NEW GCSE SCIENCE

Additional Science

For Specification Units B2, C2 and P2

Edexcel

Series Editor: Gurinder Chadha

**Authors: John Adkins,
David Applin, Gurinder Chadha**

Student Book

Contents

Biology

B2 The components of life

Chemistry

C2 Discovering chemistry

Physics

P2 Physics for your future

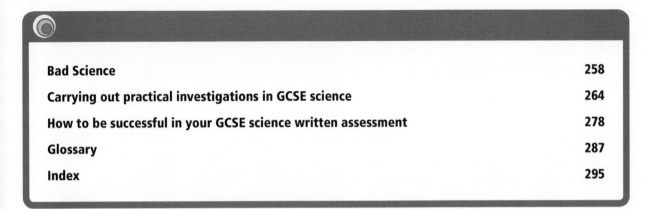

How to use this book

Welcome to Collins New GCSE Additional Science for Edexcel!

The main content

Each two-page lesson has three sections:

> The first section outlines a basic scientific idea

> The second section builds on the basics and develops the concept

> The third section extends the concept or challenges you to apply it in a new way. It can also provide information that is only relevant to the Higher tier (indicated with 'Higher tier only'). Sometimes this section may contain information that is not needed for your exam, but it is useful background knowledge and will help you in further study.

Each section contains a set of level-appropriate questions that allow you to check and apply your knowledge.

Look for:

> 'You will find out' boxes

> internet search terms (at the bottom of every page)

> 'Did you know?' and 'Remember' boxes.

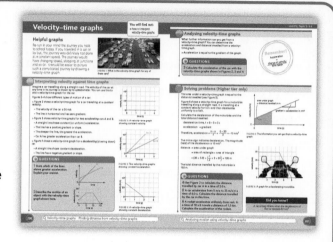

Unit introduction

Each Unit contains two Introductions – one at the start and the other midway through the Unit.

Link the science you will learn in the coming Unit with your existing scientific knowledge.

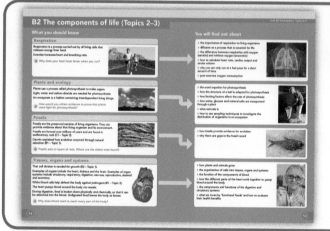

Unit checklists

Each Unit contains two graded Checklists – one midway through the Unit and the other at the end.

Summarise the key ideas that you have learnt so far and see what you need to know to progress. If there are any topics you find tricky, you can always recap them!

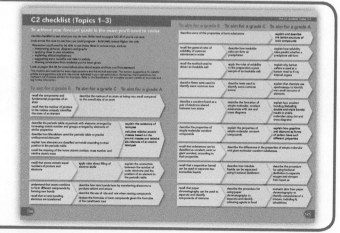

Exam-style questions

Every Unit contains practice exam-style questions for both Foundation and Higher tiers. There is a range of types of question and each is labelled with the Assessment Objective that it addresses.

There is a quick key to summarise the Assessment Objectives at the bottom of the page. A complete description of the Assessment Objectives – and how they apply to your written exam – can be found on pages 279–82 of this book and in Edexcel's specification.

Familiarise yourself with all the types of question that you might be asked.

Worked examples

Detailed worked examples with examiner comments show you how you can raise your grade. Here you will find tips on how to use accurate scientific vocabulary, avoid common exam errors and improve your Quality of Written Communication (QWC), and more. Any grades given in the worked example are target grades only. They are specific to the sample question and answer.

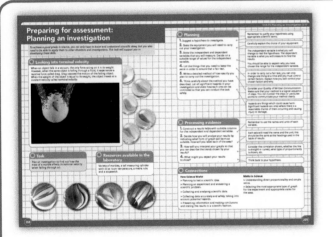

Preparing for assessment

Each Unit contains four Preparing for Assessment activities. These will help build the essential skills that you will need to succeed in your practical investigations and Controlled Assessment, and tackle the Assessment Objectives that appear throughout the Unit.

Each type of Preparing for Assessment activity builds different skills.

> Applying your knowledge: Look at a familiar scientific concept in a new context.

> Planning an investigation: Plan an investigation using handy tips to guide you along the way.

> Analysing and conclusions: Process data and draw conclusions from evidence. Use the hints to help you to achieve top marks.

Bad Science

Based on *Bad Science* by Ben Goldacre, these activities give you the chance to be a 'science detective' and evaluate the scientific claims that you hear everyday in the media.

Assessment skills

A dedicated section at the end of the book will guide you through your practical and written exams with advice on: the language used in exam papers; how best to approach a written exam; how to plan, carry out and evaluate an experiment; how to use maths to evaluate data, and much more.

B2 The components of life (Topic 1)

What you should know

Cells

Cells are the basic building blocks of all living things.

How to use a light microscope to view cells.

Animal cells contain a nucleus (the 'control centre' of the cell), a permeable cell membrane (to control the movement of substances into and out of the cell) and cytoplasm (where cell activity occurs).

Plant cells contain a nucleus, a permeable cell membrane, cytoplasm, chloroplasts (to trap light), a vacuole (to give the cell its shape) and a cell wall (to keep the cell rigid).

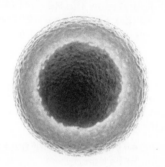

 Describe how plant cells are different to animal cells.

DNA and genetic engineering

DNA is organised into chromosomes which are found in the nucleus of cells (B1 – Topic 1).

Chromosomes are inherited from both parents.

 Describe how characteristics are inherited.

Multiplying cells

Fertilisation occurs when sex cells join.

All animals and plants begin life as one unspecialised cell. As cells grow and divide they become specialised (adapted to a specific role).

Cells multiply via cell division.

Living things with the same genetic information are called clones. Clones can be natural or man-made.

 What is the difference between sexual and asexual reproduction?

Protein synthesis and enzymes

A gene is a section of a chromosome that contains a code that enables a cell to make a protein (B1 – Topic 1).

A mutation is a change in a gene (B1 – Topic 1).

Catalysts speed up chemical reactions.

Enzymes are used in digestion.

 Why does your body need to use enzymes for digestion?

You will find out about

> how modern microscopes enable us to see cells more clearly

> how to complete simple magnification calculations

> the function of the components of bacterial cells

> the function of the components of animal cells

> the function of the components of plant cells

> the structure of DNA and how it was discovered

> the implications of using the information gathered in the Human Genome Project

> how bacteria can be genetically engineered to make human proteins

> the uses of, and controversies surrounding, GM (genetically modified) organisms

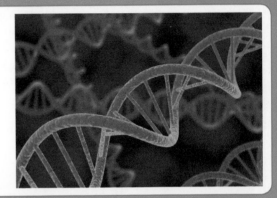

> the two types of cell division: mitosis and meiosis

> how and why plants and animals are cloned

> the arguments for and against cloning mammals

> what stem cells are and how they could be used in stem cell therapy

> the advantages and disadvantages of stem cell research

> how the code in a gene is translated into a specific protein (such as an enzyme)

> how proteins are synthesised

> how mutations change DNA and the effect of mutations

> the role of enzymes in the body

> how enzymes work like a lock and key

> the conditions that affect enzyme activity

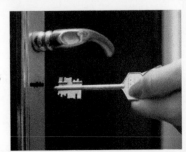

Seeing cells

You will find out:
> about using a light microscope to study cells
> how new microscope technologies improve clarity

Cell structure

In 1665, the scientist Robert Hooke looked at thin strips of cork through his microscope. He saw little box-like outlines that he called cells because they reminded him of the small rooms in which monks live.

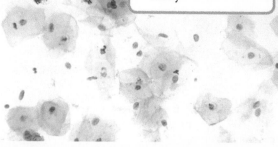

FIGURE 1: Human cheek cells stained with dyes so that the cells' nuclei are purple in contrast to pink cytoplasm. When stained, the different cell components stand out, making it easier to see them (magnification ×80).

Microscopes

Light microscopes

Most cells are too small to be seen with the naked eye. A light (or optical) microscope helps us to see them (see Figure 2).

A light source is aimed at the mirror and a beam of light passes through the cells. We can then see the cells when we look down the microscope.

Sometimes, the cells are stained with special chemicals so that components in the cell show up in contrasting colours.

eyepiece

objective lens
(choice of three
on a rotating
turret)

focusing knob

stage for
supporting the
glass slide that
holds the
specimen; clips
hold the slide
securely

light source or a
mirror that reflects
light through the
specimen

FIGURE 2: A light (optical) microscope. Suggest why there are three objective lenses.

Electron microscopes

In the 1930s, electron microscopes were invented. In an electron microscope, instead of a beam of light, a beam of **electrons** passes through the cells. We can see much more detail with an electron microscope than with a light microscope.

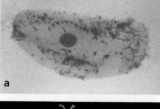

a

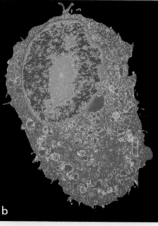

FIGURE 3: Image **a** of a human cheek cell was taken through a light microscope and shows the cells at a magnification of approximately 600 times their actual size. Image **b** of a mammalian cell was taken through an electron microscope at a magnification of approximately 4000 times its actual size. Can you think why it might be useful to be able to view cells both through a light microscope and an electron microscope?

b

QUESTIONS

1 State one difference between a light microscope and an electron microscope.

2 Suggest why a specimen of cells often is stained before being examined under a light microscope.

Using microscopes

Magnification

In Figure 2 you can see that the light reflected by a mirror passes through the specimen which is viewed through two magnifying lenses. We can calculate the magnification as follows:

$$\text{total magnification} = \begin{array}{c}\text{magnifying}\\\text{power of}\\\text{eyepiece lens}\end{array} \times \begin{array}{c}\text{magnifying}\\\text{power of}\\\text{objective lens}\end{array}$$

The magnifying power is usually stamped on the side of each lens, for example ×10 or ×40.

Resolving power

Resolving power refers to how well a microscope forms an image of a cell so that we can distinguish its different components from one another. The components may be very close together. The greater the resolving power of a microscope, the better the clarity of the images it forms.

Resolving power, and therefore clarity of image, is the measure of the quality of a light microscope.

Good-quality light microscopes can produce clear images of cells up to 2000 times their original size. At higher magnifications the images are enlarged further but they become less clear. The resolving power of an electron microscope is much greater than that of a light microscope.

Modern light microscopes can have cameras attached to them to capture the images of plant and animal cells (these images are called **photomicrographs**).

FIGURE 4: An advanced version of a light microscope with a camera attached. Why is the camera useful?

QUESTIONS

3 Calculate the total magnification of an image seen under a light microscope with a ×15 eyepiece lens in combination with a ×40 objective lens.

4 Explain the difference between the resolving power and magnification of a microscope.

5 Describe how microscopes can be used to study cells in greater detail.

More about resolving power

As you know, the electromagnetic spectrum consists of waves of different wavelengths, and visible light falls within the range of 400–720 nanometres (nm). The wavelength of electrons is less than 1 nm and therefore is much shorter than that of light.

Resolving power depends on the wavelength of the electromagnetic radiation used to 'illuminate' the specimen. The relationship is:

$$\text{resolving power} = \frac{\text{wavelength}}{2}$$

This means that, at best, the resolving power of a light microscope is 200 nm (400 nm divided by 2 = 200 nm). Therefore, cell structures less than 200 nm apart are not resolved and blur together as a single fuzzy image.

However, because the wavelength of electrons is shorter than that of light, the resolving power of an electron microscope is less than 0.5 nm (1 nm divided by 2 = 0.5 nm). This means that cell components less than 0.5 nm apart are resolved and seen in greater detail.

Table 1 summarises the resolutions of what we can see.

TABLE 1: Distances and visibility.

Unit	Fraction of a metre	Visibility
Millimetre (mm)	10^{-3} m	Unaided eye
Micrometre (μm)	10^{-6} m	Light microscope
Nanometre (nm)	10^{-9} m	Electron microscope

QUESTIONS

6 Explain why the resolving power of an electron microscope is greater than the resolving power of a light microscope.

7 State by how many times the resolving power of a light microscope is better than the resolving power of the eye.

Cell components

You will find out:
> about the components of plant cells
> about the components of animal cells
> about the components of bacterial cells

The basic unit of life

All animals and plants are made of cells. The human body is made of more than 50 trillion cells (50×10^{12}). Humans have several hundred distinct cell types, each having its own special function.

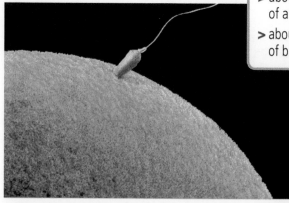

FIGURE 1: Where it all starts: a sperm cell fertilising an egg cell.

What are the components of a cell?

Cells are to bodies as bricks are to houses.

> Each of us is built of trillions of cells.

> The human body is made up of more than 200 different types of cell.

> A plant is made up of fewer types of cell.

> The term **multicellular** refers to bodies made of many cells.

A cell is made of different components:

> Some components are found in all cells.

> Other components are found just in some cells but not in others.

Did you know?

Human cells have a typical size of 10 μm (1×10^{-5} m) and a typical mass of 1 nanogram (1×10^{-9} g).

QUESTIONS

1 Use a table to list the structures found in:

   a animal cells and plant cells

   b plant cells only.

2 Close your book and draw an animal or a plant cell. Label as many components as you can from memory.

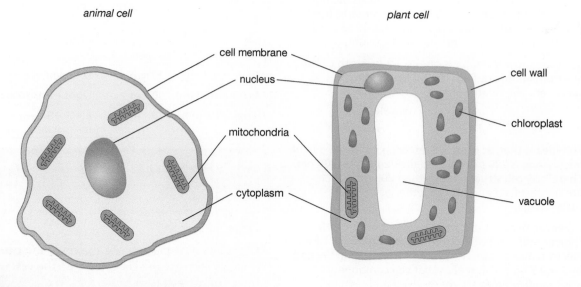

animal cell   plant cell

cell membrane
nucleus
mitochondria
cytoplasm

cell wall
chloroplast
vacuole

FIGURE 2: A typical animal cell and a typical plant cell.

Functions of cell components

Animal cells

Animal cells have the following components:

> **cytoplasm**, a jelly-like material that gives the cell shape and where most of the cell's chemical reactions take place

> a **cell membrane** that surrounds the cell and controls the movement of chemicals in and out of the cell

> a **nucleus** that contains the chromosomes, which carry genes that control the activities of the cell

> **mitochondria** where sugars are broken down by respiration releasing energy.

Plant cells

Plant cells have the same components as animal cells and these components have the same function in plant and animal cells. Plant cells also have the following additional components:

> a **cell wall** made of cellulose surrounding the cell membrane to strengthen the cell. It lets water and other chemicals pass through easily

> a **vacuole**, which is a large fluid-filled space in the cytoplasm keeping the cell **turgid**

> **chloroplasts** in the cytoplasm that contain chlorophyll used in photosynthesis.

Bacterial cells

Bacterial cells are called **microorganisms** (or microbes) because they can be seen only under a microscope.

Bacterial cells are different from animal and plant cells.

> The mitochondria and chloroplasts are absent and there is no distinct nucleus.

> Chromosomal DNA and loops of DNA called **plasmid DNA** lie loose in the cytoplasm.

> Even though the bacterial cell is surrounded by a cell wall, this is chemically different from the cellulose wall surrounding plant cells.

> Some types of bacteria have a whip-like **flagellum** (plural flagella) which propels the cell through liquid.

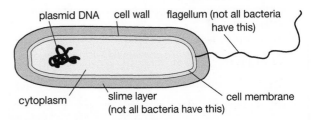

FIGURE 3: A typical bacterial cell.

QUESTIONS

3 Prepare a two-column table listing as many cell components as you can recall on the right-hand column and their functions on the left.

4 Describe the similarities and differences between bacterial cells, and plant cells and animal cells.

Managing energy needs: mitochondria and chloroplasts

The electron microscope reveals a cell's different components in much more detail than a light microscope. Figure 4 shows mitochondria and chloroplasts.

Cells use their mitochondria to release the energy they need from their food (respiration):

glucose + oxygen → carbon dioxide + water (and energy)

The cells in plants use the chlorophyll in their chloroplasts to create their food using the energy of the Sun (photosynthesis):

carbon dioxide + water → glucose + oxygen

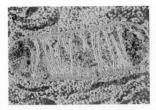
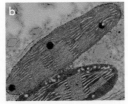

FIGURE 4:
a Mitochondria (×26000) and **b** chloroplasts (×10000) seen through a microscope. Why do plants have both?

QUESTIONS

5 The internal structures of mitochondria and chloroplasts include membranes that are folded to give a large surface area. Suggest why this is useful.

6 Use your own research to explain why the chloroplasts in seaweed often contain chlorophyll that is a different colour to plants found on the land.

Q Respiration in bacteria   Seaweed pigments

DNA

You will find out:
> about the genetic code
> the structure of DNA
> how to extract DNA from cells

Watson and Crick

In 1953, James Watson and Francis Crick built a model of the DNA molecule. Two strands are joined together and twisted around one another into a spiral shape. The shape is a double helix.

FIGURE 1: Watson (left) and Crick with their model of part of a DNA molecule in 1953. Why are models useful in science?

DNA and the genetic code

A cell's **chromosomes** are contained within its nucleus:

> Most human cells have 46 chromosomes in their nuclei.

> Each chromosome carries a double-stranded molecule of a substance called **deoxyribonucleic acid** (DNA for short).

> The double strand of DNA is wrapped round a core of protein molecules. This is called a double helix (see Figure 2).

> The strands of DNA may consist of thousands of building units joined together (see Figure 3):

> Each building unit has one of four **bases** as part of its structure: **guanine** (G), **thymine** (T), **adenine** (A) and **cytosine** (C).

> The bases come in any order along a strand of DNA.

A **gene** is a particular section of a strand of DNA. It provides the code that enables a cell to make a protein or part of a protein.

There are about 25 000 genes in a human cell. All of the base sequences of the genes make up what is called the **genetic code**. The code is universal: it works in the same way in the cells of all organisms.

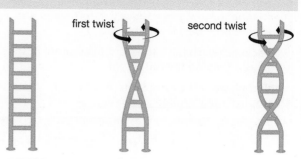

FIGURE 2: The strands of a DNA molecule twist round one another, forming a double helix like a twisted ladder.

first twist   second twist

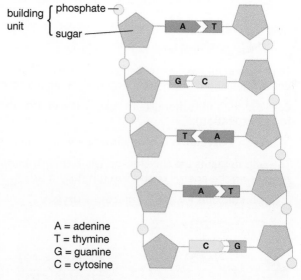

building unit { phosphate / sugar

A = adenine
T = thymine
G = guanine
C = cytosine

FIGURE 3 Part of a DNA molecule showing the two strands of DNA joined through their bases. Do you notice anything about the pairings of the bases?

QUESTIONS

1 Draw a labelled section of a DNA molecule.

2 Explain why a molecule of DNA is described as a double helix.

3 Explain the term genetic code.

DNA: its structure and extraction

Structure

A DNA molecule is made up of lots of smaller building units, as we have seen. The units are called **nucleotides**.

A nucleotide consists of the sugar deoxyribose, one of four bases and phosphate. The sugar and phosphate join together, forming a long strand (one side of the 'ladder' in Figure 3). Notice that the strand joins to its partner strand through the pairing of their bases (the 'rungs' of the 'ladder'):

> adenine (A) *always* joins with thymine (T) or vice versa

> guanine (G) *always* joins with cytosine (C) or vice versa.

The double strand is coiled into a spiral: the double helix, made up of two intertwined spiral strands.

A chromosome consists of a folded double-stranded molecule of DNA coiled around a core of proteins (see Figure 4).

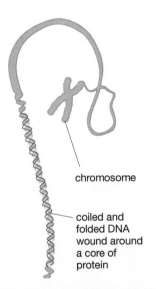

FIGURE 4:
A simplified drawing of the structure of a chromosome.

chromosome

coiled and folded DNA wound around a core of protein

Extracting DNA

It is possible to extract DNA from cells. The cells of a ripe kiwi fruit are a particularly convenient source.

If you use the cells of tissues other than kiwi fruit as a source of DNA, then a protein-digesting enzyme should be added to the mixture kept at 50 °C.

TABLE 1: Extracting DNA from a kiwi fruit.

Action	Explanation
Finely chopped kiwi fruit tissue is added to saline/detergent solution	The membranes of the cells break up, releasing their chromosomes
The mixture is kept warm at 50 °C for 15 minutes, then filtered	Protein-digesting enzymes in the cells of the kiwi fruit digest the protein part of the chromosomes, releasing their DNA
Cooled methanol is carefully added to the filtrate in equal volume	DNA precipitates from the filtrate
Watch what happens at the boundary between the layer of methanol and filtrate	DNA strands float in the methanol layer

Caution: methanol is highly flammable and toxic. This procedure should be carried out by your teacher.

QUESTIONS

4 The letters A, T, C and G stand for the bases through which a strand of DNA joins with its partner strand. State which bases join, forming a pair of bases.

5 Explain why kiwi fruit is a convenient source of DNA.

Complementary base pairings

The arrangement where the two strands of a DNA molecule are joined together through their bases, and where A always joins with T, and G with C, is called **complementary base pairing**.

The chemical bonds joining a base with its complementary partner are called hydrogen bonds. Two hydrogen bonds join A with T, three hydrogen bonds join G with C (see Figure 5).

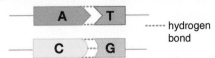

hydrogen bond

FIGURE 5: The role of hydrogen bonding in base pairing.

Hydrogen bonds are weak, which means that they are easily broken, enabling a DNA molecule to separate into two single strands. This is important when cells make protein and when they divide, forming new cells.

QUESTIONS

6 Explain the meaning of the phrase 'complementary base pairing'.

7 Explain why the weakness of hydrogen bonds is important.

Complementary base pairing

Discovering DNA

Human Genome Project

The Human Genome Project, which aimed to identify all of the genes in human DNA, is the direct result of Watson and Crick's 1953 discovery of DNA's structure. Publication of the final version of the human genome in 2003 is the stimulus for the discovery of new medical techniques.

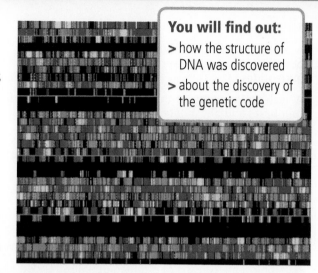

> **You will find out:**
> > how the structure of DNA was discovered
> > about the discovery of the genetic code

FIGURE 1: A computer display of a human DNA sequence as a series of coloured bands. Each colour represents a specific base.

Discovering DNA: the key events

DNA discovered

In 1869, Friedrich Miescher, a chemist, isolated a substance from the nuclei of white blood cells in pus-soaked used surgical bandages. He called the substance nuclein. We now call it DNA.

DNA chemistry worked out

In 1919, Phoebus Levene discovered the chemical make-up of nucleotides. He suggested that DNA consisted of nucleotide units joined together. In 1937 William Astbury produced the first X-ray diffraction patterns showing that DNA has a regular structure.

DNA is the genetic material

In 1944 Oswald Avery and co-workers identified DNA as the genetic material of cells.

DNA base pairs identified

In 1951 Erwin Chargaff found that in any sample of DNA, the amount of the base guanine is equal to the amount of the base cytosine, and that the amount of the base adenine is equal to the amount of the base thymine. His discovery helped Watson and Crick to establish the idea of complementary base pairing.

DNA structure modelled

In 1952 Rosalind Franklin and Maurice Wilkins, researchers at King's College in London, used X-ray crystallography to discover the arrangement of the atoms of DNA molecules.

DNA structure published

In 1953 James Watson and Francis Crick, working at Cambridge University, proposed that the structure of a molecule of DNA is a double helix. They built a model of DNA which used the information of all known features of DNA discovered by other researchers.

QUESTIONS

1 Draw a timeline of the history of the discovery of DNA.

2 Describe how the work of Franklin and Wilkins helped Watson and Crick to build a model of the DNA molecule.

Rosalind Franklin and X-ray crystallography

Rosalind Franklin's work using X-ray crystallography involved passing X-rays through a fibre of DNA on to photographic film, which produced a pattern of dots on the film. The pattern of the dots represented the positions of the atoms making up the molecule. The structure of the molecule could be worked out from the pattern of the dots.

When James Watson visited King's College in May 1952 he saw Franklin's X-ray crystallographic photograph of DNA without her permission. From this photograph, Watson realised that DNA was a helical, double-stranded molecule. Franklin's work was the vital clue that enabled Watson and Crick to build their DNA model.

Watson admitted that seeing Franklin's photograph was critical to solving the problem of DNA's structure. Whether or not her contribution was properly acknowledged by Watson and Crick is still vigorously debated.

Did you know?

Crick, Watson and Wilkins were awarded a Nobel Prize in 1962 for their work on discovering DNA's structure. Franklin was not included because she died in 1958.

QUESTIONS

3 Comment on Franklin's contribution to Watson and Crick's discovery of the structure of DNA. You may use your own research to help you.

4 Suggest what you can learn about the scientific research process from the case of Watson, Crick and Franklin.

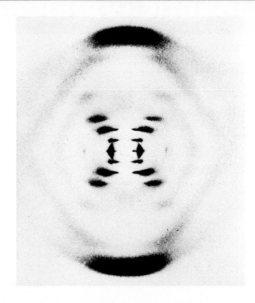

FIGURE 2: Rosalind Franklin's X-ray crystallographic photograph that gave Watson and Crick the vital clue to the structure of DNA. What does this photograph show?

Discovering the genetic code

A gene is a section of DNA carrying information which enables a cell to combine amino acid units in the correct order, making a particular type of protein. The information is carried in the sequence of bases on the nucleotides which make up the section of DNA forming the gene. We use the word **sequence** to refer to the order of the bases. 'Sequence' also refers to the order of amino acid units making a specific protein.

How does the information carried by DNA enable cells to make protein? This was the basic question asked by scientists in the early 1960s. What was the genetic code? Groups of scientists around the world worked on the coding problem. By 1965 a US scientist, Marshall Nirenberg, and his co-workers had cracked it: they had worked out the genetic code.

Nirenberg discovered that the code is a set of instructions. The instruction needed to arrange an amino acid unit in its correct place in a specific protein molecule is contained in a sequence of three bases, for example:

GCC–	ATG–	GAT–	CAA	… and so on
amino acid unit 1	amino acid unit 2	amino acid unit 3	amino acid unit 4	… and so on

The sequences of three bases (an instruction) each represents a code word known as a **codon**. Each codon specifies a particular amino acid.

Soon after its discovery scientists realised that the genetic code is universal. It works in the same way in the cells of all living things.

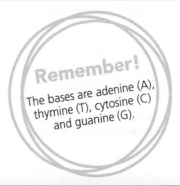

Remember!

The bases are adenine (A), thymine (T), cytosine (C) and guanine (G).

QUESTIONS

5 Explain the difference between a codon and a gene.

6 Copy the sequence of bases in the section of DNA: AATCCTGACTAG.

a Mark off the codons and state the number of codons contained in the section of DNA.

b Assume that each codon codes for one amino acid and that codons do not overlap.

> State how many amino acids are represented in the section of DNA.

> Explain the meaning of the phrase 'do not overlap'.

Use the internet to research your answer.

Q Maurice Wilkins   X-ray crystallography

Genetic engineering and insulin

Human insulin

Insulin was first used to treat a patient with Type 1 diabetes in 1922. At the time, and for many years after, the insulin was derived from animals. Since 1982 human insulin, produced by genetically modified bacteria, has been available for patients with diabetes.

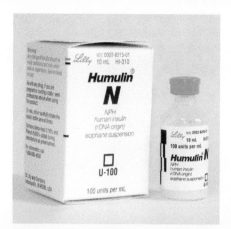

FIGURE 1: Insulin was the first medicine made by genetic engineering to be given to humans. By 1982 it was in general use.

Genetic engineering using bacteria

Genetic engineering refers to the methods that make it possible to transfer genes from the cells of one type of organism to the cells of almost any other type of organism. Today genes are routinely transferred:

> cells of plants to bacteria

> humans to bacteria

> bacteria to plants; and so on.

Why should we want to transfer genes between the cells of different organisms? In the 1970s scientists discovered that a gene continues to control production of a protein even when moved from one type of cell into another. Some of these proteins are very useful to us, for example insulin.

If a gene controlling the production of a useful protein is inserted into bacterial cells, and the cells are allowed to multiply rapidly, then large amounts of the useful protein are produced very quickly.

The term **culture** refers to the solution containing the bacterial cells, and the term **culturing** to the method of making the cells multiply rapidly.

Bacterial cells containing useful genes can be cultured in huge containers called **fermenters**. The fermenter provides an optimum environment for cell growth and so ensures maximum yield of the product. The product could be insulin, penicillin, or enzymes for washing powder, for example.

Did you know?

The genetic code is universal. It works in the same way in bacterial cells, animal cells and plant cells.

QUESTIONS

1 State why genetic engineering may be useful.

2 Explain why bacteria are used in genetic engineering.

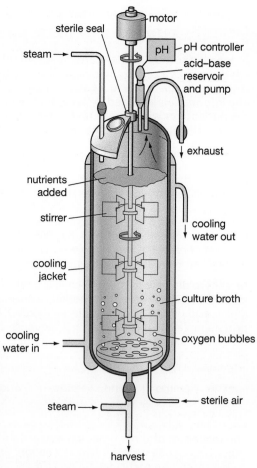

FIGURE 2: Industrial fermenters each contain up to 250 000 dm^3 of liquid and microorganisms. What does the culture broth contain?

The process of genetic engineering

In the 1970s, transferring genes from cell to cell was made possible by the discovery of enzymes produced by bacteria:

> **Restriction enzymes** are rather like molecular scissors. They catalyse reactions that cut strands of DNA into shorter pieces. They make it possible to obtain genes that enable cells to produce useful proteins.

> **Ligase** is sometimes called a pasting enzyme. It makes it possible to paste a useful gene into another piece of DNA.

The piece of DNA into which a useful gene is pasted is called a vector. The loops of DNA called **plasmid DNA** found in bacteria are commonly used vectors.

We call the vector with the useful gene pasted into place **recombinant DNA**. We say that the plasmid DNA has been genetically engineered. We also say that the organism into whose cells the genetically engineered plasmid DNA is inserted has been **genetically modified (GM)** (see Figure 3).

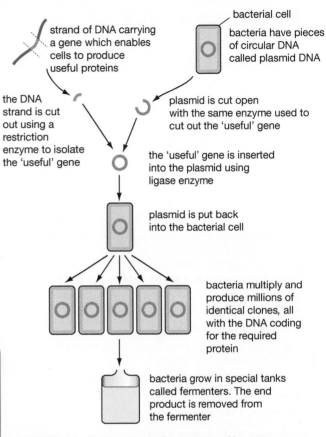

strand of DNA carrying a gene which enables cells to produce useful proteins

bacterial cell

bacteria have pieces of circular DNA called plasmid DNA

the DNA strand is cut out using a restriction enzyme to isolate the 'useful' gene

plasmid is cut open with the same enzyme used to cut out the 'useful' gene

the 'useful' gene is inserted into the plasmid using ligase enzyme

plasmid is put back into the bacterial cell

bacteria multiply and produce millions of identical clones, all with the DNA coding for the required protein

bacteria grow in special tanks called fermenters. The end product is removed from the fermenter

FIGURE 3: Producing genetically engineered bacteria.

QUESTIONS

3 Describe the difference between a restriction enzyme and ligase.

4 Describe how recombinant DNA is produced.

Producing genetically engineered insulin

The hormone insulin is produced by the pancreas and it regulates blood glucose levels.

People with Type 1 diabetes do not produce enough insulin and cannot regulate their blood glucose levels unless they inject insulin.

By 1982 genetically engineered insulin was available to treat people with Type 1 diabetes.

Before then, insulin was obtained from slaughtered cattle and pigs and had disadvantages including:

> some patients had allergic reactions as the insulin was non-human

> it was expensive to produce

> some people had ethical or religious reasons for not using a substance derived from slaughtered pigs and cattle.

Genetically engineered insulin has several advantages:

> It is cheap to produce and is available in large quantities.

> It is human insulin and so there are no allergic reactions or intolerances in users.

> It does not use animal products and so is not a problem for certain religious groups or vegetarians.

Genetically engineered insulin may have disadvantages, for example side-effects have been reported, although more research is needed into this. However, some people are concerned that GM organisms could have unknown and unforeseen effects on other organisms, including humans.

QUESTIONS

5 Suggest why some people may be prevented from using insulin obtained from cattle and pigs for religious reasons.

6 Explain why genetically engineered insulin is chemically identical to human insulin produced naturally.

GM crops

You will find out:
> the advantages and disadvantages of producing GM organisms

Should we worry?

Genetically modified (GM) organisms are at the centre of a debate: are they good or are they harmful? Some people say that GM organisms can help to increase crop yields and eradicate diseases in agriculture. Others say that we don't fully understand the consequences of GM crops and we could be heading for an environmental disaster.

FIGURE 1: Anti-GM protestors destroying a field of GM crops.

Feeding the world

Millions of people living in poorer countries do not have enough to eat. Can we look to genetically modified (GM) crops to make the difference? Developments include modified crops able to:

> grow in places with low rainfall

> produce their own chemicals to kill insects that damage them

> resist the effects of herbicides (weedkillers)

> resist diseases

> produce their own fertiliser.

GM crops, then, would seem to have real benefits. Potentially the impact on food production in dry, hot, poorer countries is immense.

Concerns about GM crops

> *Health risks*. These range from the possibility of allergic reactions to the GM food through to the danger of the mixing GM crop seeds with conventional crop seeds. This happened in the USA when maize grown for human consumption was found to contain traces of maize approved for animal feed only.

> *Environmental effects*. These include the risk to plant biodiversity, the effect on wildlife, and the chance that **herbicide** resistance could be transferred to other plants, for example weeds.

Not everyone agrees that using genetically engineered products is a problem. For example, most people think that genetically modified insulin is a good thing.

Science versus industry

The scientific breakthroughs that have made the industrial production of GM crops possible are very exciting and offer numerous commercial opportunities. However, these need to be balanced against making sure that these new products and processes are beneficial both now and in the future.

FIGURE 2: A man harvesting cotton in Algeria. Do you think drought-resistant plants would be helpful to him?

QUESTIONS

1 Describe how genetically modified crops are helping to improve food supply.

2 Draw a table to show the advantages and disadvantages of genetically modified crops.

Golden rice

We need vitamins in our food to keep fit and healthy. In particular, **vitamin A** is essential for growth and vision. The World Health Organisation estimates that each year 500 000 children are blinded because of the lack of vitamin A (vitamin A deficiency) in their food.

Golden rice is a variety which has been genetically modified to produce more of a substance called **beta-carotene** in the rice grain. Carotene is an orange–yellow pigment and gives the rice its golden colour.

Beta-carotene is called pro-vitamin A. Our cells convert it into vitamin A. With vitamin A deficiency common among millions of poorer people who depend on rice as their main food source, why is golden rice not yet available to them?

FIGURE 3: A new GM strain of golden rice (right) produces more beta-carotene than the original strain (left). Why might this be an advantage?

The issues

Although making golden rice available to people at risk from vitamin A deficiency seems an obvious response to the problem, people who are against GM food raise objections.

What do you think? These are some of the reasons for and against:

✗ There are so many regulations that golden rice will not be available to people most at risk from vitamin A deficiency until 2012 or later.
✗ Golden rice has never undergone feeding trials on animals to check that it is safe for people to eat.
✗ Trying to deal with the vitamin A problem with a single GM solution is too limiting. Aiming for a balanced diet is a better solution to vitamin A deficiency.

✔ Golden rice is not meant to be the only solution to the vitamin A problem.
✔ Golden rice will help to deal with the bigger problem of making a healthy balanced diet available to poor people.
✔ Human cells convert beta-carotene into vitamin A very efficiently.
✔ Golden rice will help to reduce cases of blindness in developing countries.

QUESTIONS

3 Explain why genetic engineering which increases the amount of beta-carotene produced by crop plants could help to prevent blindness.

4 Name the enzymes that would be used to produce golden rice.

5 Consider the arguments for and against golden rice. Prepare a pamphlet to explain your views.

Herbicide-resistant crops

Weeds compete with crops for resources such as water, sunlight and soil nutrients. In order to address the problem of weeds in crops:

> farmers have to spend time turning the soil before planting, which is time consuming and risks soil erosion

> farmers have to spray the weeds with herbicides, potentially causing crop and environmental damage.

Therefore, the introduction in the mid-1980s of herbicide-resistant crops offered an attractive solution to the problem. Herbicide resistance is introduced to the plants through genetic engineering, allowing farmers to cultivate their crops more efficiently and effectively.

The advantages of herbicide-resistant crops are clearly that the farmer is able to increase the crop yield. However, there are also disadvantages that can result from their use. For example, different weeds or invasive species taking the place of the removed weeds and possible herbicide-resistant strains of weed could develop.

QUESTIONS

6 Explain why farmers prefer their crops to be free of weeds.

7 Evaluate the arguments for and against genetically modified crops. What is your final conclusion?

Dividing cells

You will find out:
> that new cells are produced when old cells divide
> about mitosis and meiosis

Cell renewal

When animals and plants grow, their cells increase in number by dividing. Cell division also replaces the cells we lose from our skin. Much of the dust in a house consists of millions of dead skin cells.

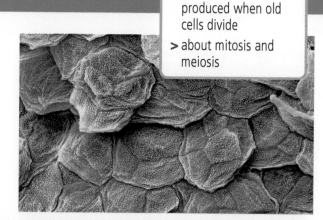

FIGURE 1: The outer layer of human skin is formed from overlapping layers of dead skin cells. These are continually scraped off and replaced with cells from the dividing layers beneath. What is the outer layer of skin called?

New cells from old

When cells divide, new cells are formed. Two overlapping processes take place:

> division of the nucleus
> division of the cytoplasm.

Dividing cells are called parent cells. The new cells produced are called **daughter cells**. 'Daughter' does not mean that the cells are female, it's just that they are the new cells formed as a result of cell division.

When a parent cell divides, the chromosomes in its nucleus are passed on to the daughter cells. This means that the genes that are carried on the chromosomes are passed on as well.

QUESTIONS

1 State which two processes take place when a cell divides.

2 Describe what happens to the chromosomes of a parent cell when it divides to produce daughter cells.

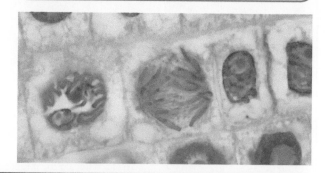

FIGURE 2: Root cells undergoing mitosis. The cell in the centre is in the final stage of mitosis before cellular division. The chromosomes have been separated and moved to opposite poles of the cell. Can you identify the chromosomes in each of the cells?

Ways of dividing

Most cells contain two sets of chromosomes: one set inherited from the male parent; the other set from the female parent.

The term **diploid** refers to cells with two sets of chromosomes (one set from each parent). The symbol **2n** represents the diploid state. How many chromosomes each daughter cell contains depends on which of two ways the nucleus of the parent cell divides: **mitosis** or **meiosis**.

Mitosis

Mitosis results in two daughter cells with the same number of chromosomes as the parent cell. The chromosomes are exact copies of the parent cell's chromosomes. Daughter cells are therefore genetically identical to their parent cell and to each other. If the parent cell is diploid then so too are the daughter cells. The nucleus of all body cells (except the cells that divide to form **gametes**) divides by mitosis.

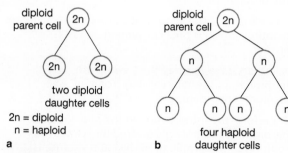

FIGURE 3: Cells divide in one of two ways: **a** mitosis or **b** meiosis. What difference between the two processes can you spot in the diagram?

Mitosis and meiosis   Cell division   Diploid and haploid

Meiosis

Meiosis results in four daughter cells each with half the number of chromosomes of the parent cell. The cells are gametes. Each gamete contains only one set of chromosomes. This means that the gamete is genetically different to the parent cell. We say that gametes are **haploid**. The symbol **n** represents the haploid state. Only the nuclei of the cells that divide to give rise to gametes divide by meiosis.

QUESTIONS

3 Describe the differences between mitosis and meiosis.

4 Explain why most cells contain two sets of chromosomes.

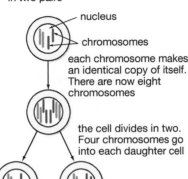

a This cell has four chromosomes in two pairs

nucleus

chromosomes

each chromosome makes an identical copy of itself. There are now eight chromosomes

the cell divides in two. Four chromosomes go into each daughter cell

each daughter cell is an exact copy of the original cell

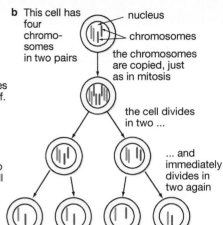

b This cell has four chromosomes in two pairs

nucleus

chromosomes

the chromosomes are copied, just as in mitosis

the cell divides in two ...

... and immediately divides in two again

this produces four gametes (eggs or sperm) each with the haploid number of chromosomes

FIGURE 4: a Mitosis and **b** meiosis: the pattern of chromosome movements compared.

Replication

Division

Before a parent cell is about to divide, the cell's chromosomes each make a copy of themselves. The copying process is called **replication**. After replication, each chromosome copy is in the form of a pair of joined **chromatids**.

Next, the pairs of chromatids follow a pattern of moves rather like a pair of dancers coming together and moving away from each other on the dance floor. The terms mitosis and meiosis describe the pattern of moves of the chromatid pairs. In each case the pattern, which is the same in both animal and plant cells, follows a strict sequence.

Eventually each pair of chromatids separates and each chromatid becomes a new chromosome in the daughter cells following division of the parent cells.

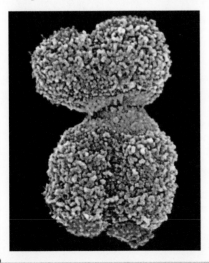

FIGURE 5: A human chromosome consists of two identical, parallel strands (chromatids, left and right), joined at a centromere (centre, green). The tips (blue) are telomeres. This is chromosome 16, which carries between 850 and 1200 genes.

Genetically identical; genetically different

During replication a chromosome (and its DNA) makes an exact copy of itself, forming a pair of joined chromatids. The weak hydrogen bonds that hold together the two strands of the chromosome's DNA double helix break. The bases of each strand attract complementary bases and a new strand of DNA builds as a complementary copy along each old strand. Now you know why pairs of chromatids are genetically identical to each other, and why daughter cells following mitosis are also genetically identical to each other and their parent cell.

However, during meiosis, each pair of chromatids of a chromosome copy pairs up with its corresponding partner.

What follows is an important difference between mitosis and meiosis. The pairs of chromosome copies exchange chromatid pieces with one another. This results in gametes produced after cell division that are not only haploid but genetically different from one another as well.

Remember!

Adenine (A) always bonds with thymine (T); guanine (G) always with cystine (C)

QUESTIONS

5 Compare chromatids and chromosomes.

Role of mitosis and meiosis

You will find out:
> about the role of mitosis
> that haploid gametes combine at fertilisation

Regeneration

A tiny animal called *Hydra* can reproduce asexually. The outgrowth seen here is the result of some of the parent's body cells dividing by mitosis. Eventually the outgrowth separates from the parent body and becomes a new individual.

FIGURE 1: *Hydra* lives in ponds and streams attached to underwater plants and other surfaces. The outgrowths are called 'buds' and become new individuals. They are genetically identical to each other and their parent. Can you explain why?

Importance of mitosis

The two diploid daughter cells that are formed as a result of mitosis are genetically identical to one another and to their parent cell. This explains how organisms:

> *Repair damage*, for example damaged or old skin cells are replaced by mitosis with identical new skin cells. This is why we generally look the same this week as we did last week. Although our skin cells die and flake off, they are replaced with genetically identical new skin cells.

> *Grow*, for example the mass of a plant root increases because the existing root cells produce more root cells by mitosis.

> *Reproduce asexually*, for example the cells of a cut plant stem divide by mitosis, producing new cells that develop into root tissue. Stem and roots grow into a new plant.

FIGURE 2: New plants – hundreds of them all the same! Can you explain why?

QUESTIONS

1 State how mitosis helps to maintain healthy body tissues.

2 Draw a diagram to show how new root cells are produced from existing cell roots.

Asexual reproduction

Why does asexual reproduction give rise to individuals genetically identical to each other and their parent?

> Asexual reproduction involves only one individual as a parent.

> The cells of the parent which develop into the new individual are produced by mitosis.

During mitosis a copy is made of each of the parent cell's chromosomes. An exact copy of the parent's genetic material passes to the daughter cells. The daughter cells and the parent cell are therefore genetically identical to each other.

Figure 3 shows an example of this using *Hydra*.

Since the daughter cells are genetically identical, the offspring that develop from them are genetically identical as well. Individuals genetically identical to each other are called **clones**.

Q Mitosis and meiosis   Asexual reproduction   Genetic variation

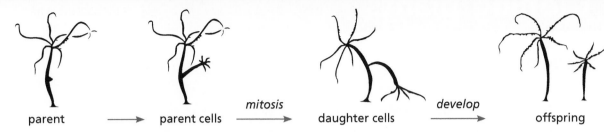

parent $\longrightarrow$ parent cells $\xrightarrow{\text{mitosis}}$ daughter cells $\xrightarrow{\text{develop}}$ offspring

FIGURE 3: Asexual reproduction. This example uses *Hydra*: a bulge forms on the column and develops tentacles. This bulge becomes a daughter *Hydra* that pulls itself away from the parent. The daughter becomes an independent animal and swims off.

QUESTIONS

3 Define the term clone.

4 Explain why asexual reproduction could not happen by meiosis.

FIGURE 4: A group of green hydra polyps, attached to a strand of water weed. The 'head' of each hydra consists of a mouth surrounded by a number of tentacles, used to capture passing water fleas and algal cells.

Did you know?

In good feeding conditions *Hydra* reproduce asexually by budding off daughter buds. In poor conditions eggs and sperm are released into the water and fertilisation occurs.

Sexual reproduction

Fertilisation restores the full set of chromosomes (diploid, 2n) in the zygote, but in a different combination compared with each parent.

Importance of meiosis

The daughter cells produced by meiosis are the gametes (sperm and eggs). Each one receives a half (haploid) set of chromosomes from the parent cell. The gametes are genetically different from one another, unlike daughter cells produced by mitosis.

During fertilisation, a haploid male gamete (sperm) fuses with a haploid female gamete (egg): the chromosomes of each cell combine. The result is a diploid **zygote** (fertilised egg) which has inherited a new combination of chromosomes (and therefore genes) contributed 50:50 from the parents.

The zygote (in this example, a human) divides again and again by mitosis. The divisions produce a ball of cells called the **embryo**. The embryo develops attached to the wall of the mother's womb into a **foetus**. The foetus becomes a baby. In humans, it takes about 9 months for the zygote to develop into a baby.

The new individual that develops from the zygote inherits characteristics from both parents. This is why offspring are genetically different from one another (except for identical twins) and from their parents. The term variation refers to the genetic differences (and therefore differences in characteristics) between individuals of the same species.

QUESTIONS

5 Explain how variation is the result of meiosis.

6 'The number of chromosomes in the nuclei of cells is kept constant from one generation to the next through meiosis and sexual reproduction.' Comment on this statement.

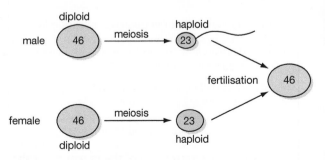

FIGURE 5: Fertilisation restores the diploid number.

Cloning plants

You will find out:
> that cloning is an example of asexual reproduction
> about the commercial application of cloning

New growth

Clones can be found in our homes. Spider plants are common houseplants and produce clones by budding off young stems each with sprouting roots and clusters of leaves. If the stems with their leaves and roots are detached from the main plant and planted, each will grow into a new plant, genetically identical to its companions and parent.

FIGURE 1: A spider plant, Chlorophytum comosum (variegatum).

Vegetative reproduction

Clones

Most types of flowering plant can reproduce asexually as well as sexually. Parts of the root, leaf or more often the stem can grow into new plants. The parts are often called vegetative parts. Therefore asexual reproduction in flowering plants is sometimes called **vegetative reproduction**.

Only one parent is involved in asexual reproduction and any new plants grown from the vegetative parts of a single parent plant are therefore genetically identical. These genetically identical individuals are called **clones**.

The usefulness of clones

Gardeners and farmers want stocks of plants with the preferred characteristics of disease resistance, colour of fruit, shape of flower and so on. Asexual reproduction passes on these characteristics from parent to offspring.

Gardeners and farmers make use of asexual reproduction to produce new plants with all of the desirable characteristics of the parent plant. In this way the quality of plants is preserved from generation to generation and from one growing season to the next.

FIGURE 2: Asexual reproduction guarantees the quality of the plants we buy.

QUESTIONS

1 State why individuals asexually reproduced from one parent are genetically identical to one another.

2 List the vegetative parts of plants.

3 State the advantages to growers of reproducing crop plants asexually.

Tissue culture

Gardeners make use of vegetative reproduction by making cuttings (see Figure 3). In a similar way, small pieces cut from a plant can be grown into new whole plants using **tissue culture**.

Plants produced by tissue culture are genetically identical to one another because they come from the same parent plant. The plants are clones. Cloning is an example of asexual reproduction in action. The process is an ideal way of producing plants with all the desirable characteristics of the parent plant that customers prefer.

Culturing plant tissue begins with small pieces of tissue cut from a parent with the characteristics we desire. The pieces are grown in a liquid or gel that provides all the substances needed for their development. Great care is taken to make sure that conditions are sterile, including the instruments used to handle the pieces of plant. Sterile conditions keep the plant pieces free of bacteria and viruses which might cause disease. The temperature at which growth of the pieces takes place is also carefully controlled.

Q Plant quality   Chitting potatoes

parent plant

this stem should have leaves on it

take a healthy plant and cut off a small length of stem

dip the end of the cut stem into hormone rooting powder

put the stem into a flowerpot full of damp compost

this will grow into a new plant

cover the pot with a plastic bag to keep it moist

QUESTIONS

4 Summarise the conditions needed for the successful culturing of plant tissue.

FIGURE 3: Making a cutting. Suggest the function of hormone rooting powder.

Did you know?

Widespread use of clones by gardeners and farmers reduces variation. Fewer alleles are available for the selective breeding of new varieties of crops.

FIGURE 4: Tissue is cultured in controlled, sterile conditions.

Commercial cloning

Commercially important plants are mass produced by tissue culture. For example, large numbers of people rely on the oil of the oil palm to sell as cooking oil or as an ingredient in soap and biofuel. The palm trees that produce most oil are chosen to grow clones from.

Pieces of tissue taken from the high-oil-yielding trees are cultured in sterile conditions. The cells of the pieces of tissue divide by mitosis. The pieces grow into clusters of identical cells.

The clusters are separated. Each one continues to grow and develop into a new plant which has the desirable characteristics (high oil yield) of the parent plant.

Oil palms grow naturally in warm tropical countries, but the cloning process can be carried out in laboratories anywhere in the world. Once produced, young plants are exported to the tropics to grow into plantations of mature trees.

QUESTIONS

5 Summarise the programme that leads to the production of high-oil-yielding palm oil trees.

6 Draw a diagram to show the movement of chromosomes during the cloning of oil palms.

breeding programme produces hybrid palm trees

selection: hybrid palm trees with fruits that produce a lot of oil are chosen

culture: tissues from selected trees are grown in a nutrient gel

FIGURE 5: Cloning oil palms: palm trees are produced which yield six times more oil than trees grown by traditional methods. What is the commercial benefit of this?

cloning: trees develop from the tissue grown in culture. They are clones since they originate from the same parent by asexual reproduction. Each tree of the clone has fruit that produces a lot of oil

Cloning animals

You will find out:

> the stages in the production of a cloned mammal

> the benefits and possible risks of cloning mammals

Cloned piglets

Animals are more difficult to clone than plants. Even so, sheep, cattle, mice and other mammals have been cloned successfully. Experts predict that genetically modified cloned pigs will be able to provide organs for human transplants in the next few years.

FIGURE 1: Millie, Christa, Alexis, Carrel and Dotcom were the world's first cloned pigs. Born in 2000, they were produced by the same gene technology company responsible for cloning Dolly the sheep.

Embryo transplants

Embryo transplants begin in the laboratory and end in normal births:

> Eggs can be taken from female animals and fertilised in the laboratory.

> The eggs are called **donor eggs**.

> Each embryo that forms from a fertilised donor egg is split up into its separate cells before the cells begin to specialise into different types of cell.

> Before specialisation the embryonic cells are called **stem cells**.

> Some of the separated stem cells are transplanted into different parts of the womb of a **host mother** – so called because the transplanted cells are not her own.

> The cells develop into identical embryos.

> Eventually the host mother gives birth to several youngsters where one or perhaps two offspring would have been more normal. The youngsters are genetically identical to one another. They are clones.

QUESTIONS

1 Draw a flowchart to show how clones are produced from embryo transplants.

Remember!

Clones are genetically identical to the parent and to each other.

Advantages, disadvantages and risks of cloning

Dolly the sheep was born on 5 July 1996 at the Roslin Institute at Edinburgh University. Although she had a normal birth, Dolly began her life in a test-tube. She was cloned from a cell taken from the mammary gland of an adult sheep, and then transferred as a 6-day-old embryo into a host mother.

Dolly became famous as the first animal cloned from an adult cell and her health and well-being became the focus of world attention. She produced six lambs in total. Although there was some concern that Dolly's DNA was more like the DNA of an older animal, investigations at the time did not reveal any evidence that she was ageing prematurely. However, in 2001 Dolly was diagnosed with arthritis and in 2003 she developed a cough. A CT scan revealed tumours in her chest and she was put to sleep while under anaesthetic. Dolly made many people ask whether it is safe to clone animals or humans.

Animal cloning

Cloning allows scientists to produce animals with desirable characteristics quickly and reliably.

For example, imagine that a mutation in a cow makes her an exceptional milk producer. Conventional breeding techniques would reshuffle her genes with the risk that the desirable mutation would be lost. Cloning to produce identical copies of the cow will conserve her milk-producing abilities in the long term.

Cloning helps to conserve rare species

Cloning also helps to build up populations of rare animals which might otherwise be threatened with extinction.

Host mothers can carry transplanted embryos of different species. The technique is useful because fertilised eggs of rare species can be cooled and preserved for years after the original parents have died. When a suitable host mother is available the fertilised eggs can be transplanted into her womb.

Zoos are developing breeding programmes which use these methods. The intention is to build up numbers of rare species. Eventually individuals may be released back into the wild from where they came and where they were driven to extinction.

Human cloning

Cloning could be carried out with the purpose of producing a fully formed person, in a similar way that Dolly was cloned and grew into an adult sheep.

Another form of cloning does not take the process beyond the embryo stage. This uses the embryo as a source of stem cells which can then generate organs and tissues that are genetically identical. This means that there is no risk of rejection by the immune system.

Attitudes towards the idea of human cloning differ. Some people feel that while cloning a whole person would be unacceptable, using stem cells from an embryo to grow a healthy new heart or kidney, for example, would be justifiable. Others consider that the use of embryos in this way is unethical for religious, political or philosophical reasons.

● QUESTIONS

2 Draw a table to show the advantages and disadvantages of cloning.

3 State, with reasons, your views on whether humans should be cloned.

Problems with cloning

The success rate in cloning is low. Depending on the species being cloned, the success rate varies from 0.1% to 3%. That is between 1 and 30 births per 1000 attempts. Reasons for this include:

> The egg and the nucleus may not be compatible.

> An egg with a newly transferred nucleus may not begin to divide properly.

> Implantation of the embryo into the surrogate mother might fail.

> The pregnancy itself might fail due to miscarriage.

> Clones are often bigger than normal at birth. This can cause birth difficulties. It can also cause breathing and circulation problems.

> Some clones have malformed brains and kidneys.

> Some clones' immune systems do not work properly.

> Clones of some species show changes in their chromosomes normally only seen in older animals.

FIGURE 2: Cloning human tissue is a very controversial area of research and is banned in many countries. Here a demonstrator makes a point in South Korea.

Production of cloned mammals (Higher tier only)

How was Dolly produced? Figure 3 shows the stages involved in producing a cloned sheep.

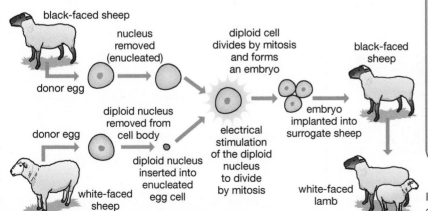

FIGURE 3: The stages in the production of a cloned sheep.

● QUESTIONS

4 Draw a flow diagram which shows the relationship between donor eggs, the biological mother and the host mother.

5 Use the internet to investigate other cloned animals. Prepare a short report on your findings.

Stem cells

Multiplying cells

Our body is made of more than 200 different types of cell: liver cells, skin cells, nerve cells and so on. Each type of cell is specialised and carries out a particular job. But if we start with just a sperm and an egg cell, where do they all come from?

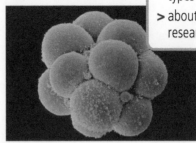

You will find out:

> that stem cells can differentiate into other types of cell

> about stem cell research

FIGURE 1: An early embryo: the mass of cells on the inside are embryonic stem cells.

Undifferentiated cells

How we begin

We each begin as a fertilised egg (called a zygote):

> The zygote soon divides into two by mitosis.

> After 3 days, the zygote has become a ball of 16 cells.

> After 5 days it is a hollow ball of cells, which starts to attach itself to the wall of the uterus. These cells start to form the embryo.

> After 14 days the zygote has become an embryo. At this stage these cells are **embryonic stem cells** and are all pretty much the same.

> As the embryo grows into a foetus, the cells undergo a process of **differentiation**. Differentiation is when the stem cells become particular types of cells with specialised functions.

> As cells mature they lose their ability to differentiate and can only make more cells like themselves.

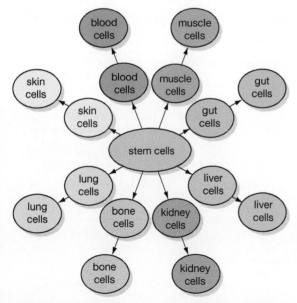

FIGURE 2: Stem cells can differentiate into different types of cells, but specialised cells, like blood cells and liver cells, can only make more cells like themselves. What process allows bone cells to form from other bone cells?

Adult stem cells

Scientists have found adult stem cells in our bodies, generally in parts of the body that can repair and renew itself. For example, bone marrow contains stem cells that form the different types of blood cells.

Adult stem cells are only called 'adult' to distinguish them from embryonic stem cells. Adult stem cells appear in children as well as adults.

Stem cell therapy

Because stem cells, both embryonic and adult, can become different types of cells, they offer the potential to repair and even regenerate organs and tissues. The use of stem cells in this way is called **stem cell therapy**.

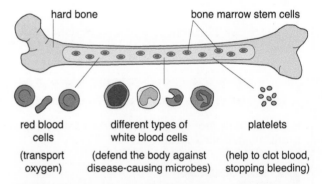

FIGURE 3: Section of a long bone cut lengthways. The bone marrow is a source of stem cells which differentiate into red blood cells, white blood cells and platelets.

QUESTIONS

1 What is special about stem cells?

2 Do the cells in the foetus divide by meiosis or mitosis?

3 Suggest an application for stem cell therapy.

What can stem cell therapy do?

Embryonic stem cells

Embryonic stem cells can differentiate into many more types of cell than adult stem cells. This makes them ideal for a range of stem cell therapies that repair damaged tissues. Treating Parkinson's disease, diabetes, different cancers and Alzheimer's disease are examples.

However, their use is controversial as sourcing embryonic stem cells destroys the embryo from which they come. Some people think this is morally wrong and therefore unethical as they believe an embryo is already a human life.

Repairing damaged tissue

Less controversial is the repair of damaged tissue using adult stem cells. Embryos are not destroyed. Also, sourcing the cells from the person to be treated avoids the risk of rejection when the cells are transplanted back into that person. For example, bone marrow stem cells have been used to treat patients with cancers such as leukaemia and lymphoma for more than 30 years.

Curing genetic disorders

Putting right genetic disorders using stem cell therapy is another possibility. You will remember that cystic fibrosis (CF) is a genetic disorder caused by mutation of the CFTR gene.

Treating CF using stem cells could run like this:

> Adult stem cells from a person with CF are genetically modified (GM) to replace the mutant CFTR gene with a normal gene.

> The GM cells differentiate into the cells lining the airways.

> The GM airway cells are transplanted back into the person.

> The GM airway cells work properly.

> The GM airway cells are not rejected because they come from the person with CF.

 QUESTIONS

4 Parkinson's disease is caused by the breakdown of a certain type of neurone in the brain. Describe how brain stem cells might be used to treat Parkinson's disease.

5 Prepare arguments for and against using embryos as a potential source of stem cells.

Risks and advances in stem cell research

There are many risks associated with both adult and embryonic stem cell research:

> The method of producing stem cell lines (stem cell cultures) must be reliable and the procedure for cell delivery in the recipient must be tried and tested.

> In therapy involving embryonic stem cells, It is possible that transplanted cells would differ in their immune profile from that of the recipient and so would be rejected.

> In therapy involving adult stem cells, the harvested stem cells may carry genetic mutations for disease or become defective during experimentation.

> Stem cells can cause side-effects and complications in the individual receiving therapy. Research is investigating concerns that stem cell therapy might trigger adverse immune responses or the development of cancers.

> Claims of the effectiveness of the therapies and treatments offered are sometimes from unregulated sources. For example, some overseas clinics advertise via the internet their poorly researched, expensive and possibly dangerous cures.

Trials in Europe, North America and Australia provide encouraging results. Stem cell therapy in China for various diseases and disorders is routine because ethical issues are not so widely discussed.

New ways of producing stem cells that have the benefits of embryonic stem cells but do not destroy embryos promise to defuse controversy. For example, embryonic-like stem cells have been sourced from umbilical cord blood. Also, embryonic-like stem cells have been produced from adult stem cells that have been programmed to reverse differentiation. Since embryos are not the source of these embryonic-like stem cells, these developments may help to make embryonic stem cell therapy less controversial.

QUESTIONS

6 Explain why stem cells used in stem cell therapy might trigger an immune response in the person receiving them.

7 Use the internet to help you explain reverse differentiation.

8 Evaluate the risks and benefits of stem cell therapy today.

The human genome

You will find out:

> about the Human Genome Project

> about reading the human genome

> about the implications of sequencing the human genome

Working together

The Human Genome Project is an example of international cooperation between scientists working to a common goal: the discovery of the sequence of bases of all of the DNA contained in a human cell. The project is more than just the sequence: work continues so that we understand its implications for medicine, agriculture, the life sciences as a whole, and ultimately for the way we live our lives.

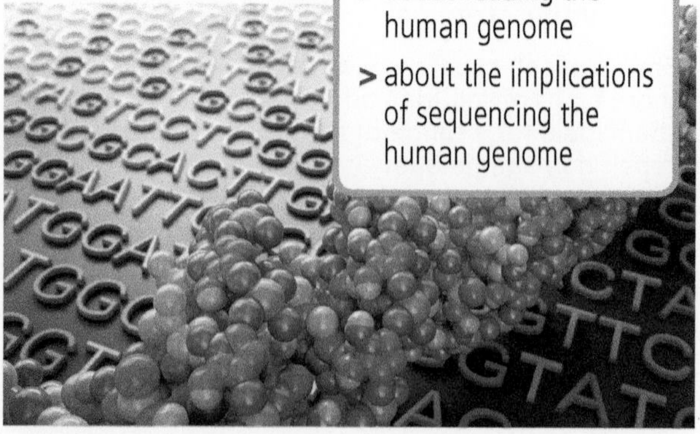

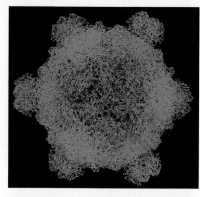

FIGURE 1: From Watson and Crick's model to the completed sequence of human DNA in 50 years.

Sequencing the human genome (Higher tier only)

The word **genome** refers to all of the DNA in each cell of an organism and **genomics** refers to the study of an organism's genome and how genome information might be used.

The techniques of genomics were pioneered by Frederick Sanger and colleagues at Cambridge University, who sequenced the genome of a virus called phi X 174: the first fully sequenced genome. The work encouraged scientists to think that sequencing the much larger human genome was possible.

The **Human Genome Project (HGP)** began in 1989 and by the next year consisted of a consortium of scientists in the USA, UK, France, Germany, Japan, China and India. This international cooperation, and advances in sequencing technology and computer-driven sequence analysis, resulted in a rough draft of the human genome.

FIGURE 2: A model of the virus phi X 174.

QUESTIONS

1 Explain the difference between the words 'genome' and 'genomics'.

2 Discuss two reasons why sequencing the virus phi X 174 genome was important to the sequencing of the human genome.

3 What methods might scientists have used to collaborate with one another during the HGP?

Reading the human genome (Higher tier only)

The sequence of the human genome is pieced together using cells from anonymous volunteers.

Chromosomes from particular cells, e.g. blood cells, are broken down into small pieces, which are replicated and then analysed by large computers called DNA **sequencers**. The results provide a likely sequence for the order of bases in a particular gene. Work continues in order to verify and build upon these findings.

FIGURE 3: A bank of DNA sequencers.

The processing, analysis, study and storage of the data produced by genome sequencing projects have become almost a science itself. **Bioinformatics** is the name given to this field.

As more information is produced, the objective of linking genes to proteins, identifying where and when genes are active within the body gets closer. Molecular atlases now exist that map particular genes with the locations of their associated proteins.

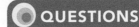

QUESTIONS

4 Explain the meaning of the word bioinformatics.

5 Explain what a molecular atlas of the cell could show scientists.

Implications of the human genome (Higher tier only)

Benefits

The finished human genome (to 99.99% accuracy) was announced in April 2003. We know the sequence (order) of the 3.1 billion bases that make up the DNA of our genome. Remarkably, genes are less than 2% of the sequence. Scientists estimate that our chromosomes carry 20 000–25 000 genes.

Our genes control how vulnerable we are to particular diseases. For example, scientists working on the **Cancer Genome Project** are studying changes in the base sequence of the genes controlling cell division. The changes are mutations which can lead to cell division running out of control. Too many cells are produced and a cancer can be the result (see Figure 4).

The discovery of the sequence of bases of our genes is the key that unlocks the possibilities of new drugs and treatments tailored to deal with diseases that have an underlying genetic cause. The emerging science of personalising drug treatment according to an individual's genome is called **pharmacogenomics**.

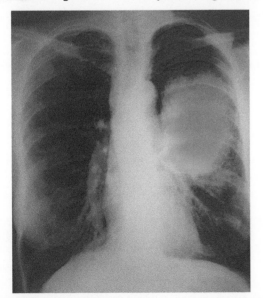

FIGURE 4: A coloured X-ray image showing an oval-shaped cancerous growth in the left lung (right of image). Recent work has discovered that the substances in cigarette smoke cause more that 49 000 mutations in genes that control cell division in lung tissue.

Criticism

If genomic-based medicine is a positive result of the HGP what might be the negative?

Studies on base sequence variations in the DNA of different ethnic (racial) groups aim to discover why some races are more or less vulnerable to particular diseases compared with others. An understanding of global patterns of disease is the goal. However, what might be the result if the government of a country used the data to identify and discriminate against particular ethnic groups within its population?

The recent history of different governments pursuing policies of **ethnic cleansing** is a warning. If genetic data identifying ethnicity were available, what then could be the outcome for ethnic groups thought by political ideologies somehow to be inferior and unwanted?

Criticism that a small group of unelected decision-makers is controlling genomic research, which could affect millions, highlights other difficult issues. For example, some people point to the potential problems of cultural differences.

Genome decision-makers are mostly part of a Western culture that emphasises individual rights; those affected are often from different cultural traditions. Their lives are bound up in collective responses to day-to-day problems and group decision-making.

Is it possible to balance different cultural traditions, so that the implications of human genomic research can benefit everyone? Many people think that to achieve balance much work remains to be done.

QUESTIONS

6 Explain the relationship between the Cancer Genome Project and the development of pharmacogenomics.

7 Using your own research, prepare a short presentation on your views about the criticisms that have been made of the HGP.

Protein synthesis

You will find out:
> about peptides, polypeptides and proteins
> about ribonucleic acid
> about the stages of protein synthesis

Making muscles

Muscles are made of protein but bodies are more than just the muscles they're made of. Proteins are essential parts of organisms and are involved in most of the processes in cells. Many proteins are enzymes that catalyse the reactions essential for life.

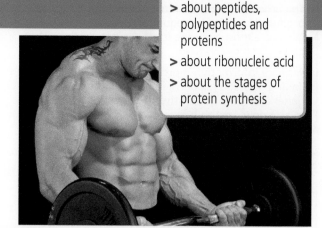

FIGURE 1: A lean man consists of about 17% protein. Are weightlifters likely to consist of more or less?

Making proteins

The word synthesis refers to the process of making something by joining other things together. For a cell to synthesise a protein, hundreds or even thousands of amino acid units must join together in the correct order. How many and in what order will specify the particular protein made.

Proteins have a complicated shape that helps them to carry out their jobs. If a protein molecule was the wrong shape, it might not be able to work properly.

DNA is responsible for getting the correct number of amino acid units joining together in the correct order.

Did you know?

The largest natural protein, found in muscles, is made of 30 000 amino acid units.

Polypeptides and **peptides** are words you will come across as well as **proteins**. What is the difference? The number of amino acid units joined together is the simple answer:

> peptide: 2–20 amino acid units
> polypeptide: 21–50 amino acid units
> protein: more than 50 amino acid units.

The more amino acid units joined together the larger the molecule. From now on we shall use proteins to include peptides and polypeptides.

QUESTIONS

1 Summarise how DNA enables a cell to make a particular protein.

2 What could happen if an antibody molecule had an amino acid unit in the wrong place?

Ribonucleic acid (RNA)

DNA is part of the chromosomes of a cell's nucleus and proteins are made on structures called **ribosomes** within the cell's cytoplasm. So how does the information for a cell to make a specific protein pass from the DNA in the nucleus to the ribosomes in the cytoplasm? The answer involves **ribonucleic acid (RNA)**.

DNA is made up of many smaller units called nucleotides, as is RNA, and each DNA nucleotide is made up of the sugar deoxyribose, one of four bases (A, T, G, C) and phosphate. Each RNA nucleotide is similar but with important differences – see Table 1.

There are different types of **RNA: messenger RNA (mRNA)** and **transfer RNA (tRNA)**. The transfer of protein-making information from DNA to mRNA enables a cell to make protein.

TABLE 1: DNA and RNA compared (U is the base uracil).

	DNA	RNA
Sugar	Deoxyribose	Ribose
Base	A, T, G or C	A, U, G or C
Phosphate	Present	Present
Structure	Double stranded	Single stranded

QUESTIONS

3 List two differences between a molecule of DNA and a molecule of RNA.

4 Arrange the order of the following terms to show the direction in which protein-making information flows within a cell: protein, DNA, RNA.

Protein synthesis (Higher tier only)

Protein synthesis is a two-stage process: transcription followed by translation. The numbers on Figure 2 correspond to the numbers in the text and are a step-by-step guide to how cells synthesise protein.

Transcription

1 The hydrogen bonds linking the complementary base pairs of double-stranded DNA sections in the cell's nucleus break. The strands separate, exposing the bases along each strand.

2 Strands of mRNA form as the bases of RNA nucleotides in solution in the cell's nucleus combine with their respective complementary bases of the single-stranded DNA. The RNA nucleotides carrying the base uracil (U) will combine with adenine (A) on the DNA.

3 The strands of mRNA separate from their respective complementary strands of DNA. They pass from the nucleus, through gaps in the membrane surrounding the nucleus, into the cytoplasm of the cell.

Translation

4 Each strand of mRNA binds to a ribosome, forming a mRNA–ribosome complex.

5 Molecules of tRNA bind to molecules of amino acid dissolved in the cytoplasm of the cell. There are as many types of tRNA molecule as there are types of amino acid. Each type of tRNA molecule binds to its particular type of amino acid.

6 tRNA/amino acid combinations pass to the mRNA–ribosome complex. Here the exposed bases of each tRNA bind to their complementary bases on the mRNA. The complementary bases come as triplets (a sequence of three) each called a codon. Each amino acid has a specific codon. The tRNA/amino acid combinations are held in place next to each other on the mRNA by the complementary pairing of codons between the mRNA and tRNAs. Chemical bonds form between the amino acids next to each other while still bound to their respective tRNAs.

7 Once the bonds form, each tRNA separates from its respective amino acid and the mRNA strand holding it, with the amino acids transferred to the ribosome.

8 The linked amino acids form a polypeptide.

Notice that the base sequence of the mRNA bound to the ribosome depends on, and is a complement of, the base sequence of the DNA strand against which the mRNA strand was transcribed in the first place. The information that controls the order in which the tRNA/amino acid combinations bind to the mRNA is therefore contained in the sequence of the mRNA's codons, themselves a complement of the codon sequence of the transcribing DNA.

QUESTIONS

5 Explain how protein-making information passes from DNA to protein.

6 HIV is an example of a virus that carries RNA and not DNA as its genetic material. Use the internet to find out how RNA viruses make proteins.

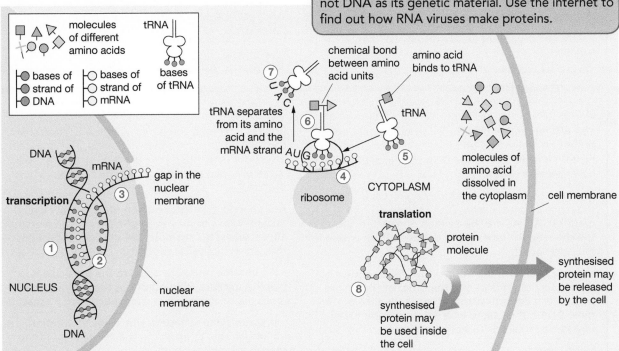

FIGURE 2: Protein synthesis simplified: follow the process 1–8.

Mutations

Mutant flies

In the early 20th century one of the first mutations to be studied was eye colour in the fruit fly. A white-eyed individual was found among a population of pure-bred red-eyed flies. White-eye is the result of a mutation in one of the genes controlling eye colour in fruit flies.

FIGURE 1: A red-eyed normal and white-eyed mutant fruit fly. *Drosophila melanogaster* is often used in genetics experiments as it is easy to take care of, breeds quickly and lays many eggs.

Variation and mutation

Mutations can occur in the genes of sperm and eggs. If either carries a mutated gene, the mutation will be inherited by offspring following fertilisation.

Often a mutation is harmful. Why is that? Think of it like this:

> A printing error is more likely to make nonsense words than to improve a book.

> A mutation is the equivalent of a printing error.

> Altering the proteins produced is more likely to disturb the activity of cells than to improve their chances of survival.

> Affected organisms are therefore less likely to survive.

However, some genes we now call normal were once mutants. The mutations added genetic variation that by chance was beneficial and favoured survival of the ancestral organisms carrying them. Their descendants inherited the genes and now are the normal versions.

Some mutations do not affect an organism's chances of survival one way or another. The mutations are neutral in their effect.

QUESTIONS

1 Describe why mutations are often harmful.

2 State why some mutations might be beneficial.

How mutations change DNA

You will remember that the information needed to order one amino acid unit into its correct place in a protein is contained in the DNA sequence of three bases called a codon.

Mutations arise because of copying errors in the sequence of bases during DNA replication (see page 23). A base may be deleted or inserted, altering the sequence of bases along the gene from where the mutation occurs.

Figure 2 compares the normal DNA base sequence of a small section of DNA and the order of the amino acid units it controls with the base sequence of the same DNA but mutated by a deletion (removal of a base) or an insertion (addition of a base).

Notice that for each mutated version of the gene, the order of amino acid units from where the mutation occurs is changed compared with the normal order controlled by the non-mutated gene. The changes affect the structure of the protein. Structure (and therefore shape) is essential to the function of a protein.

Any change in structure often changes how well the protein works or may even prevent it from working at all. Enzymes, for example, are specialised proteins that act as biological catalysts:

> An enzyme molecule binds to the molecule it is helping to react. Binding brings the enzyme and its molecule closer together. This speeds up the reaction.

> If the enzyme's shape is altered by a mutation, it is no longer able to attach to the molecule, and the reaction does not occur.

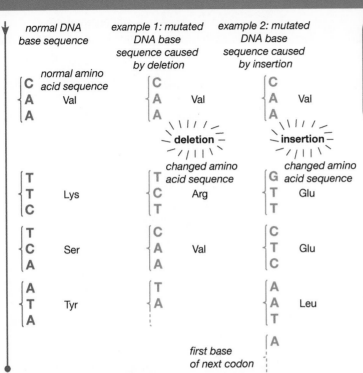

QUESTIONS

3 Describe how mutations occur.

4 Explain how a mutation might affect protein synthesis.

Remember!

Mutation in bacteria can lead to drug resistance.

FIGURE 2: The deletion or insertion of a base causes a mutation. The amino acid units and their sequence controlled by the particular short sequence of DNA bases shown here are named as their internationally recognised abbreviations. *Don't worry … you don't need to learn the names.*

Silent mutations

A codon specifies a particular amino acid, and the sequence of codons determines the position and therefore the order in which amino acid units join together, making a specific protein.

With two exceptions, each amino acid is specified by more than one codon. If a mutation changes a codon to an alternative that still specifies the same amino acid, and the sequence of codons (including the mutated codon) is unchanged, then the amino acid sequence and the structure of the protein are also unchanged. Such a mutation is called a substitution.

We say that the mutation is a **silent mutation**, that is, it is a mutation that is neutral in its effect.

QUESTIONS

5 Explain how a mutation changes an organism's genotype but might not change its phenotype.

6 Use the internet to research which amino acids are specified by only one codon.

7 The genetic code is often written as the mRNA base sequence and not the DNA base sequence. Write out the mRNA sequence transcribed from the normal DNA base sequence shown in Figure 3.

normal DNA base sequence   *mutated DNA base sequence*

normal amino acid sequence	
C A A — Val	C A A — Val
T T C — Lys	T T C — Lys
	unchanged amino acid sequence
T C A — Ser	T C G — Ser
	— substitution —
A T A — Tyr	A T A — Tyr

FIGURE 3: A silent mutation alters the base sequence of a gene but *not* the sequence of the amino acid units of the protein encoded by the gene.

Did you know?

Recent research has suggested that under certain conditions silent mutations can determine how well a final protein works.

Enzymes

You will find out:

> that enzymes are biological catalysts

> about the specificity of enzymes

> about the 'lock-and-key' hypothesis

> about the action of enzymes inside and outside cells

Putting enzymes to work

Many of the laundry-washing detergents on sale today contain enzymes. The manufacturers include different enzymes to help wash out oily marks, sticky sugars and protein stains. Only a tiny fraction (less than 1% by weight) of the powder is actually enzyme.

FIGURE 1: Biological washing powders contain enzymes which allow the washing to be done at a lower temperature. Why might this be a good thing?

Introducing enzymes

Biological catalysts

Enzymes are **catalysts**. In general, a catalyst:

> increases the rate (speed) of chemical reactions

> is effective in small amounts

> is chemically unchanged at the end of the chemical reaction it is catalysing.

Enzymes are biological catalysts. Most of them are made of proteins and they increase the rate of chemical reactions both inside and outside cells.

All of the listed features of catalysts are also features of enzymes.

However, because most of them are proteins, enzymes are also sensitive to changes in:

> temperature

> pH (acidity/alkalinity).

Enzymes are also very **specific** in their action. Each enzyme only catalyses a particular chemical reaction or type of chemical reaction.

Processes involving enzymes can take place inside and outside living cells. Examples are:

> DNA replication takes place inside cells.

> Protein synthesis takes place inside cells.

> Digestion takes place outside cells.

FIGURE 2: An enzyme called amylase in this baby's saliva starts the digestive process by converting starches in the bread to simpler molecules.

Did you know?

Enzymes used in biological washing powders are often produced by bacteria, such as *Bacillus subtilis* and *B. licheniformis*.

QUESTIONS

1 Choose from a–d which phrase best completes the sentence: Enzymes are called catalysts because they …
   a are proteins
   b are affected by changes in temperature
   c are affected by changes in pH
   d change the rate of chemical reactions.

2 What is an enzyme?

3 Suggest a reason why enzymes are often found in washing powders.

How enzymes work

The substance that an enzyme helps to react is called the **substrate**. The substance formed in the reaction is the **product**. The reaction starts when the enzyme and its substrate combine. The combination is called an **enzyme–substrate complex** (see Figure 3).

Notice that only a small part of the enzyme molecule shown in the figure binds with its substrate molecule. This part is called the **active site**. It consists of just a

Remember!

Enzymes need the correct temperature and pH to work effectively.

few of the amino acid units that make up the enzyme molecule as a whole.

The active site has a precise shape. It will only bind with a particular substrate molecule because the shape of the active site matches its shape. We say that their shapes are complementary and fit rather like a key fits into a lock.

Like a lock and key, only the shape of the particular substrate molecule fits the active site of the enzyme. An enzyme will only catalyse a particular reaction because only the shape of its active site matches the shape of the substrate molecule.

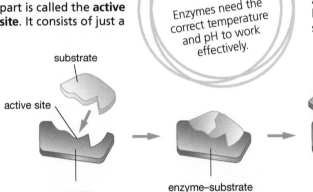

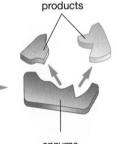

substrate

active site

enzyme

enzyme–substrate complex

products

enzyme

FIGURE 3: How an enzyme catalyses the breakdown of a molecule. Why do you think the fit of a substrate with its active site is compared with a lock and key?

QUESTIONS

4 Use your knowledge of chemistry to help you to state the difference between a reactant and a substrate.

5 Describe the relationship between an enzyme as a whole and its active site.

Enzyme actions inside and outside living cells

DNA replication

During cell division the DNA makes an exact copy of itself (see page 23) inside the cell. The weak hydrogen bonds, which hold together the two strands of the chromosome's DNA double helix, break using an enzyme called **DNA polymerase**.

DNA polymerase is a very accurate enzyme, creating an exact copy of the DNA and making less than one error in a billion bases. The base pairing of C to G and A to T allows for such high accuracy. Most DNA polymerases also check the copying. When an incorrect base pair is found the DNA polymerase reverses its direction by one base pair of DNA to correct itself.

Protein synthesis

Proteins are synthesised inside the ribosomes of cells. For this to happen hundreds or even thousands of amino acid units must join together in the correct order. DNA is responsible for getting the correct number of amino acid units to join together in the correct order. Enzymes speed up the rate of joining of the amino acid units that have been arranged in the correct order.

Digestion

Digestion is a process that enables solid food to be broken down into a form that can be absorbed into the body. The digestive enzymes speed up the chemical reactions that are involved in breaking down food.

Digestive enzymes work outside cells, for example in the mouth, in the stomach and in the small intestine, to break down the different substances that are found in food. Digestive enzymes include: amylase, an enzyme that helps to break down starches; pepsin, an enzyme that works on protein; and lipase, an enzyme that breaks down fats.

QUESTIONS

6 Suggest why the structure of DNA polymerase varies very little from species to species.

7 Explain, from an evolutionary point of view, why it is important that DNA polymerase is a very 'accurate' enzyme.

8 Draw a flowchart to show the action of enzymes in protein synthesis.

Factors affecting enzymes

You will find out:
> about the different factors affecting enzyme action
> about denaturing enzymes

Enzymic activity

Nearly all enzymes are proteins. The photograph shows you what happens when proteins (in this case milk proteins) are exposed to changes in pH. The milk has curdled because lactic acid bacteria in the milk have lowered its pH. The protein molecules have formed a white mass in the bottle because the change in pH has altered their shape. Changes in pH alter the shape of enzyme molecules, affecting their activity.

FIGURE 1: Denatured proteins can be useful, but not here.

Effect of temperature and pH on enzyme action

Figure 2 shows the effects of changing temperature and pH on the activity of **amylase** and **pepsin**.

These enzymes catalyse some of the reactions that digest food.

Enzyme activity increases as the temperature goes up and reaches a maximum. If the temperature goes up further then activity decreases. Human enzymes start to denature at temperatures above 40 °C.

The activity of pepsin and amylase is at a maximum for different conditions of pH:

> Pepsin activity is at a maximum in acid conditions.

> Amylase activity is at a maximum in alkali conditions.

Strongly acid or alkaline conditions reduce the activity of the enzymes.

Remember!

Do not describe an enzyme as being destroyed: denaturing refers to a loss of shape, not breaking up of the enzyme.

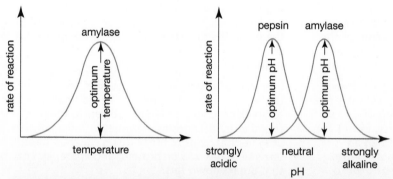

FIGURE 2: Effects of temperature and pH on the rates of reactions catalysed by the enzymes amylase and pepsin. Rate of reaction is a measure of an enzyme's activity. Which enzyme is most active at pH 5?

QUESTIONS

1 The graph shows how temperature affects an enzyme-controlled reaction.

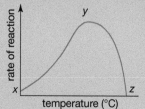

a Explain what is happening between x and y and between y and z.

b State at what temperature you would expect the reaction rate to be quickest.

c Suggest how a temperature greater than y might affect the active site of the enzyme.

Investigating factors affecting enzyme activity

Temperature and pH

Figure 2 shows that changes in temperature and pH affect enzyme activity.

> *What does 'optimum' mean?* 'Optimum' is the value of temperature or pH when the rate of formation of enzyme–substrate complexes is at a maximum. Therefore the rate of enzyme-catalysed reactions is at a maximum.

> *Why is the rate of enzyme-catalysed reactions less at non-optimum temperature values?* Enzymes are less active. As the temperature approaches 0 °C, most enzymes stop working. We say that they are **deactivated**. Many enzymes also stop working at temperatures above 60 °C. Their shape (particularly the active site) is permanently altered. We say that they are denatured.

> *Why is an enzyme less active at temperature or pH values above its optimum?* The enzyme (and its active site) is increasingly denatured at temperature and pH values above its optimum. Fewer enzyme–substrate complexes form because the shapes of the active site and substrate molecule no longer match (the 'lock' is no longer a fit for the 'key'). The rate of the enzyme-catalysed reaction is reduced.

QUESTIONS

2 What happens when an enzyme is denatured?

3 How does the concentration of substrate affect the rate of an enzyme-catalysed reaction when more than enough enzyme is present?

4 Write the outline of an experiment to investigate the effect of pH on enzyme action.

Substrate concentration

The substance an enzyme helps to react is called the substrate and the concentration of the substrate is another factor affecting enzyme activity (see Figure 3).

1 When there is more than enough (excess) enzyme, the rate of reaction is proportional to the concentration of substrate.

2 When all of the enzyme's active sites are filled with substrate molecules the rate of reaction becomes limited – it levels off.

3 Adding more enzyme increases the rate of reaction because more active sites are now available to substrate molecules which then fill them. The rate of reaction is once again proportional to the concentration of substrate.

The effects of changing substrate concentration on the rates of reaction assume that all other factors affecting enzyme activity are constant.

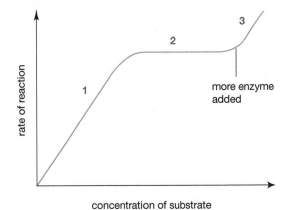

FIGURE 3: Enzyme activity varies with the concentration of substrate. How might the graph look different at point 1, if the temperature was just above optimal?

Denaturing

We have seen the effects of temperature and pH in reducing the rate of enzyme-controlled reactions. Generally, these effects are reversible. That is, if conditions return to optimal the enzyme's activity returns to normal. However, at extremes of temperature or pH the enzyme becomes denatured by permanent damage.

Enzymes have a complicated three-dimensional structure and the extremes in temperature or pH will damage the weak hydrogen bonds holding the structure together. This will alter the shape of the active site. As we have already seen, it is important that the active site matches the substrate molecule. Without a functioning 'lock' even the correct 'key' will not work.

 QUESTIONS

5 Explain the advantage of pepsin not being denatured at low pH.

6 Enzyme-controlled reactions are used to produce commercially important products. Enzymes from organisms that live in hot springs are stable up to 100 °C. Explain why enzymes extracted from bacteria that live in hot water springs might be of commercial interest.

Preparing for assessment: Applying your knowledge

To achieve a good grade in science, you not only have to know and understand scientific ideas, but you also need to be able to apply them to other situations. This task will support you in developing these skills.

✸ GM crops: famine or feast?

In the early 1990s scientists produced a variety of sweetcorn that produced a poison to kill harmful insects. The sweetcorn was named Bt-sweetcorn because it has been genetically modified to contain the poison producing genes of a bacteria called *Bacillus thuringiensis*. Once the initial plants had been successfully genetically modified, tissue culture was used to clone large numbers of genetically identical sweetcorn plants that contained the poison gene.

The poison is particularly effective at killing a type of pest called a corn borer, which every year costs the farming economy in the UK millions of pounds in lost yields.

Fortunately, the poison is harmless to humans and helpful insects such as bees and ladybirds. However, new research carried out has suggested that the Bt-sweetcorn may be responsible for the decline of the Monarch butterfly – a useful insect which feeds on unwanted plants such as milkweed. Monarch caterpillars do not feed on the sweetcorn but ingest it when pollen from Bt-sweetcorn plants lands on the leaves of milkweed.

While the benefits may seem obvious – a higher yield of sweetcorn is produced without the need for harmful chemicals – anti-GM supporters say that Bt-sweetcorn should be banned. They say that harmful insects will soon become resistant to the poison as in the case of headlice in the 1980s. They also fear that using the poison to kill harmful insects may upset ecosystems.

✸ Task 1

> What concerns might a consumer have about eating Bt-sweetcorn?

> Why is it difficult to reassure the consumer about such concerns?

Task 2

> State a feature in the structure of bacteria that makes them more suitable to be used in genetic engineering, rather than other poison-producing organisms such as jellyfish.

 Task 3

> How might the biodiversity of a sweetcorn field be affected by the introduction of Bt-sweetcorn?

> What effect might this have on the yield of Bt-sweetcorn produced in the future?

 Task 4

> Why might farmers carry on growing Bt-sweetcorn despite the damage to the Monarch butterfly population?

 Task 5

> Write a newspaper report of 300 words that argues the case either for or against the cultivation of Bt-sweetcorn in a country suffering from famine.

 Maximise your grade

These sentences show what you need to include in your work to achieve each grade. Use them to improve your work and be more successful.

E

For a grade G–E, your answers should show that you can:
> recall how farmers can produce identical copies of crops
> understand that GM crops can affect biodiversity
> outline some of the arguments for and against GM crops.

C

For a grade D–C in addition show that you can:
> understand that there are commercial and environmental factors to consider with GM crops
> explain most of the advantages and disadvantages of using genetic modification to produce new types of crops
> predict the consequences of growing GM crops on biodiversity.

A

For a grade B–A in addition show that you can:
> evaluate the arguments for and against GM crops, coming to your own conclusion.

Preparing for assessment: Planning an investigation

To achieve a good grade in science, you not only have to know and understand scientific ideas, but you need to be able to apply them to other situations and investigations. This task will support you in developing these skills.

 Investigating the effect of pH on the catalytic activity of catalase

The contents of a human stomach are so acidic that they can burn through clothes. Yet, enzymes can work in those conditions.

Catalase is an enzyme which catalyses the breakdown of hydrogen peroxide to water and oxygen.

hydrogen peroxide → water + oxygen

You are going to investigate how pH affects the ability of catalase to catalyse this reaction.

First, make a catalase solution, by crushing up a potato, mixing it with water and filtering the mixture. The filtrate contains catalase from the cells in the potato. Then divide the solution between five small beakers, and add a different buffer solution to each one (buffers keep a solution at a particular pH and can come in the range pH 3–11).

Here are two methods that you could use to measure the rate of the breakdown of the hydrogen peroxide.

Method 1

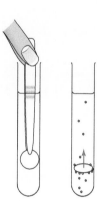

> Put some hydrogen peroxide into a test-tube.

> Cut out lots of small circles of filter paper using a hole punch.

> Using forceps, dip one circle of paper into the solution in one of the beakers.

> Push the paper circle to the bottom of the tube of hydrogen peroxide.

> Measure how long it takes for bubbles of oxygen to collect on the paper and lift it to the surface. The faster the reaction, the shorter the time this will take.

Method 2

Put some hydrogen peroxide into a small glass container. Place it on a sensitive top pan balance attached to a data logger. Add catalase solution to the container. Measure the decrease in mass as oxygen is produced and lost to the air.

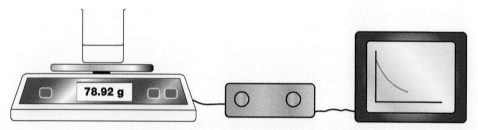

Planning

1. Suggest a hypothesis that you could test.

2. Which of the two methods would you choose? Explain your choice.

3. What would be the independent variable in your investigation? What would be the dependent variable?

4. Give the range of values that you will test for your independent variable.

5. State three variables that you would keep constant in your experiment. For each one, explain carefully how you would control this variable.

6. Write up the step-by-step instructions for the investigation.

7. Assess the risks involved with the method that you have chosen. Explain what you would do to reduce these risks.

8. Predict the results that you would expect to obtain. Explain your prediction.

 Processing evidence

1. Construct a results table in which you could record your results.

 Evaluating the investigation

1. Say briefly how you would decide whether or not your investigation had supported the proposed hypothesis.

2. Explain what you would do to evaluate the reliability (repeatability and reproducibility) of your results.

Connections

How science works

> Collecting and analysing data.

> Planning to solve a scientific problem.

> Working accurately and safely when collecting first-hand data.

> Evaluating methods of data collection.

> Planning an investigation using qualitative and quantitative approaches.

> Presenting information using appropriate language, conventions and tools.

Always give a scientific justification to support your hypothesis.

Your answer should discuss the advantages and disadvantages of each method. Finally, make your choice based on these.

Try to think of the variables that are most likely to make your results less valid if you do not control them.

Remember, your instructions should be clear enough for another student to follow them. Include detail on how you will use the equipment and how many tests you will carry out.

Look up each of the reagents used in this reaction to see if they are hazardous.

You may like to look up the optimum pH of catalase. Otherwise, use your knowledge of other enzymes to suggest an answer.

A good results table is easy for someone else to look at and understand. You may want to try out two or three designs before choosing the best one. Remember to put units in the headings of columns and rows.

Think back to the hypothesis and what results you would have expected had it been correct.

Repeatability means that, if you did your experiment again, you would get the same results. 'Reproducibility' means that, if someone else did the experiment, using different materials and equipment, they would get the same results as you.

B2 checklist (Topic 1)

To achieve your forecast grade in the exam you'll need to revise

Use this checklist to see what you can do now. Refer back to pages 10–41 if you're not sure.

Look across the rows to see how you could progress – **_bold italic_** means Higher tier only.

Remember you'll need to be able to use these ideas in various ways, such as:
> interpreting pictures, diagrams and graphs
> applying ideas to new situations
> explaining ethical implications
> suggesting some benefits and risks to society
> drawing conclusions from evidence you've been given.

Look at pages 264–86 for more information about exams and how you'll be assessed.

This checklist accompanies the exam-style questions and the worked examples. The content suggestions for specific grades are suggestions only and may not be replicated in your real examination. Remember, the checklists do not represent the complete content for any topic. Refer to the Specification for complete content details on any topic and any further information.

To aim for a grade E	To aim for a grade C	To aim for a grade A
recall why light microscopes and electron microscopes are useful when studying cells	carry out simple magnification calculations	explain why the development of modern microscopes has enabled us to see cells with more clarity and detail
recall the names of the main components in plant and animal cells	describe the function of each cell component	explain the role of mitochondria and chloroplasts
recall what a gene is recall the basic structure of DNA	describe the structure of DNA	explain what we mean by complementary base pairing
recall that the work of scientists Watson, Crick, Franklin and Wilkins helped discover the structure of DNA	evaluate the roles of Watson, Crick, Franklin and Wilkins in the discovery of the structure of DNA	**_evaluate the implications of the Human Genome Project_**
recall what we mean by genetic engineering	describe the stages of the genetic engineering technique	evaluate the advantages and disadvantages of using bacteria to produce human insulin

To aim for a grade E To aim for a grade C To aim for a grade A

state some uses of genetically modified (GM) crops recall that there are issues associated with GM crops	discuss the advantages and disadvantages of golden rice	evaluate the use of herbicide-resistant crops

recall that mitosis results in two daughter cells identical to the parent cell and that it is used for growth, repair and asexual reproduction	describe simply how mitosis results in two diploid daughter cells describe simply how meiosis results in four haploid daughter cells	explain in detail the process of mitosis and meiosis to include what happens to the chromosomes

describe how plants are cloned by using cuttings

describe how embryo transplants are used	discuss the advantages, disadvantages and risks of cloning mammals	*explain each stage of the production of a cloned mammal*

recall that stem cells in the embryo can differentiate into all other types of cells	describe how stem cell therapy can be used	evaluate the use of stem cell therapy

recall that each protein has its own specific sequence of amino acids, resulting in different shaped molecules recall that the order of bases in a gene decides the order of amino acids in a protein	describe why the order of the bases in a gene decides the shape and function of a protein	*explain what happens in each stage of protein synthesis*

recall what a mutation is	describe how a mutation can be harmful, beneficial or neither

state that enzymes are biological catalysts	use the 'lock and key' hypothesis to describe how enzymes work	explain the role of enzymes in DNA replication and protein synthesis

state what conditions affect the activity of an enzyme	explain why a change in conditions will affect the activity of an enzyme

1 Scientists use microscopes to view things that cannot be seen with the naked eye. Some microscopes are more powerful than others.

AO1 **a** Describe one way that light can enter the objective lens of a light microscope. [1]

AO1 **b** Light microscopes have been used by scientists for the past 200 years. More recently the invention of the electron microscope has allowed us to view even smaller objects such as viruses, which had not previously been seen. Suggest one advantage of using light microscopes in schools rather than electron microscopes. [1]

AO2 **c** Calculate the total magnification power of a light microscope which has an eyepiece magnifying power of ×20 and an objective lens power of ×50. Show your workings. [2]

AO1 **d** The diagram below shows a bacterium cell viewed under a light microscope. State two features which are present in animal, plant and bacterium cells. [2]

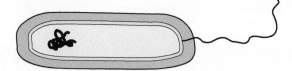

AO1 **e** Explain how the storage of genetic information is different in this bacterium compared to plant and animal cells. [2]

[Total: 8]

2 Diabetes is a serious condition that affects thousands of people in the UK. Patients often have to take daily injections of a hormone called insulin to control their blood sugar level. Previously, insulin could only be taken from the pancreas of dead pigs. More recently, scientists have managed to produce insulin in laboratories using bacterial cells.

AO1 **a** Explain why scientists can use bacteria to produce large amounts of insulin in a short space of time. [2]

AO1 **b** Suggest one disadvantage of using animals to extract insulin. [1]

AO2 **c** GM farming is a relatively new technology and involves inserting 'foreign' genes into the chromosomes of plants to give them new improved characteristics, for example making a tomato ripen on the supermarket shelf more slowly. Describe how a farmer could produce a wheat plant that is resistant to herbicides. [6]

[Total: 9]

AO1 **3** **a** Two daughter cells containing 46 chromosomes are produced during mitosis. Select the word from the list below that describes the correct term for a cell containing a full set of chromosomes. [1]

    A Zygote

    B Haploid

    C Diploid

    D Gamete.

AO1 **b** Suggest two situations whereby a cell might need to undergo mitosis. [2]

AO1 AO2 **c** Explain why the resulting number of daughter cells is different at the end of mitosis and meiosis. [3]

AO2 **d** Explain why scientists often refer to stem cells as 'the body's own repair kit'. [2]

[Total: 8]

AO1 **4** **a** Describe the function of an enzyme. [1]

AO1 **b** Explain why enzymes can be described as being specific to a particular substrate. You may draw a diagram to help with your answer. [2]

AO3 **c** Here is a graph for a mystery enzyme called 'enzyme Z', whose activity was tested over a range of pH solutions and the results plotted below.

  i Describe the pattern shown by the graph. [2]

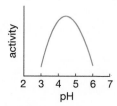

AO3 **ii** Using the information from the graph, state the enzyme's optimum pH. [1]

AO3 **iii** Suggest what happened to the enzyme at pH 6. [1]

AO3 **iv** Based on the evidence provided by the graph, in which part of the human body might you expect to find this enzyme? [1]

AO2 **v** Explain what would happen to the activity of this enzyme if it was placed in a solution of 60 °C. [3]

[Total 11]

Summary of Assessment Objectives

AO1 recall the science   AO2 apply your knowledge   AO3 evaluate and analyse the evidence

✳ Worked example

AO1 1 a Which of the following cells is not produced by mitosis? [1]

A ☑ Egg cell

B ☐ Skin cell

C ☐ Liver cell

D ☐ Nerve cell. **A correct answer**

AO2 b Why is it important that the cell you gave as your answer in part **a** is not produced by mitosis? [2]

The daughter cells would have too many chromosomes in them. ✔

They would have 92 and they need to have only 46. ✘

AO1 c Why is an organism that is produced by asexual reproduction a clone of its parent? [1]

Because during asexual reproduction the offspring receives an identical copy of the parent's chromosomes, making it genetically identical. ✔

AO2 d Children can look very similar to their parents but do not look identical. Explain why in terms of chromosomes. [3]

Chromosomes contain genes which control features about you, like way that you look. ✔

Boys get most of their chromosomes from their dad and girls get most from their mum so that's why they look similar. ✘ ✘

AO2 e Suggest why identical twins could be considered to be clones of each other. [3]

Clones are produced during asexual reproduction and have exactly the same genetic information as each other and also from their parent (their mum or their dad). ✔ ✘ ✘

The candidate has scored 5 out of 10. Overall, the candidate is familiar with key meanings and processes but gets confused when applying the knowledge correctly to the question. The candidate could improve their grade by taking time to read the question and fully answering all aspects of it.

How to raise your grade

Take note of the comments from examiners – these will help you to improve your grade.

The daughter cells would end up with 46 chromosomes in each cell. This would mean that a fertilised egg would end up with 92 instead of 46 chromosomes. The candidate has got confused with meiosis and the stages of mitosis. In meiosis the daughter cells divide twice to produce 4 haploid daughter cells. Remember meiosis – Sex cellS!

The candidate has given a good, clear definition of a clone.

While the candidate has correctly explained how we inherit our features it is not true that we inherit different numbers from our mother or father. We always inherit 23 from each. We look similar because we inherit characteristics from both of our parents but in different combinations.

The candidate has correctly described how clones are produced and has given a correct answer with regards to plants but the question asks about humans and how identical twins are produced. Identical twins are produced when a fertilised egg divides into 2 to form 2 identical zygotes. The resulting offspring are genetically identical but not to their parents but can still be considered clones of each other.

1 Cells are specialised to their role.

AO1 **a** Explain two ways in which plant cells are adapted to their role. [2]

AO2 **b** Suggest why a muscle cell might have more mitochondria than a skin cell. [1]

AO1
AO2 **c** Stem cells are unspecialised cells. Explain how muscle cells are formed from stem cells. [3]

AO1
AO2 **d** Adult stem cell therapy can be used to treat genetic disorders such as cystic fibrosis. Discuss the advantages and disadvantages of using an adult's own stem cells to treat cystic fibrosis. [4]

[Total 10]

2 Mutations are mistakes that occur during DNA replication.

AO2 **a** Explain what is meant by the term 'neutral mutation'. [2]

AO3 **b** Here is a section of the DNA base sequence taken from a goat.

A
T
A
T
T
C

The base sequence is replicated during DNA replication as:

A
A
T
T
C
A

Use this information to explain how a mutation has occurred in the DNA base sequence. [2]

AO1
AO2 **c** Mutations can sometimes be beneficial. A dairy farmer wants to clone a goat that has a gene mutation that allows her to produce more milk. Describe the stages in cloning the goat. You may draw a diagram to help with your answer. [6]

[Total 10]

3 There are over 5000 types of protein found in the body including those found in skin and hair. Proteins are made in your cells through the processes of transcription and translation.

AO1 **a** Name the building blocks found in cells from which proteins are made. [1]

AO1 **b** RNA (ribonucleic acid) plays a role in protein synthesis. Which of the following properties does **not** describe the properties of RNA? [1]

A RNA sugar is made of ribose

B RNA structure is double stranded

C RNA contains a phosphate backbone

D RNA has the following bases: U, G, C and A.

AO1 **c** mRNA is messenger RNA. It is formed when RNA nucleotide bases found in the cell's nucleus join up. Describe the role of mRNA in protein synthesis. [3]

AO2 **d** Explain how it is possible for the human body to produce over 5000 types of proteins when cells are only capable of producing 21 different amino acids. [2]

[Total 7]

4 A group of students carried out an experiment to extract DNA from the cells of a kiwi fruit. They used the following method.

1. Chop up kiwi fruit and add to saline solution.

2. Heat the solution in a water bath (temperature 50 °C) for 15 minutes.

3. Filter and collect the filtrate.

4. Add cold methanol to the filtrate.

5. Use tweezers to remove the DNA that forms at the boundary between the methanol and the filtrate.

AO2 **a** Suggest why the water bath should be heated to 50 °C. [1]

AO2 **b** Methanol was used during the experiment. State a hazard associated with methanol and the precautions that the student should take to minimise the risk associated with the hazard. [2]

AO1 **c** A kiwi chromosome is made from a folded double-stranded DNA molecule coiled around a protein.

Describe how Watson and Crick discovered the structure of DNA in the 1950s. [3]

[Total: 6]

✳ Worked example

AO1 **1 a** Describe the role of DNA in the production of proteins. [2]

DNA is responsible for arranging amino acids together in the right order ✔ *to code for a particular protein.* ✔

AO1 **b** During protein synthesis molecules of translation RNA (tRNA) bind to amino acids. Where do these amino acids come from? [2]

They come from the DNA because DNA is made up of groups of 3 bases which make an amino acid. Protease is the name of the enzyme which breaks down proteins into amino acids. ✘ ✘

AO2 **c** The Human Genome project was launched in 1989 with the aim of discovering all of the sequences of bases that appear within the total DNA found inside a human cell.

Evaluate the arguments for and against using the results from the Human Genome Project in medicine. [6]

The people who are making the decision about the Human Genome Project were not elected by anybody.

Some countries might use information about an ethnic group's resistance to getting a disease against them.

The Human Genome Project cost a lot of money, which could be spent elsewhere.

The Human Genome Project will allow scientists to create new drugs and medicines to treat more genetic conditions. Drugs will be able to be specifically given to treat a person according to their individual genome. Scientists will be able to build up more information on global patterns of diseases and design treatments as necessary.

The candidate scored 5 out of 10. They struggled with the Higher Tier concept of protein synthesis in **b** and with the quality of their written communication in **c**. This meant that they lost valuable marks. Remember that every mark counts to improve your grade.

However, they showed a good basic understanding of the Human Genome Project (a Higher tier concept) and so they show that they have the ability to access trickier scientific ideas. Careful revision of Higher tier topics and practice of extended writing would bring their work up to a grade A.

How to raise your grade

Take note of the comments from examiners – these will help you to improve your grade.

The candidate has correctly identified the role of DNA in protein synthesis.

A correct answer would have stated that the amino acids are dissolved in the cytoplasm of the cell and do not appear until they are needed to bind with the tRNA. This candidate is confused over the meanings of key terms. Make sure that you learn them carefully. The candidate has also given extra unnecessary (correct) information which does not gain them any marks.

Although this is an argument against using the results of the Human Genome Project, this point gains no marks as it is not explained or related back to the question.

Again, this point is not related back to the question.

The candidate has scored in Level 2 of the banded mark scheme used to mark 6-mark questions. They have shown a fairly detailed understanding of the Human Genome Project. However, they have not expressed themselves with full clarity, related the points back to the original question or weighed the pros and cons against each other. They have also failed to provide a conclusion (necessary in an 'evaluate' question).

B2 The components of life (Topics 2–3)

What you should know

Respiration

Respiration is a process carried out by all living cells that releases energy from food.

Exercise increases heart and breathing rate.

 Why does your heart beat faster when you run?

Plants and ecology

Plants use a process called photosynthesis to make sugars.

Light, water and carbon dioxide are needed for photosynthesis.

An ecosystem is a habitat containing interdependent living things.

 How would you collect evidence to prove that plants need light for photosynthesis?

Fossils

Fossils are the preserved remains of living organisms. They can provide evidence about that living organism and its environment.

Fossils are formed over millions of years and are found in sedimentary rock (C1 – Topic 2).

Darwin explained how evolution occurred through natural selection (B1 – Topic 1).

 Fossils exist in layers of rock. Where are the oldest ones found?

Tissues, organs and systems

That cell division is needed for growth (B2 – Topic 1).

Examples of organs include the heart, kidneys and the brain. Examples of organ systems include circulatory, respiratory, digestive, nervous, reproductive, skeletal and excretory.

White blood cells help defend the body against pathogens (B1 – Topic 3).

The heart pumps blood around the body via vessels.

During digestion, food is broken down physically and chemically, so that it can be absorbed into the blood. Undigested food leaves the body as faeces.

 Why does blood need to reach every part of the body?

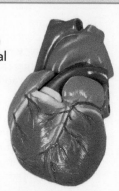

You will find out about

> the importance of respiration to living organisms

> diffusion as a process that is essential for life

> the difference between respiration with oxygen (aerobic) and without oxygen (anaerobic)

> how to calculate heart rate, cardiac output and stroke volume

> why you can only run at a fast pace for a short amount of time

> why post-exercise oxygen consumption is needed

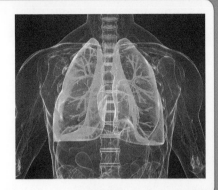

> the word equation for photosynthesis

> how the structure of a leaf is adapted for photosynthesis

> how limiting factors affect the rate of photosynthesis

> how water, glucose and mineral salts are transported through a plant

> what osmosis is

> how to use sampling techniques to investigate the distribution of organisms in an ecosystem

> how fossils provide evidence for evolution

> why there are gaps in the fossil record

> how the pentadactyl limb has provided evidence for evolution

> how plants and animals grow

> the organisation of cells into tissues, organs and systems

> the function of the components of blood

> how the different parts of the heart work together to pump blood around the body

> the components and functions of the digestive and circulatory systems

> what we mean by 'functional foods' and how to evaluate their health benefits

Respiring cells

Fuelling the machine

Respiration in the cells of all living organisms can sometimes be compared with burning fuel in engines, but there is an important difference. Burning fuel releases its energy in a single, hot, explosive reaction, whereas respiration is a slower process taking place at more moderate temperatures.

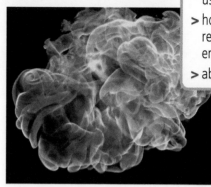

FIGURE 1: If cells respired glucose in one go, the heat released would destroy them.

Respiration

Aerobic respiration

There is less oxygen and more carbon dioxide in the air we breathe out (exhale) than in the air we breathe in (inhale).

Less oxygen:

> is the result of cells using oxygen in the chemical reactions that break down glucose molecules

> the chemical reactions are **oxidations** and release energy.

More carbon dioxide:

> is the result of the chemical reactions producing it.

The cells are respiring and the term **aerobic respiration** refers to the reaction:

glucose + oxygen → carbon dioxide + water + energy

The energy released in aerobic respiration is 16.1 kJ/g of glucose. All of the available energy is released from a glucose molecule during aerobic respiration.

Anaerobic respiration

Even when oxygen is in short supply, cells continue to respire. Molecules of glucose are broken down and the energy is released. The term **anaerobic respiration** refers to these reactions; 'anaerobic' means 'without oxygen'. For example, in muscle tissue:

glucose → lactic acid + energy

The energy released in anaerobic respiration is 0.83 kJ/g of glucose.

Notice that less energy is released per gram of glucose by cells respiring anaerobically than aerobically. This is because the glucose molecule is not fully broken down to carbon dioxide and water in anaerobic respiration and so not all of the available energy is released.

About 60% of the energy released from a molecule of glucose during aerobic respiration is heat (this is why we get warm when exercising). The rest drives life's processes, such as movement and reproduction.

QUESTIONS

1 **a** Which pathway, A or B, summarises aerobic respiration?
b Why is there a difference in energy values between pathways A and B?

A	Glucose + oxygen	→	carbon dioxide + water and 16.1 kJ/g of glucose
B	Glucose	→	lactic acid and 0.83 kJ/g of glucose

Respiration in muscle tissue

Getting ahead

You are running hard but at the end of the race you are tired and gasping for air. Why is that?

To begin with, aerobic respiration in the cells of your leg muscles gives you a flying start. Eventually you cannot breathe any faster and your heart cannot pump blood any faster. You cannot get any more oxygen to your muscle cells. When this happens, your body gets energy from glucose by anaerobic respiration, but this forms lactic acid.

The lactic acid from the anaerobic respiration reactions accumulates in the muscles. After a few minutes more of vigorous running you are exhausted.

Cellular respiration   Energy and organisms

Recovery

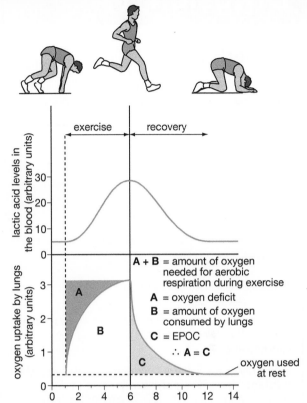

While you are recovering, rapid breathing draws more air (and oxygen) into the lungs. Your rapidly beating heart supplies more blood and its increased load of oxygen to the leg muscles, promoting aerobic respiration once more in the cells of the muscle tissue.

The extra volume of oxygen is needed because the muscle cells have to take in extra oxygen to break down the lactic acid into carbon dioxide and water. This extra oxygen used to be called the 'oxygen debt'; now we use the term **excess post-exercise oxygen consumption (EPOC)** instead (see Figure 3).

The time taken for the lactic acid to be removed and your breathing and heart rates to return to normal represents the **recovery period**:

lactic acid + oxygen → carbon dioxide + water

FIGURE 2: Athletes recovering at the end of a race. Write a word equation to show what is going on in their muscle tissue.

FIGURE 3: A summary of EPOC.

A + B = amount of oxygen needed for aerobic respiration during exercise
A = oxygen deficit
B = amount of oxygen consumed by lungs
C = EPOC
∴ A = C
oxygen used at rest

QUESTIONS

2 Why can sprinters only run at top speeds for a limited time?

3 Using graphs to illustrate your answer, explain what is meant by EPOC.

More on respiration

During aerobic respiration and anaerobic respiration, glucose is first converted in a series of reactions into a substance called pyruvic acid (don't worry, you won't have to remember the name). The reactions take place in the cell's cytoplasm. Then, if enough oxygen is available (aerobic conditions), pyruvic acid is oxidised in the cell's mitochondria in a series of reactions that produce carbon dioxide and water.

If oxygen is in short supply (anaerobic conditions), pyruvic acid in muscle cells is turned into lactic acid. Molecules of lactic acid represent a store of chemical bond energy which is only fully released when respired aerobically.

QUESTIONS

4 Explain, in terms of the end products of the chemical reactions, why less energy is released during anaerobic respiration compared with aerobic respiration.

5 Using the internet to help you, investigate how yeast cells respire and prepare a short report on how this is put to use in the baking and brewing industries.

Diffusion

You will find out:
> about diffusion
> that the human circulatory system helps diffusion
> about concentration gradients

Dinner's ready

You often know when dinner's ready because of the smell of cooking. How does the smell travel around the house? Particles that 'smell' are free to move about and travel from areas of high concentration to low concentration.

FIGURE 1: The tongue can distinguish between five tastes, while the nose can make out the difference between hundreds of different substances.

What is diffusion?

Molecules are in constant random motion. This means that:

> Molecules are likely to spread from areas where they are highly concentrated to areas of lower concentration.

> As a result there is a movement of molecules of a substance from where the substance is in high concentration to where it is in low concentration.

> This movement is called **diffusion**.

Molecules diffuse through gases as well as liquids:

> The greater the difference between the regions of high and low concentration, the faster the substance's rate of diffusion.

> Diffusion of a substance continues until it is the same concentration throughout the gas or the solution.

Substances move into and out of cells by diffusion, so it is a very important process in living things.

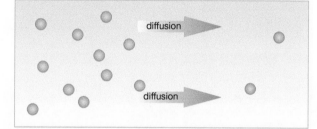

high concentration   low concentration

diffusion

diffusion

FIGURE 2: Diffusion: molecules of a substance move from where the substance is in high concentration to where it is in low concentration.

QUESTIONS

1 What does 'diffusion' mean?

2 State whether diffusion can occur through a gas, or a liquid, or both.

Diffusion in action

Blood is supplied to tissues by **capillary vessels**. These connect the arteries and veins of the circulatory system.

Blood transports glucose and oxygen *to* all of the tissues of the body and carbon dioxide *from* all of the tissues of the body. Hormones, antibodies, glucose and many of the other substances cells need or produce are also transported in the blood.

Diffusion is the way that substances pass between the blood and tissues. Figure 3 looks at the diffusion of oxygen and carbon dioxide in the blood:

> The concentration of oxygen in the air inside the alveoli is higher than in the blood supplied to them, so oxygen diffuses from the air in the alveoli into the blood in the capillaries.

> The concentration of carbon dioxide in the blood supplied to the alveoli is higher than in the air within them, so carbon dioxide diffuses from the blood into the air.

Breathing in constantly supplies the alveoli with air:

> The concentration of oxygen in the alveoli therefore remains high even though diffusion removes it to the blood.

> The concentration of oxygen in the blood passing through tissues decreases. Why? The oxygen diffuses from the blood into the tissues. The circulatory system returns blood to the alveoli, where more oxygen diffuses from them into the blood passing through.

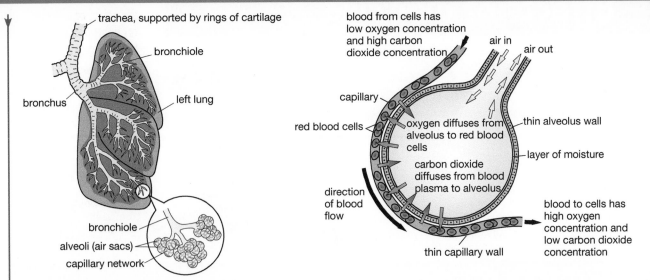

FIGURE 3: Gas exchange to and from blood in an alveolus.

QUESTIONS

3 State why carbon dioxide diffuses from respiring cells into the blood of the capillaries supplying them.

4 Prepare a flowchart to show how oxygen enters and carbon dioxide leaves the body.

Concentration gradients

The difference in concentration of a substance between the regions where it is in high concentration and lower concentration is its **concentration gradient**. The greater the difference between the regions, the greater the concentration gradient. As a result the rate of diffusion is maximised.

Capillaries form dense networks in tissues called capillary beds. No cell is very far from a capillary vessel (see Figure 4):

> The concentration of oxygen and glucose in the blood supplied to the cells of the body's tissues is higher than within the cells. Why? The cells are respiring and therefore consuming oxygen and glucose. Oxygen and glucose therefore diffuse from the blood in the capillaries into the cells.

> Respiring cells produce carbon dioxide. The concentration of carbon dioxide within the cells is therefore higher than in the blood supplied to them.

Carbon dioxide therefore diffuses from the cells into the blood in capillaries.

> Decrease in blood glucose levels because respiring cells consume glucose is balanced by its absorption into the blood from the small intestine. Glucose is also released into the blood from the liver.

Notice that glucose, oxygen and carbon dioxide diffuse from where they are in high concentration to where they are in lower concentration.

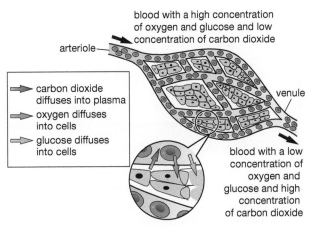

FIGURE 4: A capillary bed: oxygen and glucose diffuse from the blood to body cells and carbon dioxide diffuses from the cells to the blood.

QUESTIONS

5 Suggest why the movement of oxygen molecules is referred to as 'net movement'.

6 Explain the diffusion of glucose and carbon dioxide between the blood and the body's tissues in terms of concentration gradients.

Effects of exercise

You will find out:
> the effect of exercise on heart rate and breathing rate
> how to investigate the effects of exercise
> how to calculate heart rate, stroke volume and cardiac output

Pushing the body

Rowing is a vigorous form of exercise. The action at the start of a race makes big demands on the muscles, heart and lungs of each rower.

FIGURE 1: Rower Matthew Pinsent (front) had a heart rate of 45 beats per minute before the Olympic final; after winning the race it was 190 beats per minute.

Exercise and rates

Exercise affects the heart rate and breathing rate in proportion to the intensity of the exercise. Rowing is an intense form of exercise. The heart rate and breathing rate will increase sharply when racing.

> For the period of a race, the rowers' lungs will absorb more oxygen and the heart will pump more blood with its load of oxygen and glucose to the muscles.

> The chemical reactions of aerobic respiration in the muscle cells release energy, enabling their muscles to contract quickly and strongly.

> The chemical reactions produce carbon dioxide which passes from the muscle cells to the blood.

> The concentration of carbon dioxide in the blood increases, raising its acidity and therefore lowering its pH below 7.0.

> The lowered pH stimulates an increase in the heart rate and breathing rate of the rowers.

The rowers' heart and breathing rates remain high for some minutes after the race while they recover. This allows:

> More blood with its load of carbon dioxide to be passed to the lungs where it is exhaled (breathed out).

> The concentration of carbon dioxide in the blood to decrease, restoring the pH of the blood to its normal value of 7.4.

> The heart rate and breathing rate to return to normal.

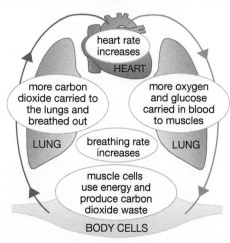

FIGURE 2: A summary of the effects of exercise on the body.

QUESTIONS

1 State the effects on the heart and lungs when the pH of the blood falls below pH 7.0 (neutral).

2 Why does it take a while for your body to return to normal after exercising?

Investigating the effects of exercise

You can carry out simple experiments into the effects of exercise on your body. For example:

> comparing the amount of carbon dioxide in your breath before and after exercise

> counting before and after exercise the number of breaths and heart beats per minute.

Investigating breathing rate

You will already know about the limewater test for carbon dioxide. It can be used in a simple experiment to investigate breathing rate.

If you breathe out through a straw into limewater (calcium hydroxide solution), the solution turns from

Exercise and blood pH   Limewater test   Exercise and breathing rate being clear to cloudy white. The carbon dioxide in your breath reacts with calcium hydroxide, producing a white **precipitate**, calcium carbonate.

Noting the time taken for the limewater to turn cloudy while you breathe out through a straw into it is an easy way of measuring your output of carbon dioxide.

Counting the number of times your back rises and falls in a minute gives the breathing rate.

Investigating heart rate

Each heartbeat sets up a ripple of pressure along the arteries. The ripple is felt as a **pulse**. Feeling the pulse therefore is an easy way of measuring heart rate (number of pulses per minute).

QUESTIONS

3 Where are the best locations on the body to measure a pulse?

4 When investigating the effect of exercise on the breathing rate and heart rate of a person, state the controls you could put into place to make the investigation a valid one.

5 Why are modern electronic methods of recording things such as heart rate better than older methods?

Breathing and heart rates

Calculating heart rate

One complete contraction and relaxation of the heart produces an unmistakable two-tone sound called the **heartbeat**. The sound is easily heard through a stethoscope.

In a healthy adult the resting heart beats on average 72 times a minute. This is the **heart rate** controlled by the heart's natural **pacemaker**.

Two nerves from the brain affect the pacemaker: nerve impulses from one speed up the heart rate; nerve impulses from the other slow it down. Our resting heart rate results from the balance between these opposite effects.

The volume of blood pumped from the heart each minute (called the cardiac output) depends on the heart rate and volume of blood pumped out with each beat (called the stroke volume). Heart rate, stroke volume and cardiac output measure the heart's effectiveness and fitness. Each can be calculated using the equation:

cardiac output = stroke volume × heart rate

If a student has a heart rate of 72 beats per minute and a stroke volume of 0.065 dm^3, their cardiac output can be calculated as follows:

cardiac output = 0.065 × 72 = 4.68 dm^3 per minute

Remember!

A fit person recovers more quickly and has a shorter recovery period than an unfit person.

Calculating breathing rate

Approximately 5.5 dm^3 of air fills a pair of human lungs. At rest about 0.5 dm^3 of air moves into and out of the lungs each time a person breathes.

The breathing rate is the number of breaths taken in a given time (a minute, for example):

number of breaths in a minute × volume of air per breath = volume of air exchanged per minute

The more air that is breathed in, the more oxygen reaches the muscles.

The muscle cells are respiring aerobically so more glucose is oxidised and more energy released. The muscles contract more vigorously, enabling a person to exercise more.

The increased rate of aerobic respiration in the muscle cells produces more carbon dioxide. The increased breathing rate rapidly removes the carbon dioxide from the lungs.

QUESTIONS

6 A sedentary office worker has a heart rate of 80 beats per minute and a stroke volume of 0.06 dm^3. Calculate his cardiac output. The office worker has to run to catch his train home. What effect is this likely to have on his cardiac output?

7 The heart rate of an athlete running on a treadmill was 120 beats per minute. The athlete's cardiac output from the left side of the heart was 6.0 dm^3 per minute. Calculate the stroke volume of the athlete's heart. Show your working.

Photosynthesis

You will find out:
> how the adaptations of a leaf maximise photosynthesis
> how photosynthesis uses light energy

Life on Earth

Plants provide much of the Earth's oxygen. During photosynthesis plants produce oxygen as well as glucose. Oxygen diffuses from the leaves into the atmosphere (or water in the case of submerged aquatic plants). This oxygen enables the cells of all living things to oxidise glucose in the reactions of aerobic respiration.

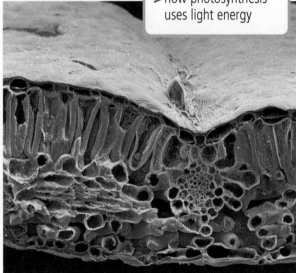

FIGURE 1: A micrograph of a leaf: notice the waxy upper surface and numerous vertical cells containing chloroplasts. What other cell component can you spot?

 Light and photosynthesis

Plants use sunlight, carbon dioxide and water to produce glucose, through the process of **photosynthesis**:

> Green plants are green because of the green pigment chlorophyll inside their cells. The **chlorophyll** is held in **chloroplasts**.

> The Sun floods the Earth with light.

> Chlorophyll absorbs light.

> Light energy drives the reactions that enable plant cells to combine carbon dioxide and water, producing glucose and oxygen.

> Photosynthesis refers to these reactions.

> Chloroplasts are where the reactions take place.

This word equation describes the process:

$$\text{carbon dioxide} + \text{water} \xrightarrow{\text{light energy}} \text{glucose} + \text{oxygen} + \text{water}$$

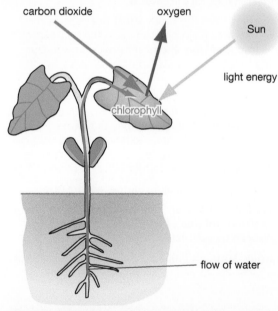

FIGURE 2: A summary of photosynthesis: light, carbon dioxide and water.

QUESTIONS

1 What chemicals are used up in photosynthesis?

2 What chemicals are made in photosynthesis?

3 State from where the plant obtains the chemicals you named in question 1 and question 2.

Leaves and photosynthesis

Figure 3 shows the inside of a leaf. Its characteristics are adaptations that help to maximise the rate of photosynthesis.

> The leaf is thin and flat, exposing a large surface area which maximises the absorption of light.

> The cells just under the upper surface of the leaf are packed with chloroplasts containing chlorophyll. Here light is brightest and the concentration of chlorophyll the greatest. Together, these features help to maximise the rate of photosynthesis.

> Air spaces enable gases and water vapour to circulate freely within the leaf. This means that the water and carbon dioxide needed for the reactions of photosynthesis are easily absorbed in solution by the leaf's cells. This helps to maximise the rate of the reactions.

> Oxygen is a product of photosynthesis and, together with the reactants carbon dioxide and water vapour, it diffuses between the leaf's air spaces and the atmosphere through the gaps called **stomata** (singular stoma) that perforate the underside of the leaf.

 QUESTIONS

4 Describe three adaptations of the leaf that help to maximise the rate of photosynthesis. Draw a diagram to help your answer.

5 Explain how gases and water vapour diffuse into and out of a leaf.

Did you know?

Chlorophyll is used as a food colorant and it even has a registered E number, E140.

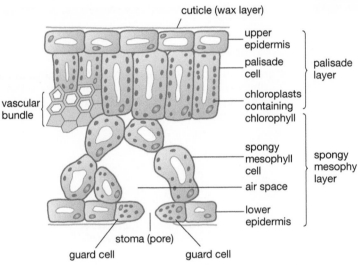

FIGURE 3: Inside a leaf. Suggest the purpose of the cuticle.

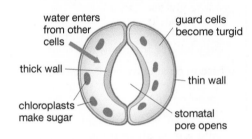

FIGURE 4: A stoma.

Gas exchange

Gas exchange in plants occurs through the stomata. During the day a plant, on average:

> Produces more oxygen by photosynthesis than it uses in aerobic respiration. The surplus oxygen diffuses down its concentration gradient through the stomata from inside the leaf to the outside.

> Produces less carbon dioxide by aerobic respiration than it uses in photosynthesis. Carbon dioxide therefore diffuses down its concentration gradient through the stomata from the outside of the leaf to the inside.

During the night photosynthesis stops:

> Plants use oxygen in aerobic respiration. Oxygen therefore diffuses down its concentration gradient through the stomata from outside the leaf to the inside.

> Plants produce carbon dioxide by aerobic respiration. Carbon dioxide therefore diffuses down its concentration gradient through the stomata from inside the leaf to the outside.

QUESTIONS

6 Sketch two graphs to show the volume of oxygen and carbon dioxide produced by a plant during the day and at night.

7 What advice would you give to a gardener about watering plants?

8 Algae live at different depths in the sea, where they photosynthesise. Explain why they are differently coloured.

Q Photosynthetic pigments   Light energy drives photosynthesis

Limiting photosynthesis

You will find out:
> about factors that limit the rate of photosynthesis

Deserts

No wonder hot deserts are virtually plant-free environments, even though the warmth and bright sunlight are just right for encouraging plant growth. Photosynthesis needs water; its absence limits photosynthesis.

FIGURE 1: Where there is water, there is life. How are these plants able to survive in a desert?

 ## The rate of photosynthesis

Limiting factors

Plants make glucose through the process of photosynthesis. The rate at which plants are able to carry out photosynthesis is affected by conditions of:

> temperature – chlorophyll works best in warm conditions

> light intensity – chlorophyll absorbs more light energy when light intensity is high

> carbon dioxide concentration – the higher the concentration in the atmosphere (or water), the more is absorbed

> water – an adequate supply is needed for the reactions of photosynthesis.

If any one of these conditions falls to a low level, the rate of photosynthesis slows even if the others are in abundant supply. This is called a **limiting factor** because it slows the rate at which plants make glucose.

Greenhouses remove limiting factors

A greenhouse provides all the conditions plants need for photosynthesis. Conditions are controlled so that the rate of photosynthesis is at a maximum. Limiting factors are removed.

Remember!
Photosynthesis needs light energy for the process:
carbon dioxide + water → glucose + oxygen + water

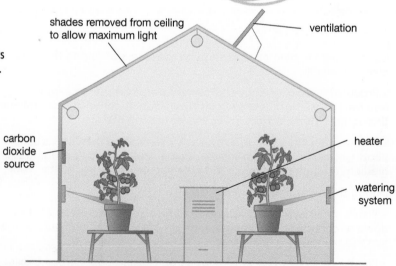

shades removed from ceiling to allow maximum light

ventilation

carbon dioxide source

heater

watering system

FIGURE 2: Plants grow quickly under glass because the greenhouse environment maximises the rate of photosynthesis.

Investigating limiting factors

A simple experiment for measuring the rate of photosynthesis is shown in Figure 3. The rate of photosynthesis is measured by counting the number of bubbles of oxygen produced by the water-weed in a given time.

How do we know that the gas produced is oxygen? Use the glowing splint test to see if oxygen is present.

Using this set-up will allow you to investigate the effects of changing light intensity, carbon dioxide concentration and temperature on the rate of photosynthesis.

 QUESTIONS

4 The rate of photosynthesis was measured at different light intensities. The results are shown in the table below.

Light intensity	1	2	3	4	5	6	7
Bubbles per minute	6	15	21	25	27	28	28

a Draw a graph to show the results of the experiment.
b At which light intensity was the rate of photosynthesis highest? Explain your answer.
c State the controls for the experiment.

Here are a few ideas for you to think about:

> Moving a lamp fixed distances away from bubbling water-weed alters the amount of light received by the weed.

> Using different concentrations of sodium hydrogen carbonate solution is a simple way of altering the amount of carbon dioxide available to the water-weed.

> If a temperature-controlled waterbath is not available then ice and hot water provide a simple way of investigating the effect of changing temperature on the rate of photosynthesis.

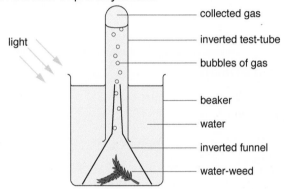

FIGURE 3: An experimental set-up to investigate the rate of photosynthesis. What is the gas collected?

Limiting factors at work

Different limiting factors affect the rate of photosynthesis, as we have seen. Asking questions will help you to understand how.

Why do most plants grow best in warm conditions?

The higher the temperature, the faster the rate of photosynthesis and the faster the production of materials that enable plants to grow, within limits.

If the temperature continues to increase beyond an optimum (when the rate of photosynthesis is maximal), then the rate of photosynthesis decreases. The optimum temperature for many plants is about 30 °C. Above this the enzymes controlling the different reactions of photosynthesis are denatured.

Why do plants grow more vigorously in bright sunlight?

High light intensity maximises the rate of photosynthesis and therefore the production of the materials that enable plants to grow. At night photosynthesis stops. The rate of photosynthesis increases up to a maximum value (called the optimum light intensity). If light intensity increases further the rate of photosynthesis does not.

Why do plants grow better in greenhouses with carbon dioxide added to the atmosphere?

The rate of photosynthesis increases as the concentration of carbon dioxide increases and the rate of plant growth increases, within limits. Any further increase in the concentration of carbon dioxide beyond its optimum does not result in a further increase in the rate of photosynthesis.

 QUESTIONS

5 The inverse square law states that the intensity of light is inversely proportional to the square of the distance from its source. How can this law be applied to the experiment described in question 4?

6 Design a greenhouse for growing cactus plants. Explain what features should be included to help them thrive.

Transport in plants

You will find out:

> that xylem tissue transports water and mineral salts

> that phloem tissue transports glucose

Nutrient movements

A large oak tree can lose up to 150 000 dm^3 of water through transpiration each year. Transpiration from the leaves draws the water and mineral salts absorbed in the roots up through the xylem tissue. Another tissue, phloem, transports glucose from the leaves to the rest of the tree.

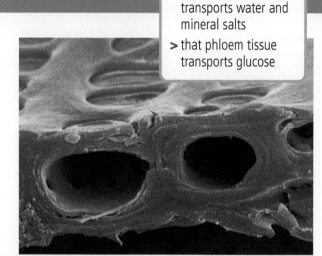

FIGURE 1: Coloured scanning electron micrograph (SEM) of a section through the xylem vessels of an oak tree (*Quercus robur*).

Transport tissues

Figure 2 shows the tissues that transport water, glucose and mineral salts to all parts of a plant:

> The tissues are called **xylem** and **phloem**

> Each tissue consists of tube-like cells.

Xylem tissue:

> runs from the tips of the roots through the stem and out into every leaf and flower

> carries water and mineral salts in solution to all parts of the plant.

Phloem tissue:

> runs by the side of the xylem

> carries dissolved glucose and other substances in solution to all parts of the plant.

At the soil's surface the central core of xylem and phloem in the root changes to a ring of vascular bundles in the stem. This arrangement helps the plant to resist the force of the wind tugging at the roots and bending the stem.

A **waxy cuticle** covers the leaf. This waterproof layer prevents the leaves from losing too much water. Plants growing in hot, dry environments have a thick cuticle, which cuts down water losses even more.

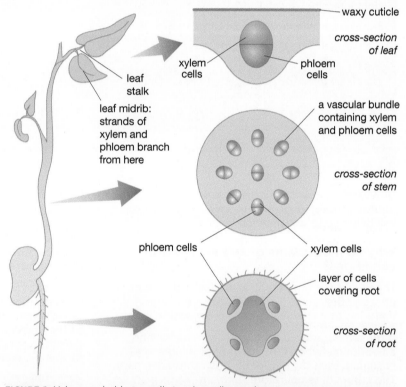

FIGURE 2: Xylem and phloem cells in a broadbean shoot.

QUESTIONS

1 Arrange the parts listed in the order that correctly describes the passage of water through a plant: stem, root hairs, leaves, root.

2 Describe differences in the arrangement of phloem tissue and xylem tissue in the root of a broad-leaved non-woody plant compared with its stem.

Q Vascular tissue of plants   Lignin in plants   Water transport in plants

Transport systems

Transpiration

In plants, water evaporates from the underside of leaves through the tiny gaps called stomata in a process called **transpiration**.

> As water is lost from the leaves, more is drawn up through the **xylem** tissue (columns of hollow, dead cells) from the roots.

> The roots in turn, absorb more water from the soil.

> The effect of evaporation is to move water and mineral salts from the roots to the leaves.

> The result is an unbroken column of water and mineral salts in solution moving up the plant from roots to leaves. This is called the **transpiration** stream.

Active transport

Mineral salts do not pass easily across a cell membrane. Therefore the plant uses an **active transport** mechanism. This involves special carrier proteins in the cell membrane reacting with mineral ions in the soil to bring them against their concentration gradient, inside the cell. This process requires energy released by aerobic respiration.

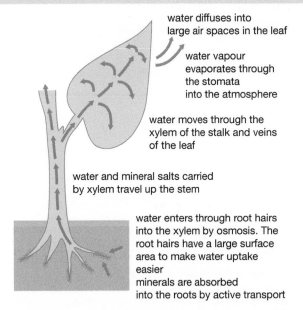

water diffuses into large air spaces in the leaf

water vapour evaporates through the stomata into the atmosphere

water moves through the xylem of the stalk and veins of the leaf

water and mineral salts carried by xylem travel up the stem

water enters through root hairs into the xylem by osmosis. The root hairs have a large surface area to make water uptake easier

minerals are absorbed into the roots by active transport

FIGURE 3: A summary of transpiration. Why doesn't water evaporate through the stem?

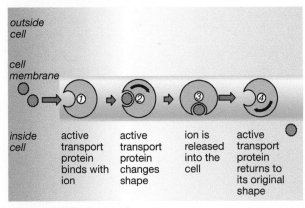

outside cell

cell membrane

inside cell | active transport protein binds with ion | active transport protein changes shape | ion is released into the cell | active transport protein returns to its original shape

FIGURE 4: The process of active transport.

QUESTIONS

3 Complete the following by inserting the correct terms: Root hairs _____ the surface area available for the _____ uptake of water. Water also moves across the root by _____ into the _____. The uptake of minerals in solution is by _____. Water moves through the _____ in unbroken columns, connecting the root with the leaves of the plant. Water vapour is lost from the leaves by _____ through the _____.

4 Compare the process of transpiration and active transport

Transport of glucose

Translocation is the process of transporting dissolved glucose through the phloem tissue. Glucose is produced by photosynthesis and used in respiration. Its concentration is higher where it is produced (leaves) than where it is used (all tissues). The differences in concentration of glucose in different parts of a plant drive the transport of dissolved glucose through phloem tissue.

Phloem tissue consists of two types of cell: tube-like **sieve cells** and **companion cells**. Dissolved glucose passes through the sieve cells. Their function is supported by the companion cells. The concentration of dissolved glucose in the leaf is often lower than

the concentration of glucose in the upper ends of the sieve tubes nearby. This is why active transport is needed to move glucose from the leaf into the sieve cells.

QUESTIONS

5 Explain why pressure in sieve cells drops as the cells of other tissues use glucose or convert it to starch.

6 Compare the features of xylem tissue with those of phloem tissues.

Osmosis and root hairs

You will find out:
> about osmosis
> that root hair cells are adapted to take up water by osmosis

Water gives shape

When a plant lacks water, its leaves droop. We say the plant is wilted. Cells need a non-stop supply of water and the substances dissolved in it to stay alive.

FIGURE 1: How could you help this flaccid plant to recover?

Osmosis

Diffusion is the movement of a substance in a gas or solution from where it is in high concentration to where it is in lower concentration. **Osmosis** is used to describe the diffusion of water through a partially permeable membrane.

> Watering increases the concentration of water in the soil compared with the root cells of the plant.

> Water passes from the soil into the root across the membrane surrounding each of its cells.

> Once water is absorbed by roots, it passes through the xylem to the leaves by transpiration.

> Here osmosis fills the leaf cells with water and the leaves lift and spread out as normal.

Now you know how a wilted plant recovers after it is watered.

Water passes into (and out of) all types of cell, not just plant cells.

> Water passes through a partially permeable membrane in both directions.

> The net flow of water molecules is from the more dilute solution outside the cell (the concentration of water is high) to the more concentrated solution inside the cell (the concentration of water is lower).

> The net flow of water molecules in one direction continues until the two concentrations are equal. Then, the flow of water molecules is the same in both directions.

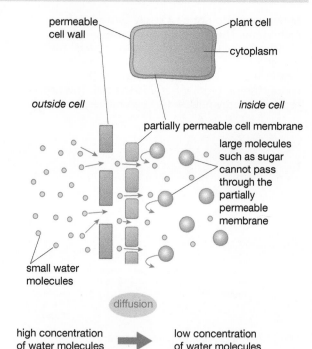

permeable cell wall

plant cell

cytoplasm

outside cell

inside cell

partially permeable cell membrane

large molecules such as sugar cannot pass through the partially permeable membrane

small water molecules

diffusion

high concentration of water molecules → low concentration of water molecules

FIGURE 2: Osmosis in action.

Remember!
When each plant cell contains as much water as it can hold, it is fully turgid.

QUESTIONS

1 State what is meant by osmosis.

2 What is meant by a partially permeable membrane?

3 Why does a plant deprived of water recover when watered?

Root hairs absorb water

Some of the cells that form the layer covering the surface of root tips are called root hair cells because they are drawn out into fine hair-like extensions. Roots themselves branch in all directions from the base of the stem. Branching roots and root hair cells cover a large surface area, anchoring the plant and maximising the absorption of water and mineral salts in solution from the soil.

Recall that plant cells, including root hair cells, contain a permanent space in the cytoplasm called a vacuole. This contains a solution of salts and sugars. It helps to maintain the difference in concentration of water between the inside of the cells and the outside. The solution outside the cells is more dilute than inside. Water therefore flows into the cells by osmosis.

The large surface area of root hair cells, each with a liquid-filled vacuole, is an adaptation that enables plants to maximise their absorption of water from the soil.

QUESTIONS

4 Describe the ways in which a root hair cell is adapted to facilitate osmosis.

5 Explain why osmosis might be described as a special case of diffusion.

6 Explain why animal cells are not turgid in the same way that plant cells are.

Did you know?

New research has focused on increasing root hair length as a potential way of increasing crop yields

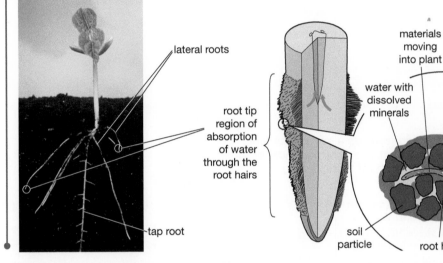

lateral roots

root tip region of absorption of water through the root hairs

tap root

materials moving into plant

water with dissolved minerals

root cells

soil particle

root hair

FIGURE 3: Water absorption through a plant's root system. Why do roots have hairs?

Root hairs absorb mineral salts

As well as water, root hair cells take up mineral salts in solution. Table 1 shows that solutions of mineral salts are much more concentrated in the cells of root tissue than in the soil where the dissolved salts come from.

Potassium, for example, is 1000 times more concentrated in root tissue than in soil. With this difference in concentrations you would expect root tissue to quickly lose mineral salts to the soil by diffusion.

So how then do mineral salts pass from the soil into root tissue? Active transport is the answer. During active transport molecules of substances (in this case mineral salts) pass from where they are in low concentration to where they are in higher concentration.

The process needs more energy than diffusion. The extra energy comes from the aerobic respiration of glucose.

TABLE 1: Comparison of mineral salt concentration in soil and roots (arbitrary units).

Mineral salt	Concentration in soil	Concentration in root tissue
Potassium	0.16	160
Nitrate	0.13	38

QUESTIONS

7 Explain why you might expect root tissue to lose mineral salts by diffusion. Use the data in Table 1 to support your answer.

8 Explain why the process of active transport requires more energy than diffusion.

Investigating osmosis

Life in salty solutions

How are some fish able to live in the sea? They have adapted to drink seawater and excrete some of the salt through their gills.

FIGURE 1: A salmon spends some of its life in seawater and some in fresh water. Why might this be a useful adaptation?

Osmosis in cells

Using red onions can help you to investigate osmosis in cells:

> Each layer of onion consists of leaves that are tightly packed together joining the stem.

> Snapping a layer in two produces rough edges that makes it easy to peel even thinner layers using tweezers.

> With practice you can peel layers so thin that each is only one cell thick.

Cover a one-cell-thick layer of red onion tissue on a microscope slide with a few drops of concentrated salt solution (sodium chloride) or sugar solution. Leave for 10 minutes and then dab off the excess liquid with a tissue.

Notice that the salt and sugar solution has caused the cytoplasm of the cells in Figure 2b to shrink away from the cell wall. You can easily see what has happened because of the red pigment in the cells. This is why it is best to use red onions (or other pigmented tissues such as rhubarb) to investigate osmosis.

The term **plasmolysis** refers to the shrinkage. As water passes out of the cells the turgor pressure, which was pressing the cytoplasm against the cell wall, decreases. This results in shrinkage of the cell's contents away from the cell wall and the appearance of the small patches of colour within cells. The cell becomes **flaccid** (limp), rather like a partly blown-up balloon.

Remember!

Osmosis is used to describe the diffusion of water.

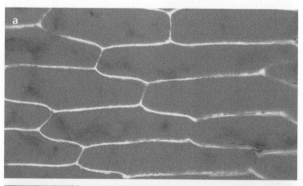
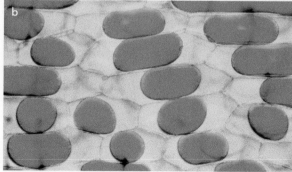

FIGURE 2: Plasmolysed red onion cells: **a** before the experiment and **b** afterwards.

QUESTIONS

1 Suggest why red onion cells are suitable for investigating osmosis.

2 Explain why most plants cannot grow in soil contaminated with seawater.

A model cell

Visking tubing is a partially permeable membrane. You can tie off each end of a length of tubing and use it as a sausage-like model to investigate the movement of substances into and out of cells. Figure 3 shows a simple example.

Note the appearance of each of the Visking 'sausages'. You can feel the texture of the sausages if you do the experiment. Try to explain what is happening in each case.

As water enters a cell, the pressure inside it increases. We call the pressure **turgor pressure** and the cell becomes turgid.

In the case of experiment **b** (in Figure 3), if you leave the 'Visking model' of a cell for 30 minutes, the model cell will become very turgid. Turgor pressure has built up inside the model.

 QUESTIONS

3 Explain why a Visking 'sausage' is a useful model of a cell.

4 What is the purpose of using water inside the first model in Figure 3?

5 Explain what is happening in experiment **c**. Use the term 'turgor pressure' in your answer.

6 Evaluate the pros and cons of using the Visking model to investigate osmosis, compared to using a microscope slide.

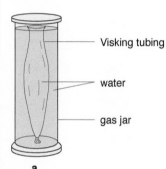

a

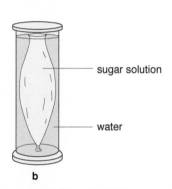

b

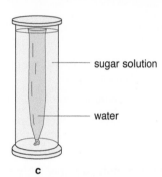

c

FIGURE 3: The Visking tubing experiment. **a** Filled with water and standing in water. **b** Filled with a sugar solution and standing in water. **c** Filled with water and standing in a sugar solution.

Water potential

Water molecules are in a constant state of motion. As water molecules move inside a cell they hit the membrane surrounding it and generate pressure called the **water potential**. We can now think of osmosis in a different way.

The more water molecules hitting a membrane the higher the water potential and the more likely they are to pass through it. A dilute solution of a particular substance contains more water molecules per unit volume than a more concentrated one. In other words, the water potential of the dilute solution is higher than the water potential of the more concentrated solution. Osmosis can now be defined in terms of different water potentials: osmosis occurs across a partially permeable membrane from a region of high water potential to a region of lower water potential, until the water potential on either side of the membrane is the same.

Water potential is a measure of the tendency of water to leave a solution. Instead of talking about a concentration gradient of water, we can now understand osmosis in terms of a water potential gradient.

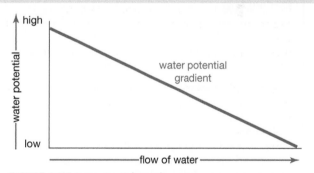

FIGURE 4: Water potential graph.

 QUESTIONS

7 Explain what water potential measures.

8 Starch is insoluble in water. Explain why water does not accumulate in plant cells that store starch. Use the term water potential in your explanation.

Organisms and their environment

Suited for their place

Why do woodlice live under logs and rocks and in any other damp place? In dry air the woodlouse body quickly loses water. Damp areas cut water loss and so improve the chances of woodlouse survival. This is an example of how environmental conditions affect where organisms can be found.

FIGURE 1: Woodlice are crustaceans, like crabs and lobsters, but live on the land. What is a crustacean?

Ecology

Organisms affect each other. The environment affects organisms. Studying these effects is all part of the science of **ecology**.

The places where life on Earth is found are collectively called the **biosphere**. Each place is made up of:

> a non-living **(abiotic) environment** of air, soil and water

> a living **(biotic) community** of different **species** of plants, animals, fungi and microorganisms. The individuals of different species group into **populations**.

Environment and community together form an **ecosystem** which is a more or less self-contained part of the biosphere. 'Self-contained' means that each ecosystem is identified by its own species, and those species are not usually found in other ecosystems. A pond and woodland are examples.

The way that organisms relate to their environment can be investigated practically using a number of fieldwork techniques. The findings from these investigations can help to build a picture of the number, variety and habits of organisms in an ecosystem.

 **QUESTIONS**

1 Draw a diagram showing the relationship between ecosystem, biotic community, species, population, and individual.

Remember!

An ecosystem can be as large as a forest or as small as a puddle.

Fieldwork techniques

'Fieldwork' refers to scientific investigations (the work) carried out in ecosystems (the field). Investigations are designed to find out more about where organisms live (their distribution) and why they live where they do. Techniques refers to the equipment and methods used in the investigations.

Ecosystems and their population are usually too large for it to be practical to study everything about them. Instead we study small parts called samples. Each sample is assumed to be typical of the ecosystem we are studying.

The techniques used in an investigation depend on the type of ecosystem investigated and what we want to find out. The diagrams show you the different types of equipment and methods used to investigate two different ecosystems: a pond and woodland.

 **QUESTIONS**

2 Describe the technique you would use to collect insects and spiders living in long grass.

3 Describe how fieldwork enables you to investigate biodiversity in a particular environment.

4 Ponds and woodlands are two examples of an ecosystem. Name two different ecosystems in your area that you could investigate.

Did you know?

'Ecology' comes from the Greek for 'study of house'.

Collecting samples

The following methods can help you to collect samples in a pond or in a wood:

> *Pooters*: suction tubes to suck up small insects.

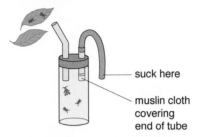

suck here

muslin cloth covering end of tube

> *Pond nets*: to collect underwater animals.

> *Sweep nets*: swishing the net in long grass knocks small animals into the net.

> *Pitfall traps*: to collect small animals that walk along the surface of the ground.

lid (a piece of bark or flat stone) prevents flooding of the trap by rain

stick support

plastic cup sunk to ground level

> *Quadrats*: used to count the number of animals or plants in a known area.

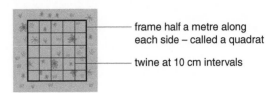

frame half a metre along each side – called a quadrat

twine at 10 cm intervals

Environmental investigations

The following methods can help you to gather data on the environment you are studying:

> *Temperature/pH probes*: to measure environmental conditions.

scale

probe

meter

> *Light intensity meters*: to measure how much light a particular habitat receives.

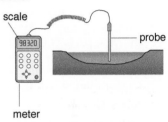

light meter

sensor

Getting reliable data

Taking a single sample of whatever is being investigated (the number of spiders in an area of grassland, for example) is not enough to provide reliable data. Accurate sampling requires a number of repeat samples to ensure that your results are reliable, repeatable and reproducible.

Errors can be reduced in different ways including:

> consistent methods of working

> taking a number of samples (the more the better within practical limits)

> standardising the samples taken (for example, at the same time of day, same season, similar weather conditions)

Taking samples at random (not selected) is important to successful fieldwork. By random we mean that any part of the ecosystem has an equal chance of being sampled. Different methods, including random number generators or random number tables, are used to make sure that sampling is random.

Random sampling avoids bias in the data collected during an investigation. Biased data might lead to false conclusions. However, we can never be completely sure of any conclusions made from data. The conclusions are tentative (not definite). We can improve confidence in data by making sure it is obtained randomly and by reducing error in sampling methods.

QUESTIONS

5 Why it is important to standardise fieldwork techniques?

6 Explain the importance of random sampling.

7 If you were to carry out a sampling investigation, how would you plan to minimise errors in your findings?

8 Describe how you would investigate what conditions black beetles prefer.

Preparing for assessment: Analysing and interpreting data

To achieve a good grade in science, you not only have to know and understand scientific ideas, but you need to be able to apply them to other situations and investigations. This task will support you in developing these skills.

 Buttercups and soil moisture

Hypothesis

Ewan cycles to school on a path across a meadow. In spring, the meadow is full of buttercups.

Ewan noticed that there were two different kinds of buttercup. One kind seemed to grow in the drier parts of the meadow, and Ewan identified this one as the bulbous buttercup. The other kind seemed to grow in wetter places, and he identified this as the creeping buttercup.

Ewan decided to collect data to test this hypothesis: Creeping buttercups grow in wetter places than bulbous buttercups.

Method

He laid out a 40-metre long tape to form a transect across part of the meadow, where the ground changed from being quite dry to very wet.

He put down 0.5 metre square quadrats at every 4 metres along the tape.

He estimated the percentage of each quadrat that was covered with each kind of buttercup. He made his estimates to the nearest 10%.

Ewan also measured the percentage of water in the soil, using a soil moisture meter and a data logger.

He did this twice in each quadrat, in two slightly different places.

Results

Ewan's results are shown in the table.

Quadrat	1	2	3	4	5	6	7	8	9	10
Water content in the soil – test 1 (%)	33.6	32.8	38.2	41.5	49.3	54.6	56.1	66.2	67.9	71.7
Water content in the soil – test 2 (%)	32.9	34.1	38.1	43.9	49.5	56.2	56.4	38.4	70.3	72.8
Cover of bulbous buttercup (%)	60	40	60	50	40	20	10	0	0	0
Cover of creeping buttercup (%)	0	0	20	10	0	30	50	60	80	70

Processing evidence

1. Calculate the mean percentage water content of the soil in each quadrat. Take care – there is an anomalous result that you will need to deal with.

2. Think about possible ways in which you could use Ewan's results to draw a graph or chart showing the relationship between the percentage cover of the two kinds of buttercups and the percentage water content of the soil.

Choose one way, and draw a graph or chart.

> The mean should have the same number of decimal places as the numbers you used to calculate it.

> There is no 'right' way to display these results. Would you draw a line graph, bar chart or scattergram? If you know about histograms or kite diagrams, you might choose to use one of these instead.

Evaluating the method and conclusions

1. Comment on these choices that Ewan made, and how they might affect the validity or repeatability of his investigation:

a using a soil moisture meter and data logger to measure the soil water content

b measuring the soil water content twice in each quadrat, in slightly different places

c using 10 quadrats

d estimating percentage cover to the nearest 10%

2. Ewan's friend said that the difference between the two measurements of soil water content in each quadrat meant that the soil moisture meter was not accurate or precise. Ewan disagreed. Who was right, and why?

3. Suggest the most important probable source of error in Ewan's investigation. Was this a random error or a systematic error?

4. Suggest what Ewan could do next, in order to improve his method and obtain extra evidence to increase the confidence with which he can draw a conclusion.

5. How could Ewan reword his hypothesis in light of the results obtained?

> Validity means that Ewan measured the appropriate variables to test his hypothesis, and that he controlled other important variables. Repeatability means that, if he did the same investigation again, he would expect to get similar results.

> Think about where Ewan made the two measurements.

> Make sure that your suggestions would allow Ewan to find more evidence in relation to the same hypothesis, not a different one.

> Be sure to use correct scientific and mathematical language to gain Quality of Written Communication marks.

Conclusions

1. Describe the relationship between soil moisture content and the distribution of each of the two species of buttercup.

2. Assess the extent to which Ewan's data supported the hypothesis.

> Remember that you cannot prove that a hypothesis is correct with just a few experiments. You can find that it is supported. However, one investigation could disprove it.

Connections

How science works

> Collecting and analysing data.

> Collecting data from secondary sources.

> Interpreting data to provide evidence for testing ideas.

> Presenting information and drawing conclusions using appropriate language, conventions and ICT.

Maths in science

> Calculate arithmetic means.

> Plot and draw graphs.

> Extract and interpret information from charts, graphs and tables.

> Translate information between graphical and numeric forms.

Fossils

Fossil hunting

In 1812, 12-year-old Mary Anning uncovered an almost complete skeleton of what looked like a crocodile in the limestone cliffs near Lyme Regis in Dorset. Eventually scientists realised the fossil skeleton was that of an ancient type of lizard called *Ichthyosaurus*, adapted to swim in the sea like a fish, and was over 90 million years old. *Ichthyosaurus* lived entirely in the water and gave birth to live young.

FIGURE 1: An artist's representation of *Ichthyosaurus*. The name means 'fish-lizard'. Similar to modern aquatic mammals, they were thought to have evolved from terrestrial animals moving back into the water. How did scientists find out about the fish-lizard?

The fossil record

Fossils are the remains of, or impressions made by, dead organisms. They are usually preserved in **sedimentary rocks** which are formed layer upon layer when the mud, sand and silt in suspension in ancient seas settled and compacted over millions of years.

The fossils in each layer are a record of the life on Earth at the time when the layer was formed. The sequence of fossils can be used to trace the history and evolution of life on Earth.

Careful study of fossils in successive layers of rock reveals that:

> Vertebrate animals did not exist 600 million years ago. The animals represented in the layers are all **invertebrates**.

> Fish were the first vertebrates to appear, about 510 million years ago.

> Reptiles appeared about 310 million years after fish.

The sequence of fossils also tells us that the older the fossils, the more likely they are to differ from present-day living things. From the fossil record we can conclude that organisms change through time.

Darwin's theory of natural selection explained that organisms have gradually changed over time, resulting in new species through the process of evolution. Fossils are evidence of the changes and a record of evolution.

FIGURE 2: An ammonite found on Lyme Regis beach. This is an extinct invertebrate animal that swam or floated in the sea. What sort of tissue formed the impression?

○ QUESTIONS

1 Draw a diagram to show how fossils form.

2 Explain how fossils can be used as evidence of evolution.

 Fossil record   Fossil formation   Mary Anning   Punctuated evolution

Why are there gaps in the fossil record?

Fossil formation depends on particular conditions that preserve organic material before it all decays away. Hard tissue like bones and shells is more likely to be preserved as fossils because it decays more slowly than soft tissue.

It might be expected that there would be a continuous series of changes to show between ancestors and their descendants. This is rarely the case. The fossil record is incomplete; there are gaps. One reason is that:

> Fossils do not always form. Most organisms decompose quickly when they die, and so only a small number find their way into an environment that preserves their shape and form.

> Even if a fossil forms, it may not survive the movement and weather of geological cycles.

> Many fossils are yet to be found. After all, fossil formation is by chance, and finding fossils even more so.

Another reason for gaps in the fossil record is that evolution is not always a slow and gradual process. The absence of a graded series of fossils is possibly the result of relatively short periods of species change, followed by longer periods of stability.

QUESTIONS

3 Explain why there are gaps in the fossil record.

4 Use the internet to evaluate five reconstructions from fossils of organisms that lived long ago. Your research should include examples of plants and animals.

5 Suggest what it may not be possible to learn from a fossil.

Fossil anatomy as evidence of evolution (Higher tier only)

Most modern-day vertebrate animals have a **pentadactyl limb**. This is a forelimb of five 'fingers' or 'toes' (*penta* is Greek for five). Scientists have discovered the pentadactyl limb in fossils and think that modern-day vertebrates and the fossils share a **common ancestor** from which all vertebrates have directly descended and use this as evidence of evolution taking place.

The fossilised remains of the extinct fish, *Eusthenopteron*, show lobed fins with bony projections that were thought to have allowed movement along river beds. This bone structure resembles the structure in our own hands and feet.

Figure 3 shows the arrangement of limb bones in vertebrates. You can see that while the basic pattern is similar, the structure reflects the different functions of limbs: grasping, swimming or flying. Despite the differences in function, they have a similar anatomy since they have all evolved from a common ancestor.

QUESTIONS

6 Explain why the anatomy of the pentadactyl limb is evidence for evolution.

7 The panda appears to have six fingers. Write a short report on why this is different to other vertebrates and suggest an evolutionary reason for it. You may carry out additional research to help you.

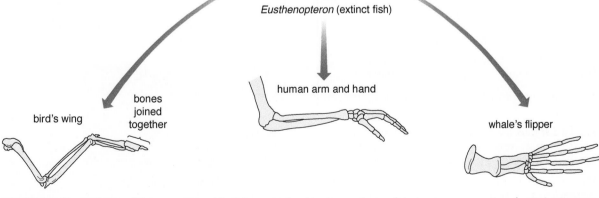

Eusthenopteron (extinct fish)

human arm and hand

bird's wing

bones joined together

whale's flipper

FIGURE 3: Different forms of the pentadactyl limb have evolved in descendants of the common ancestor of vertebrates over many millions of years.

Q Evidence of evolution   Pentadactyl limb   Common ancestor

Growth

You will find out:
> what growth is
> about differentiation of cells in plants
> about percentile charts

Growing up

Mammal growth is steady; insect growth is not because the insect body is surrounded by a hard exoskeleton that does not stretch. Growth only occurs when the old exoskeleton is moulted (removed) and replaced with a soft, stretchy new one. The body tissue grows before the new exoskeleton hardens.

FIGURE 1: A young cicada crawls out of its old skin. Which other animals grow in this way?

What is growth?

An organism's growth is measured as an increase in its size, length and mass. The increase is the result of:

> cell division: the number of cells increases

> cell elongation: the length of cells increases

> synthesis of organic materials (carbohydrates, proteins, fats and oils): the mass of cells increases.

The way plants and animals grow is one of the differences between them. A plant grows throughout its life; an animal only when juvenile, although its mass may continue to increase when an adult.

 QUESTIONS

1 List the processes that enable plants and animals to grow.

2 Describe the difference in the way plants and animals grow.

3 State the difference between cell division and cell elongation.

Growing

Plant growth

Cell division in plants is restricted to tissues called **meristems**:

> Apical meristems are located in the tips of shoots and roots.

> Lateral meristems are located next to the tissues of the xylem and phloem within the plant body.

Plants grow from their meristems:

> Apical meristems extend shoots and roots, increasing a plant's length, making it taller.

> Lateral meristems add to a plant's width, increasing its girth.

Figure 3 shows the tip of a root seen under a light microscope. Its meristem lies just behind its tip.

The cells of the meristem divide very quickly. Behind the meristem is the region where cells elongate and increase in size. Water flowing into the cells by osmosis accounts for 90% of their elongation.

Synthesis of organic materials makes up the rest and adds to their mass.

Recall that plants grow from meristems and to begin with the cells are undifferentiated. As growth continues, differentiation of cells begins. Some of the meristem cells in roots become the cells of phloem tissue, others form the cells of xylem tissue. Differentiation in the meristem cells of the growing shoot produces the other types of cell that make up the tissues and organs of the plant.

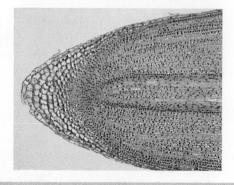

FIGURE 2: The growing root tip of a lily. What are the black spots in each cell?

Animal growth

Cell division in animals is not restricted to a particular type of tissue but occurs in all the tissues of the body. In young animals tissues grow because cell division produces more cells than die through age or damage. The individual increases in length. Synthesis of protein that adds to the cytoplasm of cells increases cell mass and therefore the individual's mass.

Animals continue to elongate until the gain of cells balances the loss of cells as the result of cell death. Elongation then stops, marking the start of becoming an adult. However, the mass of an individual may continue to increase as protein synthesis adds more mass to cells and the tissues that the cells form.

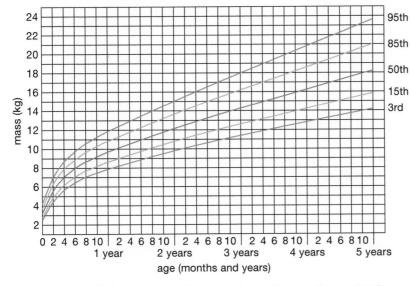

FIGURE 3: The blue whale is the largest animal ever known to have existed: over 33 metres in length and 180 tonnes or more in weight.

QUESTIONS

4 Explain how a plant increases in length and in girth.

5 Describe the differences in the way cell mass increases in plants and animals.

Growth charts and percentiles

A baby grows to become a child and children develop into adolescents who become adults at around the age of 20 years. These are stages signposting the route of human growth and development.

Growth charts help parents and doctors to monitor children's development. The figures on the chart are different **percentiles**: 95th, 85th, 50th, 15th and 3rd, each representing the spread of values for the

characteristic (such as height or mass) selected. The 50th percentile represents the average value.

How are the readings to be interpreted? For example, a 2 year old who falls in the 95th percentile for height means that the child's height measurement is equal to or greater than 95% of children of the same age. Only 5% of children at that age are taller than that child.

FIGURE 4: A growth chart for mass of boys aged up to 5 years. (Source: WHO Child Growth Standards.)

QUESTIONS

6 From Figure 4 calculate to the nearest kilogram:

a the average mass of babies aged 2 years 10 months

b the difference in mass between babies in the 95th and 3rd percentiles

c the increase in mass between birth and 5 years for an average baby.

7 Discuss the possible uses for the data in growth charts.

Cells, tissues and organs

You will find out:

> that cells group into tissues, tissues into organs, and organs into organ systems

> about differentiation of cells in animals

Starting with cells

The photograph shows a human embryo at 7–8 weeks. During this early stage, organ differentiation overshadows growth and all the major organs have been formed. At this age the embryo is about 4 cm in length and less than 10 g in weight.

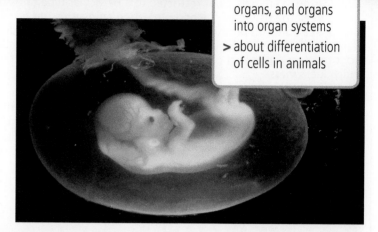

FIGURE 1: A human embryo. Does this embryo have specialised cells?

Cells join together

More than 200 different cell types make up the human body. Groups of each type of cell form a particular **tissue**. Tissues group to form **organs**, which group to form organ systems:

> Cells are the building blocks from which humans and all other living things are made.

> Tissues are a group of similar cells with a particular function.

> An organ is a group of different tissues which work together and has a particular function.

> An organ system is a group of different organs which work together and has a particular function.

cells: cardiac cells

tissue: cardiac muscle

organ: the heart

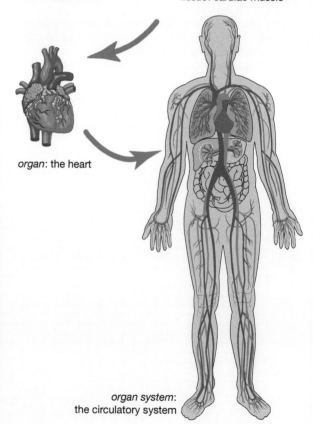

organ system: the circulatory system

FIGURE 2: Cells form tissues which form organs which form organ systems.

Did you know?

The major organ systems of humans include:

> digestive system
> respiratory system
> excretory system
> circulatory system
> reproductive system
> nervous system

> endocrine system
> skeletal system
> muscle system
> integumentary system (skin, hair and nails)
> lymphatic system

QUESTIONS

1 Arrange the following words in order to show how simpler parts combine to make a whole multicellular organism: living thing, organ systems, cells, organ, tissues.

2 Look at Figure 2. Draw a similar diagram to show the system that is made up of pulmonary (lung) cells.

3 Explain why cells can be described as the building blocks from which living things are made.

Differentiation

All of us start as a single fertilised egg that divides into two cells by mitosis soon after its fertilisation. The cells divide by mitosis and the repeated mitoses that follow are how the process of development produces the hollow ball of cells that we call the **embryo**. The cells of the embryo are all descendants of the fertilised egg. They are all the same. We say that the cells are undifferentiated.

As development of the embryo continues, forming the foetus, cells become more and more different from one another. We say that they differentiate and call the process **differentiation**. All the different types of human cell are the result of differentiation during the development of the egg to the embryo and then to the foetus.

Each of the different types of human cell is specialised in ways that enable each type to carry out a particular function: for example, neurones (nerve cells) transmit nerve impulses and muscle cells contract (shorten). Figure 3 shows some other examples.

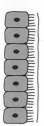

ciliated cells line the windpipe. Their cilia sweep away a covering layer of mucus

muscle cells help us move

skin cells cover the body

nerve cells send impulses to muscles and glands

ovum (egg) – the female sex cell

white blood cells help to defend the body against disease

red blood cells absorb oxygen

sperm – the male sex cell

bone cells produce bone

FIGURE 3: Different types of human cell.

QUESTIONS

4 Explain why the cells of an embryo are genetically identical and all the same.

5 Is mitosis necessary for sexual reproduction?

6 Draw an outline diagram of the human body and using labels indicate where you might expect the cells in Figure 3 to appear.

How do cells become different?

Mitosis produces daughter cells that are genetically identical to one another and to their parent cell, which means that all of the cells of the foetus and baby that develops from it are genetically identical (except the gametes). How can cells differentiate and yet genetically be the same?

The answer is in the pattern of gene activity. Genetically the cells may be the same, but the pattern of genes switching on and off (gene activity) is different depending on the position of the cells in the developing embryo. The same process occurs in the development of all organisms.

QUESTIONS

7 Explain how cells differentiate.

8 Use the internet to help you find out how genes switch on and off.

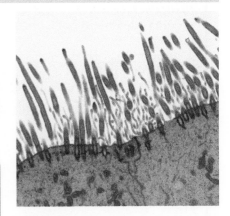

FIGURE 4: The cilia in the nasal lining are examples of specialised cells. How do these cells become different?

Blood

What does blood do?

In 2009, 1.6 million people in England donated blood. Every day donated blood is used to carry out treatments that help save lives. So why is blood so important? It transports oxygen, digested food, hormones and other substances *to* the tissues and organs of the body. It also takes carbon dioxide and other waste substance produced by the chemical reactions in cells *from* the tissues and organs of the body.

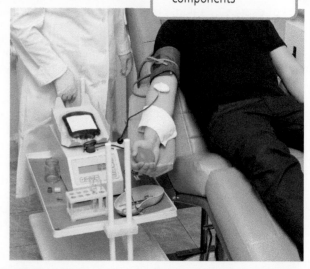

FIGURE 1: An adult human contains about 5 dm^3 of blood and can donate 0.45 dm^3 every 4 months.

Blood's components

Blood cells

Figure 2 shows a micrograph of blood, which consists of the following types of cell:

> *Red blood cells*: contain the pigment **haemoglobin**. They do not have a nucleus. Their disc-shape increases their surface area maximising oxygen absorption. A thin membrane allows the oxygen to diffuse easily into and out of the cell.

> *White blood cells*: they have a nucleus. They also have cytoplasm that has a flowing movement. This helps them to squeeze through the cells in the blood capillary walls into tissues where they are able to engulf bacteria and viruses. They also secrete digestive enzymes which destroy the bacteria and viruses.

> *Platelets*: small fragments of cells that do not have a nucleus, but they contain proteins that enable them to stick to breaks in the blood vessel wall and also to stick to each other. A clot forms that stops the bleeding.

Plasma

Plasma is the straw-coloured liquid part of blood that is mostly water (90% by volume). It transports in solution:

> carbon dioxide produced by aerobic respiration in the cells of the body's tissues and organs to the lungs

> the soluble products of digestion absorbed from the small intestine to the body's liver

> urea, which is a waste substance produced by liver cells, to the kidneys.

Plasma also circulates the heat released by the chemical reactions in cells round the body, helping it to keep warm.

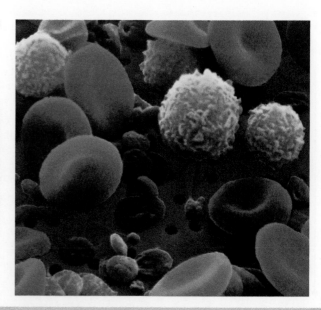

FIGURE 2: A micrograph of human blood showing red and white cells and platelets. Can you identify red and white blood cells and platelets?

QUESTIONS

1 Draw a diagram to show the different types of blood cell.

2 Suggest why blood cells separate from plasma when blood samples are spun in a centrifuge.

Blood cells

Red blood cells

Red blood cells are red because the haemoglobin inside the cytoplasm of the cell is a red-coloured pigment.

In tissues where the concentration of oxygen is high, haemoglobin combines readily with oxygen, forming **oxyhaemoglobin**. Oxyhaemoglobin breaks down to release oxygen to tissues where the concentration of oxygen is low.

$$\text{haemoglobin} + \text{oxygen} \underset{\text{other body tissues}}{\overset{\text{lungs}}{\rightleftharpoons}} \text{oxyhaemoglobin}$$

Blood containing a lot of oxyhaemoglobin is called **oxygenated blood** and is bright red in colour. Blood with little oxyhaemoglobin is called **deoxygenated blood** and is a deep red–purple colour.

QUESTIONS

3 Match the different components of blood with the correct description.

Plasma	Absorbs oxygen
Red blood cell	Contains wastes which are removed by the kidneys
White blood cell	Helps to stop bleeding
Platelet	Helps to protect the body from disease

4 Briefly explain what happens when blood becomes oxygenated.

White blood cells

White blood cells protect the body by working to destroy viruses and bacteria that may cause disease or harm to the body.

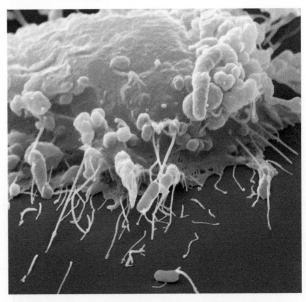

FIGURE 3: A micrograph of a white blood cell engulfing *Escherichia coli* bacteria (pink rods). *E. coli* is usually harmless, but some strains are harmful. What is *E. coli* known to cause?

Did you know?

1 cm³ of blood contains 3000 white blood cells and 5 000 000 red blood cells.

Platelets

When platelets are damaged by a cut or torn tissue, they release a substance which begins the process of forming a blood clot.

The substance triggers a cascade of chemical reactions in the blood that end with the soluble plasma protein called fibrinogen changing into insoluble **fibrin**.

Fibrin forms a tangled mesh of fibres across the wound and traps red blood cells, forming a clot. The clot plugs the wound and stops any bleeding. It also restricts bacteria and viruses from entering the body.

QUESTIONS

5 Explain how a wound is plugged.

6 Why is it important that a blood clot forms?

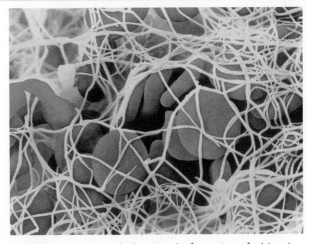

FIGURE 4: A micrograph showing the formation of a blood clot. Red blood cells are trapped by a sheet of fibrin threads (green). As the red blood cells become trapped they will begin to lose their normal rounded shape.

Oxygenating blood   Blood clotting

The heart

The muscle that can't rest

The heart is an organ that pumps blood through a circulatory system. Its walls are made of involuntary muscle which means that your heart beats without you having to think about it.

Remember!
Heart diagrams are shown as they appear in the body, so the right side is on the left and vice versa.

You will find out:
> about the heart's major blood vessels
> about atria and ventricles
> about the direction of blood flow
> how valves prevent backflow

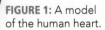

FIGURE 1: A model of the human heart.

The heart pumps blood

The heart lies inside the chest cavity protected by the rib cage. Much of the wall of the heart is made of **cardiac muscle**. The rhythmic contractions and relaxations of the muscle pump blood through the circulatory system.

Inside the heart there are four chambers:

> two **atria** (singular atrium)

> two **ventricles**.

The atria are smaller and have thinner walls than the ventricles.

There are different blood vessels associated with the heart:

> *pulmonary artery*: transports blood from the heart to the lungs

> *pulmonary vein*: transports blood from the lungs to the heart

> *aorta*: transports blood from the heart to the head and the rest of the body

> *vena cava*: transports blood from the head and the rest of the body to the heart.

The black arrows in Figure 2 show the direction of blood flow through the heart:

> blood from the vena cava flows into the right atrium

> blood from the pulmonary vein flows into the left atrium

> blood to the lungs flows through the pulmonary artery from the right ventricle

> blood to the rest of the body flows through the aorta from the left ventricle.

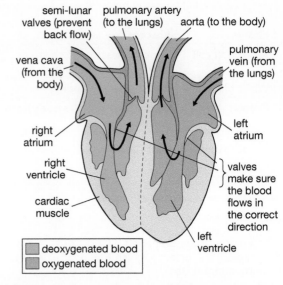

FIGURE 2: A drawing of the human heart viewed from the front. Why do the atria have thinner walls?

You can see that the wall of the left ventricle is thicker than that of the right ventricle.

The left ventricle has to pump blood to all areas of the body while the right ventricle only has to pump blood to the lungs – a shorter distance. The muscle on the left ventricle needs to be thicker for the extra effort.

QUESTIONS

1 Briefly outline the structure of the heart.

Blood circulates

Figure 3 shows a simplified arrangement of the circulation of blood:

> The left atrium pumps **oxygenated blood** from the lungs to the left ventricle which in turn pumps blood around the rest of the body.

> The right atrium pumps **deoxygenated blood** to the right ventricle which in turn pumps it to the lungs where it can be oxygenated.

In effect, the heart is a double pump, each ventricle pumping blood along a different route through the body. The distance travelled by blood through the head and body circuit is greater than the distance it travels through the lung circuit, and therefore needs to be pumped at a higher pressure.

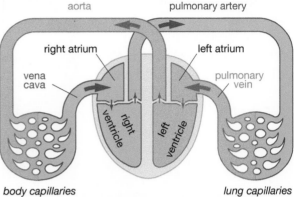

FIGURE 3: The heart and circulatory system showing the lung circuit and the head and body circuit.

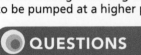 **QUESTIONS**

2 Draw a fully labelled diagram showing the path taken by blood through the heart.

3 Explain how the heart works as a double pump.

How does the heart pump blood?

When the muscular walls of the heart relax, blood fills the chambers. When the muscles contract, blood is forced from the chambers. The valves control the flow of blood through the heart and into the arteries leading from the heart, preventing backflow.

Figure 4 shows the sequence:

1 When relaxed, the atria fill with blood. To begin with, the valves separating the atria from the ventricles are closed. As the atria fill up, the pressure within increases and pushes open the valves.

2 When filled with blood, the atria contract. Their volume decreases and the increase in blood pressure opens the valves separating the atria from the ventricles. Blood is forced into the ventricles.

3 When filled with blood the ventricles contract. Their volume decreases. The increase in blood pressure closes the valves separating the atria from the ventricles, and opens the valves which guard the openings of the arteries. Blood is forced into the arteries.

> ### Did you know?
> It has been estimated that a human heart beats over two billion times in a lifetime.

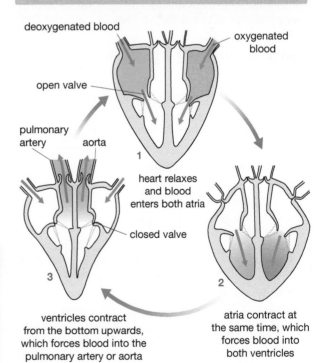

FIGURE 4: The heart's pumping cycles. What causes the valves to open and close?

 QUESTIONS

4 Explain how changes in blood pressure within the atria and ventricles open and close the valves of the heart.

5 During intense exercise muscles can respire anaerobically. Using your own research, investigate whether this happens with cardiac muscle. Explain why.

Circulatory system

Well-travelled cells

During its short life (about 4 months), a human red blood cell covers about 15 km every day for a total of 1500 km. In a litre (1 dm^3) of blood there are normally about 5000 million red blood cells.

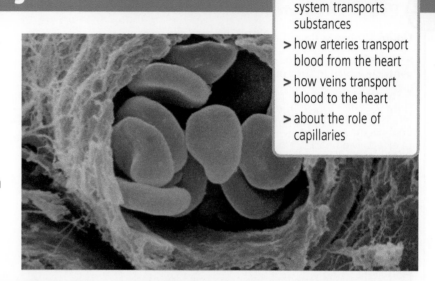

FIGURE 1: A micrograph of a group of red blood cells travelling through a small branch of an artery.

You will find out:

> how the circulatory system transports substances

> how arteries transport blood from the heart

> how veins transport blood to the heart

> about the role of capillaries

 ## Circulation

The circulatory system consists of a network of tube-like vessels through which blood passes to, and drains from, the tissues of the body. The tube-like vessels are **arteries** and **veins**:

> The heart pumps blood through arteries to the tissues of the body.

> Blood drains from the tissues through the veins back to the heart.

> Smaller vessels branch from arteries and veins. The smallest are called **capillaries**. They link arteries and veins.

Table 1 summarises the components of the circulatory system.

QUESTIONS

1 Table 1 shows sections through an artery and a vein.

a Give two differences in structure between an artery and a vein.

b Briefly explain how the differences you have given in **a** are linked to the way in which arteries and veins work.

c Complete the following: An artery carries blood from the _____ at _____ pressure and a vein carries blood to the _____ at _____ pressure.

TABLE 1: Arteries, capillaries and veins compared.

Arteries	Capillaries	Veins
layer of cells elastic fibres and muscle tough non-elastic fibres	wall: one cell thick	layer of cells elastic fibres and muscle non-elastic fibres
Carry blood away from the heart to the organs and tissues of the body	Receive blood from arteries and drain blood into veins	Carry blood to the heart from the organs and tissues
Narrow diameter	Narrow diameter	Wide diameter
Thick walls consisting of muscles and elastic fibres that withstand the high pressure of the blood flowing through	Walls are only one cell thick. Substances can easily diffuse between blood within the capillaries and the tissues in which capillaries form a dense network	Thin walls consisting of muscles and elastic fibres that easily expand, reducing resistance to the flow of blood returning to the heart
Valves absent	Valves absent	Valves present

Veins and arteries

Veins

Blood flows through veins slowly because it is at a lower pressure than the blood in the arteries (the veins only receive blood after it has travelled through the arteries). This is why the diameter of a vein is larger than the diameter of an artery. More space enables the blood to flow more easily.

Blood flow through veins is also helped by the contractions of the muscles in the arms and legs through which the veins pass. These contractions squeeze the veins, and so move the blood inside them towards the heart.

Valves in the veins prevent blood from flowing in the opposite direction (backflow) because of low pressure.

Arteries

The heart pumps blood into arteries at high pressure as the blood needs to reach every extremity of the body. The elastic fibres of the artery walls stretch and then contract. This elastic recoil helps to maintain the flow of blood away from the heart and prevent backflow. Therefore, there are no valves inside arteries.

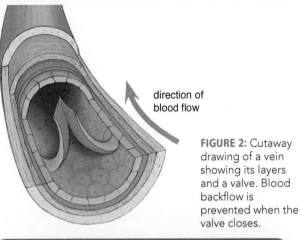

direction of blood flow

FIGURE 2: Cutaway drawing of a vein showing its layers and a valve. Blood backflow is prevented when the valve closes.

QUESTIONS

2 Explain the role of elastic fibres in the wall of an artery.

3 Briefly explain why there are valves inside veins but not inside arteries.

Capillaries: the blood at work

A capillary is only about 0.005 mm in diameter. Capillaries form dense networks, called **capillary beds**, in the tissues of the body. This means that no cell is very far from a capillary. Capillary beds provide a large surface area for the efficient exchange of materials between the blood and tissues.

Arteries carry blood to, and veins drain blood from, the capillaries. In the capillaries blood is at work. It supplies the nearby cells, and the tissues the cells form, with nutrients, oxygen and other substances. The blood also carries away **urea**, carbon dioxide and other wastes produced by the cells' metabolism. With the wall of the capillaries only one cell thick, substances easily pass between the blood within and surrounding cells.

The blood is at a higher pressure at the artery end of the capillary bed. The higher pressure forces plasma through the thin capillary walls. The liquid, called **tissue fluid**, carries nutrients and oxygen to the surrounding cells.

There is just enough room in capillaries for red blood cells to pass through in single file. As a result, pressure drops as blood passes from the artery end to the vein end of a capillary bed. The drop in pressure allows tissue fluid to diffuse into the capillaries with its load of carbon dioxide, urea and other dissolved wastes produced by the cells' metabolism.

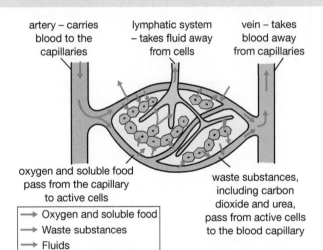

artery – carries blood to the capillaries

lymphatic system – takes fluid away from cells

vein – takes blood away from capillaries

oxygen and soluble food pass from the capillary to active cells

→ Oxygen and soluble food
→ Waste substances
→ Fluids

waste substances, including carbon dioxide and urea, pass from active cells to the blood capillary

FIGURE 3: Substances are exchanged between the blood flowing through capillaries and the cells of the surrounding tissues.

QUESTIONS

4 During times of exertion, blood pressure increases. Suggest why this does not damage the thin walls of capillary beds.

5 Draw a flowchart to show the movement of blood to and from the heart and leg muscles.

Digestive system

You will find out:
> about the digestive system
> how peristalsis moves food along the alimentary canal

Eating satisfies hunger

Eating, chewing and swallowing food might stop us feeling hungry, but we need to break down our food so that it can be absorbed and used by the body to fuel life's processes. This is the job of the digestive system.

FIGURE 1: The digestive system starts at the mouth. Where does it finish?

What is the digestive system?

The alimentary canal is a muscular tube through which food passes from mouth to anus. The food is processed as it passes through. Gut and intestine are terms sometimes used instead of alimentary canal.

The liver and pancreas also play their part in processing food. The alimentary canal, liver and pancreas together make up the digestive system.

Figure 2 shows the digestive system:

> *Mouth*: chewing food in the mouth breaks up the food into small pieces. This increases the surface area of the food to the action of digestive enzymes and makes it easier to swallow. Saliva makes the food slippery for easier swallowing and contains an enzyme which begins its digestion.

> *Oesophagus*: this muscular tube pushes food and liquid from the mouth down into the stomach.

> *Stomach*: muscles in the stomach wall contract and relax to mix food with digestive juices, containing digestive enzymes that continue digestion.

> *Pancreas*: pancreatic juice is produced, which contains digestive enzymes that pass to the small intestine.

> *Small intestine*: enzymes break down food molecules further. This is where most of the digestion and absorption of food takes place.

> *Liver*: processes the nutrients absorbed from the small intestine and produces **bile**, which plays an important role in digesting fat.

> *Large intestine*: absorbs water from the remaining indigestible food matter.

As food passes through the digestive system, it is broken down into smaller soluble molecules which the body can absorb. The process runs as follows:

> *Ingestion*: food and the nutrients it contains are taken into the mouth.

> *Digestion*: large insoluble nutrient molecules are broken down into smaller soluble molecules.

> *Absorption*: the small molecules of digested food pass through the wall of the intestine into the blood on its way to the liver.

> *Egestion*: undigested remains of food are removed from the body as faeces through the anus.

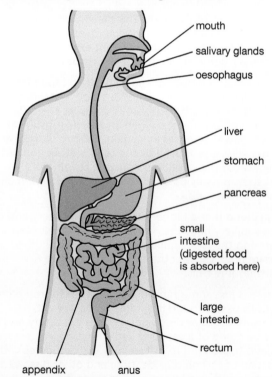

FIGURE 2: The different parts of the human digestive system. What do the salivary glands do?

mouth
salivary glands
oesophagus
liver
stomach
pancreas
small intestine (digested food is absorbed here)
large intestine
rectum
appendix
anus

○ QUESTIONS

1 State what the digestive system does.

2 List the different parts that make up the digestive system, in order, from mouth to anus.

Moving food through the alimentary canal

The time taken for food to move from mouth to anus through the alimentary canal varies. It depends on the individual and also on the sort of food eaten. For example, high **fibre** foods like salad and vegetables tend to move more quickly through the alimentary canal than lower fibre foods. On average, clearance of the undigested remains of food from the alimentary canal through the anus takes anything from 18 hours after eating (ingestion) to 3 days.

Repeated contraction and relaxation of the muscle layers forming the wall of the alimentary canal move food through. This muscular action is called **peristalsis**.

Longitudinal muscles run along the length of the alimentary canal. When they contract the alimentary canal shortens, pushing food along. Circular muscles surround the alimentary canal. Their contraction squeezes food into the next region of the alimentary canal, where the muscles are relaxed.

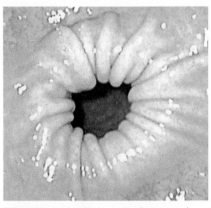

FIGURE 3: Peristalsis – a circular smooth muscle in the stomach contracting at the beginning of a peristaltic wave.

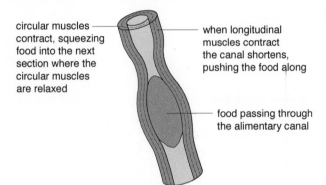

circular muscles contract, squeezing food into the next section where the circular muscles are relaxed

when longitudinal muscles contract the canal shortens, pushing the food along

food passing through the alimentary canal

FIGURE 4: Peristalsis – the alimentary canal narrows when the circular muscle contracts and shortens when the longitudinal muscles contract.

QUESTIONS

3 Describe how the action of the muscles moves food through the alimentary canal.

4 Draw a flowchart to show the progress of food from ingestion to egestion. Explain what is happening at each stage.

The gall bladder (Higher tier only)

Figure 4 shows you that the **gall bladder** lies next to the liver.

The human gall bladder is a small sac-like structure connected to the small intestine by the bile duct. It stores a greenish alkaline liquid called bile. Bile is produced by the liver and breaks down fats in partly digested food.

During storage in the gall bladder, the bile becomes more concentrated, which increases its potency and intensifies its effect on fats.

QUESTIONS

5 Explain how bile passes from the gall bladder into the small intestine.

6 Using your own research, explain why the recent discovery that the gall bladder produces the hormone insulin might lead to new treatments for people with Type 1 diabetes.

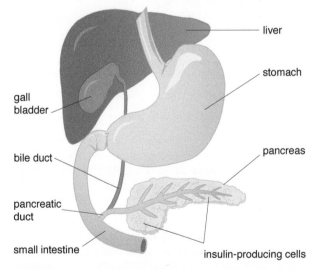

FIGURE 5: The wall of the gall bladder is muscular. When the muscle contracts, bile squirts into the bile duct, sending it on its way to the small intestine. The bile duct and pancreatic duct share the duct that empties into the small intestine.

Digestion and absorption

You will find out:

> the role of digestive enzymes

> about investigating digestive enzymes

> about bile

> how villi absorb digested food

Energy from food

To get the energy from the food we eat, our bodies need to break the food down, digest and then absorb it into the blood where it can reach every part of the body. The recommended daily energy intake for young adults and men is 10 MJ.

FIGURE 1: A 100 g portion of lettuce contains about 64 kJ of energy: less than 1% of your daily energy requirements.

What is digestion and absorption?

Digestion is the process that breaks down our food into the nutrients our bodies can absorb.

In digestion:

> Chemical and mechanical processes break down food as it passes through the digestive system.

> Different digestive **enzymes** speed up many of the chemical reactions of digestion. Table 1 summarises the digestive enzymes.

Absorption:

> is the process where the nutrients are taken into the body

> takes place in the small intestine.

> The digested food passes into the blood through the wall of the small intestine.

QUESTIONS

1 State the difference between digestion and absorption.

2 State where in the digestive system starch is digested.

3 Which enzymes produce amino acids?

TABLE 1: Digestive enzymes.

Enzyme group	Examples	Location	Food component acted on	Substance eventually produced
Carbohydrases digest carbohydrates	Amylase	Mouth and small intestine	Starch	Glucose (simple sugars)
Proteases digest proteins	Pepsin	Stomach	Proteins	Amino acids
Lipases digest fats and oils	Lipase	Small intestine	Fats and oils	Fatty acids and glycerol

Processing food

In humans, digestion begins in the mouth, and continues in the stomach and small intestine.

Chemical processes break down large, insoluble molecules of carbohydrates, fat and oil, and protein that the body cannot absorb into smaller molecules which it can absorb.

Solutions of digestive enzymes are in the juices produced in different parts of the digestive system.

Mechanical processes include:

> teeth chewing food, which breaks it up into small pieces

> contractions of the muscles of the wall of the alimentary canal, which mix food with solutions of digestive enzymes.

Investigating digestive enzymes

A model is something that mimics the real thing. Visking tubing is very useful for making biological models because the membrane it is made from is partially permeable and so it can be used to make a model cell. Here you can use it to make a model alimentary canal.

Figure 2 suggests a set-up for investigating digestive enzymes: amylase and maltase, for example.

Amylase is an enzyme that catalyses the chemical reactions that break down starch into molecules of the sugar maltose. Maltase catalyses the breakdown of maltose into glucose:

$$\text{starch} \xrightarrow{\text{amylase}} \text{maltose} \quad \text{and} \quad \text{maltose} \xrightarrow{\text{maltase}} \text{glucose}$$

Maltose and glucose are reducing sugars and you can detect their presence using Benedict's solution. A positive test for maltose or glucose would indicate that digestive enzymes have broken down the starch molecules. By using different concentrations of these enzymes, the optimum conditions for enzymatic activity can be investigated.

Iodine solution can be used to detect the presence of starch.

Think of the Visking model as representing part of the small intestine, the water in which it is suspended as its blood supply and, because the water is warm, it is at body temperature as well. You can set up different models using Visking tubing with different sizes of membrane pore.

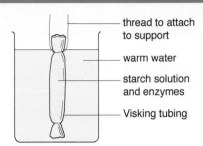

FIGURE 2: Modelling the alimentary canal. Why must the water be warm?

thread to attach to support

warm water

starch solution and enzymes

Visking tubing

QUESTIONS

4 Suggest why some of the mechanical processes of digestion start before the chemical processes.

5 Write a plan to test the process of the digestion of starch to maltose in the presence of the enzyme amylase.

Bile and villi (Higher tier only)

Bile

Bile, produced by the liver and stored in the gall bladder before release into the small intestine, contains salts that break down fats and oils into small droplets. The process is called **emulsification**.

Emulsification increases the surface area of fats and oils exposed to the action of lipase, speeding up their digestion. Lipase catalyses reactions which break down fats and oils into fatty acids and glycerol.

As bile is strongly alkali, it also neutralises stomach acid. This ensures optimum conditions for enzymes to work in the small intestine.

QUESTIONS

6 Explain the importance of bile.

7 Explain how the small intestine enables efficient absorption of the soluble products of digestion.

Villi

The upper part of the small intestine is where most of the digestion of food is completed. The lower part is where most of the soluble products of digestion are absorbed.

Tiny finger-like protections called **villi** (singular villus) project into the space of the small intestine. They increase its surface area, allowing more efficient absorption of the soluble products of digestion.

Each villus has:

> a single-layer covering of cells, making absorption of soluble products easier and therefore even more efficient

> a good supply of capillary vessels, which make absorption still more efficient because the surface area available for absorption of soluble products into the bloodstream is increased.

The soluble products of digestion are transported in solution in the bloodstream to the liver.

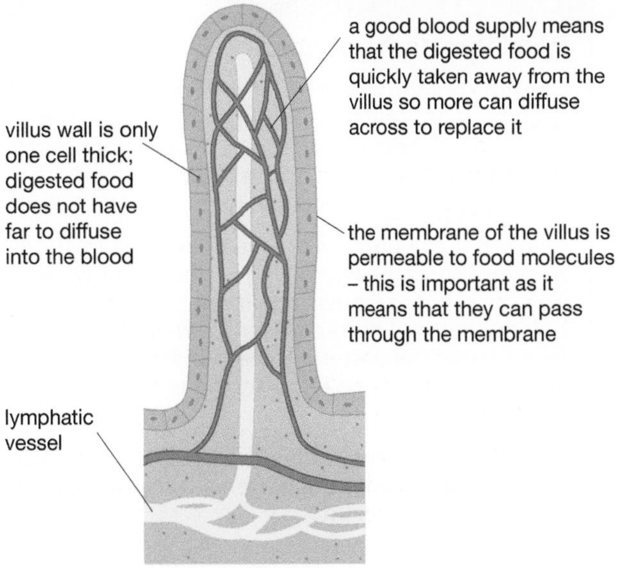

a good blood supply means that the digested food is quickly taken away from the villus so more can diffuse across to replace it

villus wall is only one cell thick; digested food does not have far to diffuse into the blood

the membrane of the villus is permeable to food molecules – this is important as it means that they can pass through the membrane

lymphatic vessel

FIGURE 3: The small intestine wall is covered in finger-like extensions called villi with a surface area of approximately 9 m².

Functional foods

You will find out:
> about different functional foods
> the claimed health benefits of functional foods

A bit fishy?

Omega-3 fats found in oily fish are claimed by manufacturers to be able to increase brain power. However, government scientists say that they have been shown to maintain good heart health but do not generally support the brain power claim. What is going on?

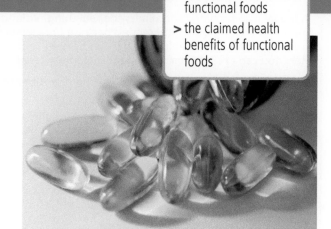

FIGURE 1: Fish oil supplement: part of the UK's £1 billion a year functional foods business.

What are functional foods?

Functional foods are defined, according to the British Dietetic Association, as 'foods that have health-promoting benefits over and above their basic nutritional value'.

Functional foods include:

> **Probiotic foods**: which contain bacteria such as *Bifidobacteria* and lactic acid bacteria *Lactobacillus* that are claimed to maintain a healthy digestive system.

> **Prebiotic foods**: which contain added sugars called oligosaccharides that cannot be digested, but act as a food supply to the bacteria in our alimentary canal.

> **Plant stanol esters**: which come from plant stanols and are found naturally in food such as wheat and maize and have been clinically proven to reduce the absorption of **cholesterol**.

QUESTIONS

1 Give two examples of functional foods that you might include in your diet.

2 For your two examples, state their beneficial properties.

Prebiotics, probiotics and plant stanol esters

Prebiotics and probiotics

Our gut contains hundreds of different species of bacteria. Although there is still a lot we don't yet know about these bacteria, they do assist our bodily functions in many ways, such as helping to digest certain types of food and aiding our immune system.

Changes in the number or type of bacteria in our gut, for example, caused by taking antibiotics or by poor diet can result in illness and disease. This may be because harmful bacteria flourish when there are fewer beneficial bacteria to keep them at bay and also digestion may be less effective without so many beneficial bacteria.

Taking prebiotic and probiotic foods aims to restore the number of beneficial bacteria in our gut, and so keep us in good health.

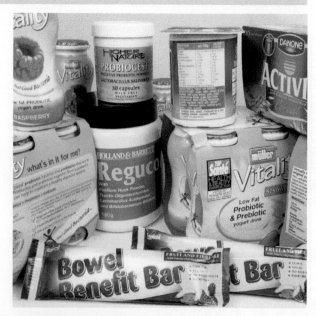

FIGURE 2: A selection of food products and supplements containing probiotic cultures and prebiotics.

Plant stanol esters

The margarine Benecol is a type of functional food. It has had plant stanol ester added to the spread.

Cholesterol is an important fat that the body uses in cell membranes, nerve fibres, to make bile acids and hormones. However, high levels of cholesterol in the blood can lead to diseases of the arteries and increase the risk of heart attacks and strokes.

Studies have shown that consuming 2–3 grams of plant stanol esters per day in the food that we eat can reduce the effects of too much cholesterol in the blood by 10–15% without any side-effects.

Reducing the levels of blood cholesterol therefore reduces the risk of heart disease and stroke. The scientific evidence supports the health benefit claims of the makers of Benecol.

QUESTIONS

3 Explain how prebiotic foods work.

4 Explain why Benecol can reduce the risk of heart disease.

Did you know?

Porridge and other oatmeals can help to lower cholesterol and do not contain added ingredients.

Evaluating functional foods

In the past, food producers have made health claims for their products unsupported by clear scientific evidence.

More recent scientific evidence suggests that certain kinds of bacteria can treat and even prevent some illnesses. *Lactobacillus* and *Bifidobacterium* are two genera especially associated with boosting health. They are often components of yoghurt, fermented milks and cheese. These foods in particular lead the field in the development of probiotics.

Concerns about functional foods

There are concerns about *Lactobacillus* and *Bifidobacterium*'s effectiveness involving:

> how well the bacteria survive the manufacture and storage of probiotics before sale

> their passage through the digestive system

> competition with the trillions of other microorganisms already in the gut.

Overcoming the concerns

Prebiotics are alternatives that get round these potential problems as they:

> resist digestion in the stomach and small intestine

> are preferred by *Lactobacillus* and *Bifidobacterium* as a source of energy.

Prebiotics therefore encourage the growth of these bacteria already living in the digestive system (particularly the large intestine) at the expense of less useful and even harmful residents.

Since the 1990s, scientific studies seem to support the idea that some types of bacteria (particularly *Lactobacillus* and *Bifidobacterium* species) living in the digestive system are beneficial to:

> keep in check potentially harmful bacteria also living there

> help digestion and the absorption of the products of digestion

> help to prevent/treat diseases of the digestive and urinary systems

> boost the function of the immune system.

Future of functional foods

In a few cases the scientific evidence supporting claims for the health benefits of functional foods is strong; for example, plant stanol esters in spreadable margarines. However, the health claims made for including prebiotics, probiotics and other functional foods as part of the diet remain unproven. Much more research is still needed.

QUESTIONS

5 Discuss why there are doubts about the effectiveness of probiotics as functional foods.

6 Evaluate the claims about functional foods promoting good health. You may wish to carry out extra research. Prepare a short report on your findings.

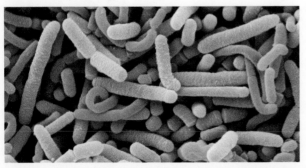

FIGURE 3: A micrograph of *Lactobacillus acidophilus* and *L. casei* cultured from a commercial probiotic food. Magnification: ×6500.

Preparing for assessment: Applying your knowledge

To achieve a good grade in science, you not only have to know and understand scientific ideas, but you also need to be able to apply them to other situations. This task will support you in developing these skills.

✳ Artificial blood – the end of blood donation?

Blood is essential to human life – without it your body would be unable to transport oxygen and other substances to all of the billions of cells inside you.

The average person contains 5 litres of the stuff – about 8% of your total mass. However there are occasions when a person may lose too much of their blood, for example, following an accident, and they need to be given some more. When this happens they receive blood that has been donated from somebody else in a blood transfusion.

Blood donation is fraught with problems – not enough people are willing to donate their blood and donated blood has to be a correct match to the recipient's blood type, it can only be stored for 35 days and it has to be carefully screened for diseases such as HIV.

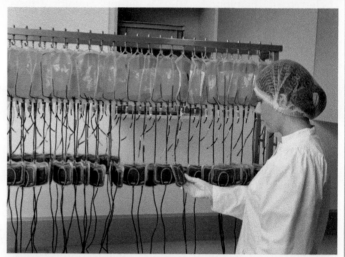

In recent years scientists have worked hard to overcome these issues by producing a substance called synthetic or artificial blood. The liquid looks like blood and contains tiny plastic molecules that have an iron atom at their core. They are able to mimic red blood cells and carry oxygen around the body 100 times more efficiently than their natural counterparts. Moreover, the 'blood' can be stored for years at a time and can easily be sterilised before use.

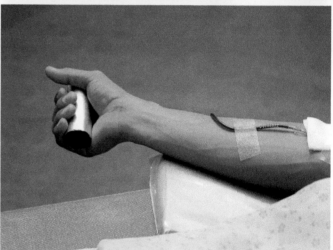

Scientists hope that this artificial blood will become more common for use in blood transfusions and save many lives in the future.

✳ Task 1

Why is it important that your cells receive oxygen?

Task 2

90% of the artificial blood is made up of a watery substance called plasma.

> What is the role of this artificial plasma?

 Task 3

The molecules in artificial blood contain iron atoms at their core.

> State which substance in red blood cells the iron atoms are mimicking.

> Explain the function of the iron atoms.

 Task 4

Doctors have warned that artificial blood must be used to complement the patient's own blood – it cannot completely replace it. This is because the artificial blood does not contain two essential components.

> Suggest what these components might be, including what they look like and their role within the blood.

> Why might it be an issue if a patient is only given blood that does not contain these components?

 Task 5

> Explain the advantage and disadvantage of using artificial blood in blood transfusions. Then, do the same for 'natural blood'.

> Explain whether you think natural blood or artificial blood is best used in blood transfusions. Give a reason for your answer.

 Maximise your grade

These sentences show what you need to include in your work to achieve each grade. Use them to improve your work and be more successful.

For a grade G–E, your answers should show that you can:
> describe the role of the blood in facilitating the diffusion of oxygen from the capillaries into respiring cells.
> describe the role of each component of the blood
> understand the need for artificial blood.

E

For a grade D–C in addition show that you can:
> explain the function of the blood cells that make up blood
> describe the advantages and disadvantages of using artificial blood and natural blood in transfusions.

C

For a grade B–A in addition show that you can:
> relate the structure of platelets, red blood cells and white blood cells to their function
> suggest why artificial blood cannot replace natural blood completely
> evaluate the usefulness of artificial blood.

A

B2 checklist (Topics 2–3)

To achieve your forecast grade in the exam you'll need to revise

Use this checklist to see what you can do now. Refer back to pages 54–91 if you're not sure.

Look across the rows to see how you could progress – **bold italic** means Higher tier only.

Remember you'll need to be able to use these ideas in various ways, such as:
> interpreting pictures, diagrams and graphs
> applying ideas to new situations
> explaining ethical implications
> suggesting some benefits and risks to society
> drawing conclusions from evidence you've been given.

Look at pages 264–86 for more information about exams and how you'll be assessed.

This checklist accompanies the exam-style questions and the worked examples. The content suggestions for specific grades are suggestions only and may not be replicated in your real examination. Remember, the checklists do not represent the complete content for any topic. Refer to the Specification for complete content details on any topic and any further information.

To aim for a grade E	To aim for a grade C	To aim for a grade A
recall the word equation for aerobic respiration recall the word equation for anaerobic respiration	describe why muscles may start to respire anaerobically describe what EPOC is	
state that diffusion is the movement of particles from an area of high concentration to an area of lower concentration	describe how the movement of oxygen and glucose in the body is facilitated by diffusion	apply the term 'concentration gradient' to explain diffusion
explain why heart and breathing rate increase with exercise		calculate heart rate, stroke volume and cardiac output
recall the word equation for photosynthesis state the conditions that affect the rate of photosynthesis	describe how the structure of a leaf is adapted for photosynthesis	explain how limiting factors affect the growth of a plant
describe how water, glucose and mineral salts are transported through a plant via the xylem, phloem and roots	explain why transpiration is important in the movement of water and mineral salts	

To aim for a grade E To aim for a grade C To aim for a grade A

To aim for a grade E	To aim for a grade C	To aim for a grade A
state the definition of osmosis as the movement of water molecules from an area of high concentration to an area of lower concentration through a partially permeable membrane	describe how root hair cells are adapted to take up water by osmosis describe simply the process of active transport	explain how active transport is used in the absorption of mineral salts through the roots
describe how fieldwork techniques are used to investigate the distribution of organisms in an ecosystem		explain how to reduce errors when using sampling techniques
recall that fossils are evidence for evolution	explain why there are gaps in the fossil record	*explain how the pentadactyl limb provides evidence for evolution*
state that growth is an increase in size, length and mass that occurs through cell division	describe how growth and development happens in both plants and animals	interpret growth by using percentile charts
recall the components in blood	describe the function of the components in blood	explain the clotting process
state the names of the four chambers of the heart and the four major blood vessels associated with it	describe how the circulatory system transports substances around the body	explain how the heart pumps blood
recall the names and functions of the parts of the digestive system	describe how food is moved along by the alimentary canal by peristalsis	*explain the role of the gall bladder in digestion* *explain how the structure of villi allows efficient absorption of products from digestion into the blood*
recall the function of the digestive enzymes carbohydrases, proteases and lipases	evaluate Visking tubing as a model of the small intestine	
state what is meant by the term 'functional food'	describe some examples of functional foods	evaluate the evidence for the claimed benefits of the use of functional foods

1 Aerobic respiration releases energy from glucose. The chemical reaction can be represented by the following word equation:

glucose + oxygen → carbon dioxide + water + **energy**

AO1 **a** State where the glucose needed for aerobic respiration comes from. [1]

AO2 **b** The air that you breathe in contains approximately 0.04% carbon dioxide. Suggest why the air you breathe out contains almost 10 times that amount. [1]

AO1 **c** Describe the change in a runner's heart rate and breathing rate when they are exercising. [1]

AO2 **d** At the end of a race, a runner's heart rate is 135 beats per minute and the volume of blood pumped out of the heart with each beat (stroke volume) is 0.65 dm³. Cardiac output can be calculated using the equation: cardiac output = stroke volume × heart rate. Calculate the cardiac output of the runner's heart. Show your workings and give your answer in dm³/min. [2]

AO1 **e** By the end of the race, the runner's muscle
AO2 cells are getting their energy from anaerobic respiration.

i Write the word equation for anaerobic respiration. [1]

ii Explain why our muscle cells do not respire using anaerobic respiration in normal circumstances. [2]

[Total 8]

2 A plant cannot move around to catch food. Instead it produces its own food in a reaction that uses light energy. This process is called photosynthesis.

AO1 **a** Copy and complete the word equation for photosynthesis. [2]

$$\text{......... + water} \xrightarrow{\text{light energy}} \text{glucose + ... + water}$$

AO1 **b** In which cell structure does photosynthesis take place? [1]

AO1 **c** The water produced in photosynthesis leaves the plant in a process called transpiration. Describe how transpiration occurs in plants. [2]

AO2 **d** Plants require certain conditions in order to photosynthesise.

i Suggest why water could be described as a limiting factor in the rate of photosynthesis. [1]

ii Farmers growing lettuces often use large commercial greenhouses to maximise their crop. Here, they can control the factors that could limit

the rate of photosynthesis in lettuces. Explain why a farmer would want to keep his greenhouse at approximately 30 °C. [2]

[Total: 8]

3

AO1 **a** Match the components of the blood to their function. [2]

Red blood cell	Carries oxygen
Plasma	Forms blood clots
	Transports carbon dioxide, urea and the soluble products of digestion around the body

AO1 **b** Describe one way in which red blood cells are adapted to their function. [1]

AO2 **c** Human immunodeficiency virus (HIV) can enter the blood through an open wound. It multiplies within certain white blood cells, killing those cells.

Explain why people infected with HIV are less able to fight infections. [2]

[Total: 5]

4 Bella set up a model to investigate how the concentration of amylase affects how quickly starch is digested. She used Visking tubing to model the small intestine. She added a mixture of starch solution and amylase enzymes to the tubing. Then, she sealed the tubing and placed it in warm water for half an hour.

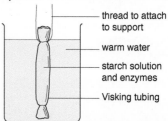

thread to attach to support

warm water

starch solution and enzymes

Visking tubing

AO2 **a** **i** Name the substance that Bella will find in the water at the end of the experiment. [1]

AO2 **ii** Explain how you would test for the presence of this substance. [1]

AO2 **b** Why is Visking tubing a good model of the small intestine? [2]

AO3 **c** Bella repeated her experiment three times, increasing the concentration of amylase each time. She tested the water after 5 minutes. Explain what you would expect her results to show. [3]

AO1 **d** Explain how the digestive system breaks
AO2 down protein into a form that the body's cells can use. [6]

[Total: 13]

✳ Worked example

AO1 **1 a** Name the chamber where blood first enters the heart. [1]

The left atrium. ✗

AO2 **b** Suggest why it is important that the heart wall is made of muscle tissue. [1]

Muscle tissue is needed to contract and expand the heart to pump the blood in and out of the heart. ✔

AO1 **c i** Explain the role of arteries in the circulatory system. [1]

The arteries pump oxygenated blood away from the heart to other parts of the body. ✔

AO2 **ii** Why is the pulmonary artery an unusual artery? [1]

The pulmonary artery is different in that it carries deoxygenated blood from the heart to the lungs. ✔

AO1 **d** Describe what happens to the blood as it passes through
AO2 the heart during one heartbeat. [6]

Stage 1 – The left atrium receives the blood from the vena cava, this opens the valves between the atrium and ventricle and the blood flows into the ventricle. Oxygenated blood then comes into the right atrium and then into the ventricle below it.

Stage 2 – The ventricles are now filled with blood so they squeeze together and the blood goes through some more valves.

Stage 3 – The oxygenated blood goes through the aorta and the deoxygenated blood goes into the pulmonary vein to the lungs.

The candidate has 7 scored out of 10. A silly mistake early on in confusing the sides of the heart meant that they missed on marks further into the question. Take your time when writing down your answer and make sure you go back and double-check any answers that you were unsure about.

How to raise your grade

Take note of the comments from examiners – these will help you to improve your grade.

It is the right atrium. The candidate has made the common mistake of forgetting that heart diagrams are labelled according to how they appear in the body.

A good, clear answer. Watch out – candidates sometimes confuse themselves by thinking that the pulmonary artery carries blood back to the heart and that is why it is unusual.

The candidate has answered this challenging question quite well and scored within Level 2 of the banded mark scheme used to mark 6-mark questions. They have communicated with clarity throughout and organised the information logically. However, the candidate lost valuable marks by incorrectly describing the first stage in the process.

An ideal answer to this question might read as follows:
Stage 1 – Deoxygenated blood flows into the right atrium from the vena cava. Oxygenated blood flows into the left atrium from the pulmonary vein.
Stage 2 – The valves between the atria and the ventricles open due to increased pressure upon them. The blood flows from the atria into the ventricles.
Stage 3 – The ventricles contract forcing blood towards through valves whereby the aorta takes oxygenated blood to the rest of the body and the pulmonary vein transports deoxygenated blood to the lungs.

1 Emma investigated the distribution of a green alga called *Pleurococcus* on tree trunks. She created a quadrant on a piece of transparent plastic, with 100 squares of 1 cm². Emma placed the quadrat on the south side of a tree trunk, 1 m up from the ground. She counted the number of squares in which *Pleurococcus* was present. She repeated this on the north side of the tree trunk. She then repeated the counts on nine more trees within one hour. Her results are shown in the table.

Tree		1	2	3	4	5	6	7	8	9	10
Squares with alga	South side	38	38	12	29	16	49	4	38	27	13
	North side	69	69	91	54	49	87	43	94	86	81

AO2 **a** Suggest why it was a good idea to divide the quadrant into 100 squares. [2]

AO2 **b** Describe how Emma could improve the quality of her results. [3]

AO3 **c** Describe the distribution pattern of *Pleurococcus* shown in Emma's results. [1]

AO3 **d** Explain the pattern that Emma saw in her results. [2]

[Total 8]

2 a Root hair cells enable a plant to take in water and mineral salts.

AO1 **i** Describe how a root hair cell is adapted to increase its uptake of water via osmosis. [2]

AO1 **ii** Describe how mineral salts are transported from the soil to cells in the plant's leaf. [4]

b Luke carried out an experiment to investigate osmosis in plants. He cut two small sections potato, and put one section in distilled water and the other in a high sugar solution. He left the experiment overnight. In the morning he looked at the potato cells under a microscope and drew diagrams of how the cells looked.

AO3 **i** Which diagram represents a plant cell from the potato section put in high sugar solution? [1]

AO2 **ii** Explain why cell B has become flaccid. [3]

[Total: 10]

3 a This is a growth chart for children aged 0–5 years old.

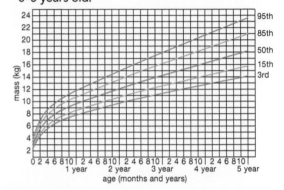

AO3 **i** Describe the correlation shown by the graph. [1]

AO3 **ii** What is the average weight for a child of 2 years old? [1]

AO3 **iii** Baby James is 1 year and 10 months old. He has a mass of 13 kg. State the percentile that he would fit into on the graph. [1]

AO3 **iv** Calculate the percentage of babies who are James's age but weigh more than him. [2]

AO2 **v** Explain why growth charts are used in hospitals. [2]

AO1 AO2 **b** Compare how a baby and seedling will grow into adult organisms. [6]

[Total: 13]

AO1 **4 a** Where in the body is bile produced? [1]

AO1 **b** Explain the role of bile in the digestive system. [2]

AO1 **c** The small intestine contains villi. These villi allow the efficient absorption of soluble digested food. Describe two properties of villi that enable them to facilitate the absorption of digested food. [2]

AO2 **d** Coeliac's disease is a condition affecting a person's small intestine, causing the villi in the small intestine to be destroyed or damaged. Describe the effect of the disease on the sufferer. [3]

e 'Healthy Balance' is a newly launched prebiotic yoghurt drink. The manufacturers guarantee that consumers will feel great after trying it for one month.

AO2 **ii** Explain why 'Healthy Balance' could be called a functional food. [2]

AO1 AO2 **i** Evaluate the effectiveness of prebiotics and probiotics in improving a person's health. [6]

[Total: 16]

Summary of Assessment Objectives

| AO1 recall the science | AO2 apply your knowledge | AO3 evaluate and analyse the evidence |

Worked example

The photograph shows a fossilised mesosaurus that lived over 90 million years ago. Modern amphibians today such as lizards and crocodiles are ancestors of the mesosaurus.

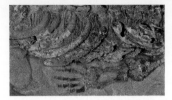

AO2   Evaluate how far this fossil can be used as evidence that amphibians evolved from mesosauruses.   [6]

Organisms change and adapt over time to become more suited to their environment. In the process, organisms can evolve to become new species. This is known as evolution.

Fossils are preserved examples of species that lived millions of years ago. They can provide evidence of how organisms used to look and how the same species changed over time. The mesosaurus fossil is evidence of how the mesosaurus used to look. If a scientist compared the skeleton of a mesosaurus with that of a modern amphibian, they would see that they both have a pentadactyl limb. This is a shared characteristic and could indicate that modern amphibians evolved from mesosauruses.

This fossil cannot tell scientists what the mesosauruses' habitat, skin or diet was like. This means it is difficult to decide whether a mesosaurus really was similar to a modern amphibian and whether it was the ancestor of an amphibian.

Also, this mesosaurus fossil is just one piece of evidence. There may be other mesosaurus fossils that scientists have not found yet because they have been damaged or destroyed. Also, not all mesosauruses would have formed fossils when they died. It would be impossible for scientists to find fossils from all the mesosauruses that have ever existed. One day, we may find mesosaurus fossils that show characteristics that are very different from amphibians. If enough of these fossils are found, the fossil record would provide evidence that suggests that amphibians did not evolve from mesosauruses.

This mesosaurus fossil can be used as evidence that amphibians evolved from mesosauruses as they show similar characteristics. But, more evidence would be needed to be sure that amphibians evolved from mesosauruses.

How to raise your grade

Take note of the comments from examiners – these will help you to improve your grade.

A good statement, but the question did not ask for a definition of evolution.

The candidate has given a clear and accurate answer to score maximum marks. They have made good use of scientific terms, organised their answer into a logical structure of 'for' and 'against' and related their answer completely to the example given in the question. The final statement gives a clear conclusion to their answer and shows the ability to form an independent, mature scientific opinion.

The candidate has scored 6 out of 6. They have obviously revised this topic thoroughly and been able to pull together their ideas to form accurate answers. Their extended writing is very strong and shows that they are confident in expressing their ideas.

C2 Discovering chemistry (Topics 1–3)

What you should know

Atomic structure and the periodic table

Materials are composed of particles and atoms are the smallest particles that take part in chemical reactions.

Materials can be classified based on their properties.

Elements are arranged in the periodic table with elements in the same group being similar to each other and metals on the left and non-metals on the right.

 Describe the structure of an atom.

Ionic compounds and analysis

Elements bond to form compounds.

A salt is made when an acid neutralises a base (C1 – Topic 3).

Substances can be identified using chemical tests (C1 – Topic 3).

A precipitate is a solid that is sometimes formed when two chemicals react.

 Describe a chemical test for carbon dioxide.

Covalent compounds and separation techniques

Compounds and mixtures can be separated using filters, evaporation, distillation and chromatography.

A mixture of hydrocarbons can be separated using fractional distillation.

 Describe the separation of crude oil using fractional distillation.

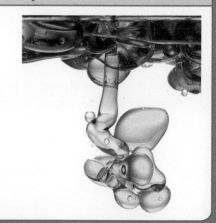

You will find out about

> the structure of an atom and the properties (including charge and mass) of protons, neutrons and electrons

> the terms atomic number and mass number

> isotopes

> calculating relative atomic mass

> Mendeleev's construction of the periodic table

> the information contained in the periodic table including the classification of elements

> the relationship between electron configuration and an element's position in the periodic table

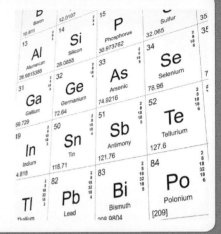

> the formation of ions and ionic compounds of elements in groups 1, 2, 6 and 7

> naming ionic compounds and writing their formulae

> the structure and properties of ionic compounds

> the rules of solubility

> the methods used to prepare an insoluble salt

> tests used to identify some of the more common ions

> the use of spectroscopy to discover new elements

> the formation of molecules with covalent bonds

> the use of dot and cross diagrams to represent covalent bonds

> the formation of giant covalent structures

> the relationship between properties and structure

> using properties to classify elements and compounds

> using separation techniques including fractional distillation, separation funnels and chromatography

Atomic structure

You will find out:

> about the structure of atoms

> about elements

> the relative size and relative mass of protons, neutrons and electrons

It's a small world

Atoms are incredibly small but very powerful. When atoms are split huge amounts of energy can be released. In a nuclear power station 1 kg of uranium can produce the same amount of energy as burning 2 million kg of coal.

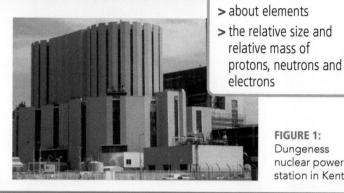

FIGURE 1: Dungeness nuclear power station in Kent.

The nature of matter

Chemistry is the study of **matter** and its behaviour. So, what is matter? Matter is anything that occupies space (volume) and has mass. The smallest particles of matter that can be studied using chemistry are called **atoms**. Atoms are very small, too small to be seen with the naked eye.

Atoms are composed of:

> a central core called the **nucleus**

> negatively charged particles called **electrons**, surrounding the nucleus.

The nucleus is made up of:

> **protons** that have a positive charge

> and **neutrons** that have no charge.

Most atoms have no overall charge. This is because each atom often contains an equal number of positively charged protons and negatively charged electrons.

The number of protons in the nucleus uniquely determines the identity of an atom. The simplest atom has one proton in the nucleus with one electron surrounding the nucleus. This atom is called hydrogen. All atoms of hydrogen have one proton in their nucleus. Next, atoms with two protons in the nucleus are called helium.

Electrons can have only certain energies when they surround the nucleus. We sometimes say that electrons that have the same energy are found in the same **shell** of an atom. There are many different shells around the nucleus:

> The first shell which is closest to the nucleus holds a maximum of two electrons.

> The second and subsequent shells, up to and including atomic number 20, can each hold a maximum of eight electrons.

Elements are substances made from one type of atom. So, the element hydrogen is made of hydrogen atoms all of which have one proton in their nucleus.

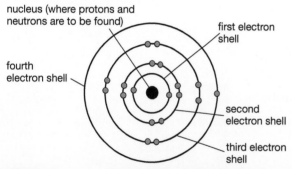

nucleus (where protons and neutrons are to be found)

first electron shell

fourth electron shell

second electron shell

third electron shell

FIGURE 2: Electron shells (energy levels) for a potassium atom.

QUESTIONS

1 Describe the structure of an atom.

2 A scientist looks at the atoms in an unknown element. State how they can identify the element.

Masses

Table 1 shows the mass of a proton as 1. One what? The typical unit for mass is the kilogram, but there are no units indicated. What is going on?

Scientists have solved a difficult problem in the simplest way possible. The mass of a proton is 1.67×10^{-27} g. Imagine trying to do maths with that

TABLE 1: Atomic particles.

Name of particle	Relative mass	Relative charge
Proton	1	+1
Neutron	1	0
Electron	1/1836	−1

kind of number. The number is so small that regular units are difficult to work with. To simplify the problem, the mass of a proton was arbitrarily set to 1 **atomic mass unit** (amu). The mass of a neutron is so similar to that of the proton that it also has a mass of 1 amu.

Electrons are even smaller that protons and neutrons. It would take 1836 electrons to equal the mass of a proton. They are so small that when calculating the mass of an atom the electrons are often ignored.

QUESTIONS

3 Explain why all atoms have zero charge, if the number of protons and electrons is equal.

4 Where in the atom is most of the mass found?

5 State how many protons are in an atom of lithium, if it has an atomic number of 3.

What do atoms look like?

In the late 1890s, a picture began to emerge that gave more information about the appearance of atoms. J.J. Thomson (1856–1940) discovered electrons. He deduced that they had a negative charge because they were repelled by negatively charged plates and attracted by positively charged plates. Since Thomson knew that atoms had no charge, he concluded that atoms must be composed of positive and negative charges.

Robert Millikan (1868–1953) carried out an experiment to determine the charge of an electron. This is very difficult to do because electrons cannot be seen, and their charge is very small. In this experiment, small oil drops made in an atomiser were squirted into a container, and given a negative charge by firing electrons at each drop. Then the oil drop was held suspended in mid-air by changing the voltage across two plates until the drop stayed in the same place. The measurements were then used to calculate a value for the charge of the electron.

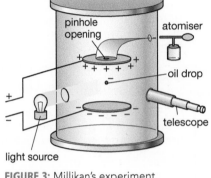

FIGURE 3: Millikan's experiment.

The next question was how are the positive and negative charges put together? Thomson incorrectly described the atom as a plum pudding (like a Christmas pudding) of positive charge with electrons scattered, like currants, throughout the pudding. In 1909, Hans Geiger (1882–1945) and Ernest Marsden (1889–1970) used alpha particles (small, positively charged particles) from radioactive substances to get a better model of atoms. Geiger and Marsden aimed alpha particles at a sheet of gold foil and observed how they were scattered:

> The majority of the alpha particles went straight through the foil. This meant that most of the atom was empty space, showing that the plum pudding model of the atom was incorrect.

> A very small number of alpha particles were scattered through large angles of 90° or more. They realised that the alpha particles were colliding with a nucleus, which was extremely small. The diameter of the nucleus is about 10^{-15} m, whereas atoms as a whole are 10^{-10} m across. Hence a nucleus' diameter is only a hundred thousandth of that of an atom! A modern model of the atom is shown in Figure 4.

This will not be assessed in your GCSE Additional Science exam but it will be useful for further study in Unit 3 and at A level.

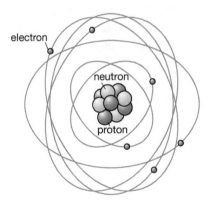

FIGURE 4: A model depicting the structure of an atom. What can you say about the scale of this drawing?

QUESTIONS

6 Explain why only a few alpha particles were scattered through large angles in Geiger and Marsden's experiment.

7 Suggest why it took so long to discover the neutron in an atom (it wasn't discovered until 1932).

8 Using the internet, research Ernest Rutherford and write a short report on his contribution to our knowledge of science.

Did you know?

If you had an atom as big as a football stadium the nucleus would be the size of a grain of sand.

The periodic table

You will find out:
> how the elements are organised in the periodic table
> about atomic number, mass number and relative atomic mass
> about isotopes
> how to calculate relative atomic mass

A place for everything ...

Dmitri Mendeleev (1834–1907) found a way of classifying (putting into classes) the chemical elements. The modern periodic table is built on Mendeleev's table and his table is now considered to be one of the most remarkable ideas in the whole of science.

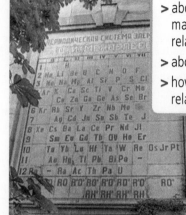

FIGURE 1: Monument to Mendeleev. The Russian words at the top say 'periodic system of elements' followed by Mendeleev's name.

Recognising patterns

In 1869, Mendeleev proposed a new scheme to organise the known elements into some kind or order. He produced the **periodic table** of elements where he:

> Arranged the elements in order of increasing atomic weight (later replaced by atomic number).

> Arranged elements with similar chemical properties is the same **group**.

> Left gaps for undiscovered elements and predicted their properties.

The periodic table is organised into rows and columns:

> Elements are arranged in rows in order of increasing atomic number; these rows are referred to as **periods**.

> Elements with similar properties are arranged in vertical columns called groups.

Each box in the modern-day periodic table usually contains the following information:

> **Atomic number**: the number of protons in the nucleus of an atom.

> **Mass number**: The number of protons and neutrons in the nucleus. This is approximately equal to the mass of the atom in amu.

> **Symbol**: an internationally recognised abbreviation used to identify the element using up to two letters. The first letter is always a capital letter; if there is a second letter it is lowercase, for example, copper is Cu.

The broadest division on the periodic table is that of metals and non-metals. The red line in the right-hand portion of the periodic table in Figure 2 marks the divide between metals and non-metals. All of those elements to the left of the line are metals. All those elements to the right of the line are non-metals.

FIGURE 2: A modern periodic table. Can you identify which number is the atomic number and which is the mass number?

Did you know?

Gallium was discovered 9 years after being predicted by Mendeleev as an element that belonged in one of his empty spaces.

QUESTIONS

1 Describe how Mendeleev organised the periodic table of elements.

2 Use the periodic table to name three metals and three non-metals.

Isotopes

It was once believed that all atoms of an element were identical. However, as technology improved, it was discovered that atoms of an element could differ in mass.

The number of protons in the nucleus was the same for all atoms of an element, so what accounted for the different masses? The answer was neutrons. Atoms of an element could have different numbers of neutrons in their nuclei. These atoms with different numbers of neutrons, but the same number of protons, are called **isotopes**.

Hydrogen has two stable isotopes:

> The most common form of hydrogen has one proton in its nucleus and therefore an atomic mass of 1.

> The other form of hydrogen has one proton and one neutron in the nucleus and an atomic mass of 2. It is called hydrogen-2 or deuterium.

Both are hydrogen because the identity of an element is based on the atomic number.

Some periodic tables include **relative atomic mass** rather than atomic mass. The relative atomic mass takes into account the relative abundance of the different isotopes of the elements. This means that most relative atomic masses are not whole numbers.

FIGURE 4: The isotopes of carbon.

 QUESTIONS

3 Explain why atoms with different numbers of neutrons are not considered different elements.

4 Define the term isotope.

5 An aluminium atom has 13 protons and 14 neutrons present. What is its mass number and how many electrons are there? What is its atomic number?

hydrogen-1 nucleus
(1 proton)

hydrogen-2 (deuterium) nucleus
(1 proton plus 1 neutron)

FIGURE 3: The isotopes of hydrogen.

carbon-12 nucleus
(6 protons plus 6 neutrons)

carbon-13 nucleus
(6 protons plus 7 neutrons)

Calculating relative atomic mass (Higher tier only)

The mass number of carbon listed on a periodic table is 12. However, carbon has a less common isotope that has an atomic mass of 13 amu. Periodic tables that include the relative atomic mass instead of the mass number will list carbon's mass as 12.01 amu.

 QUESTIONS

6 Use the information in the following table to show that the relative atomic mass for chlorine is 35.5.

Isotopes of chlorine	
Atomic mass (amu)	Relative abundance (%)
35	75
37	25

To calculate the relative atomic mass of an element we need to know the relative abundance of each of the isotopes. Table 1 shows this for two carbon isotopes.

The relative atomic mass is the sum of the individual isotope masses multiplied by their fractional relative abundance. So for carbon:

$$\left(12 \times \frac{98.93}{100}\right) + \left(13 \times \frac{1.07}{100}\right) = 12.0107$$

This is rounded to 12.01.

TABLE 1: Common isotopes of carbon and their relative abundance.

Atomic mass (amu)	Relative abundance (%)
12	98.93
13	1.070

Electrons

You will find out:
> the number of electrons in an atom
> the rules for electron configuration of the first 20 elements
> the connection between outer electrons and position in the periodic table

What's on tonight?

Electrons were the first part of the atom to be discovered. This was in 1898 when J.J. Thomson carried out experiments using a cathode-ray tube. These devices work in a similar way to bulky, old-fashioned TV sets.

FIGURE 1: A cathode-ray tube has a source of electrons before striking a fluorescent screen that can be deflected using a magnetic field screen – just like an old TV.

Completing the picture

As the structure of the nucleus became clearer, attention turned to the electrons. Eventually scientists realised that:

> the electrons are separated from the nucleus

> protons are individual particles inside the nucleus.

By the 1930s, it was clear that atoms were composed of:

> positively charged protons

> uncharged neutrons

> negatively charged electrons.

It was also clear that, overall, atoms had no charge. This implied that the number of protons and the number of electrons must be equal since the positive charge is balanced by the negative charge.

But, where were the electrons located? In 1913, Niels Bohr (1885–1962) offered a possible solution. His proposal stated that:

> electrons surround the nucleus

> electrons are grouped into layers called **electron shells** or energy levels

> each shell can hold a specific number of electrons

> the innermost shell or level can hold up to two electrons

> the next two shells or levels can hold up to eight electrons each

> each shell must be filled before electrons can go into a higher shell.

From these proposals, a system of notation can be created to indicate the **electron configuration** for each element. The number of electrons in each shell or energy level is indicated by a number and each shell is separated by a full stop as shown in Table 1.

TABLE 1: The first three periods of the periodic table showing the electron configuration.

Element	Atomic number	Electron configuration
Hydrogen	1	1
Helium	2	2
Lithium	3	2.1
Beryllium	4	2.2
Boron	5	2.3
Carbon	6	2.4
Nitrogen	7	2.5
Oxygen	8	2.6
Fluorine	9	2.7
Neon	10	2.8
Sodium	11	2.8.1
Magnesium	12	2.8.2
Aluminium	13	2.8.3
Silicon	14	2.8.4
Phosphorus	15	2.8.5
Sulfur	16	2.8.6
Chlorine	17	2.8.7
Argon	18	2.8.8

Did you know?

The neutron was not discovered until 1932 by James Chadwick when he identified that neutral particles were emitted from a beryllium target bombarded by alpha particles.

Q Niels Bohr   Periodicity   Metalloids

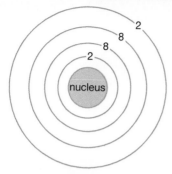

FIGURE 2: Electron shells, or energy levels, surrounding the nucleus. What is this element?

QUESTIONS

1 Give one piece of evidence to show that atoms have an equal number of protons and electrons.

2 Use the periodic table at the back of this book to help you to write the electron configuration for potassium and calcium.

3 Draw diagrams to show the electron configuration of: **a** helium, **b** nitrogen, and **c** aluminium.

Location, location, location

If the electron configuration of an element is compared to the same element's position in the periodic table, the following can be seen:

> Each period (or row) in the table represents an electron shell or energy level being filled up.

> Each vertical group in the table is made up of elements that have the same number of outer shell electrons. This is the origin of the group numbers.

Look at helium and lithium in Table 1.

> Notice that helium has two electrons and a full shell, because the inner shell can only hold two electrons.

> The next element, lithium, has one more electron, which has to be placed in the next shell.

> If you now look at the periodic table, you will see that lithium is the first element in a new period.

> So, as we move across the periodic table from one element to the next, an electron is added to the electron shell. When the shell is full the next electron added must go in the next electron shell and a new period begins.

By knowing where an element is in the periodic table, we know its electron configuration. Moreover, by knowing an element's electron configuration we know where it fits into the periodic table. For example, aluminium, 2.8.3, is in group 3, as it has three electrons in its outer shell, and in the third period as it has three shells containing electrons.

QUESTIONS

4 Describe the relationship between position in the periodic table and electron configuration.

5 Using the periodic table at the back of this book, identify the element that has three electrons shells with two electrons in the outer shell.

6 An element has 14 electrons. In which group of the periodic table would the element be found?

Periodicity

Mendeleev recognised a repeating nature to the elements. He referred to this as **periodicity**. For instance, lithium, sodium and potassium all react with chlorine in a 1 to 1 ratio (see Table 2). These are the kind of similarities that Mendeleev recognised and used to form his groups.

TABLE 2: Reactions of some group 1 elements with chlorine.

$2Li (s) + Cl_2 (g) \rightarrow 2LiCl (s)$
$2Na (s) + Cl_2 (g) \rightarrow 2NaCl (s)$
$2K (s) + Cl_2 (g) \rightarrow 2KCl (s)$

Some of the trends that Mendeleev saw and used to organise the periodic table start to make sense once we start to look at electron configurations. If you

look at the electron configuration of the elements of group 1 you will see that they all have one outer shell electron. The reason these elements all react similarly is their electron configuration.

QUESTIONS

7 Magnesium reacts with chlorine in a 1 to 2 ratio: $Mg (s) + Cl_2 (g) \rightarrow MgCl_2 (s)$. Use this information to predict how calcium will react with chlorine.

8 Neon is one of the noble gases in group 0 of the periodic table. Explain how its electron configuration may affect its properties.

Q Electron configuration   Cathode-ray tube

Ionic bonds

You will find out:
> how atoms combine to form compounds
> how ionic bonds are formed
> that ions are positively or negatively charged
> about sodium and chloride ions

When sodium met chlorine

Table salt (sodium chloride) is an everyday substance that we scatter on our food without much thought. But in the lab its formation from its constituent elements, sodium and chlorine, is a fiery, explosive reaction, as you can see in Figure 1.

FIGURE 1: The reaction of sodium and chlorine.

Bonding: when elements get together

Atoms of elements that are very different can combine to form new compounds. This happens when the atoms join together by making new chemical bonds.

Sodium chloride is a good example of atoms from two different elements bonding together to make a new compound.

> Sodium is a soft, silvery metal that reacts vigorously with water.

> Chlorine is a light green poisonous gas.

> The two elements bond together to form the compound sodium chloride.

When sodium and chlorine bond:

> the sodium atom and chlorine atom transfer electrons

> the sodium atom becomes positively charged as it loses an electron

> the chlorine atom becomes negatively charged as it gains an electron.

An atom or a group of atoms with a positive or a negative charge is called an **ion**, so in this case the sodium atom (Na) becomes a sodium ion (Na$^+$) and the chlorine atom (Cl) becomes a chloride ion (Cl$^-$).

The attraction between the positive and negative ions holds the atoms together **electrostatically**. This type of bonding is called **ionic bonding**.

FIGURE 2: Sodium chloride contains two very reactive elements bonded together. We know it as table salt.

QUESTIONS

1 State two differences between the elements sodium and chlorine and the compound sodium chloride.

2 Write a word equation for the reaction between sodium and chlorine.

3 Define the term ionic bond.

Making ions

Ionic bonding involves the transfer of electrons between atoms. It creates a stable electron configuration.

Notice that an atom of neon has a full outer shell of electrons. This is what makes neon, and other elements such as helium and argon, so unreactive. A full outer shell is very stable for atoms. However, a sodium atom has one outer electron and a chlorine atom has seven outer electrons.

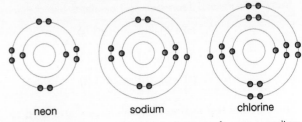

neon   sodium   chlorine

FIGURE 3: Electron configuration diagrams for neon, sodium and chlorine.

Forming sodium ions

A sodium atom can obtain a full outer shell by giving up or donating the outer electron. This means that the atom would change from having 11 electrons to having only 10 electrons. Remember, the atom will still have 11 protons in the nucleus. The atom will have one more positively changed proton than negatively charged electrons.

When a sodium atom donates its outer electron it changes from an atom into an ion. The sodium ion has a charge of +1.

> **QUESTIONS**

4 Explain how an ionic bond forms.

5 How many electrons does:

a a sodium atom and

b a chlorine ion contain?

6 Calcium has the atomic number 20 and fluorine has the atomic number 9. Predict:

a the charges on the calcium and fluoride ions

b the likely formula for calcium fluoride.

Forming chloride ions

A chlorine atom can obtain a full outer shell by accepting an extra outer electron. This means that the atom would change from having 17 electrons to having 18 electrons. Remember, the atom will still have 17 protons in the nucleus. The atom will have one more negatively charged electron than positively charged proton.

When a chlorine atom accepts an outer electron it changes from an atom into an ion. The chlorine atom changes its name to chloride and the ion has a charge of −1.

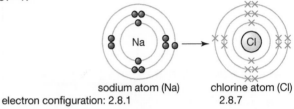

sodium atom (Na)   chlorine atom (Cl)
electron configuration: 2.8.1   2.8.7

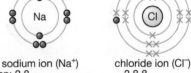

sodium ion (Na⁺)   chloride ion (Cl⁻)
electron configuration: 2.8   2.8.8

FIGURE 4: Sodium and chloride ions being formed.

Ionic bonds

In the periodic table the metallic elements are to the left, mainly in groups 1 and 2 and in the central block of transition metals. Metallic atoms can obtain electronic structures like those of the noble gases by donating electrons. Metallic atoms form into positive ions:

> positive ions are called **cations**.

In the periodic table the non-metallic elements are to the right, mainly in groups 5, 6 and 7. Non-metallic atoms can obtain an electronic structures like those of the noble gases by accepting electrons. Non-metallic atoms form negative ions:

> negative ions are called **anions**.

When a metallic element bonds with a non-metallic element the metal atoms transfer electrons to the non-metal atoms. This forms positive and negative ions and these are attracted together to form a bond. In ionic bonding a metal is needed to act as a giver or donor of electrons. Sometimes ions are made up of more than one atom and sometimes the atoms are from different elements.

> **QUESTIONS**

7 Explain how an ionic bond forms between calcium and oxygen. Use a diagram to illustrate your answer.

8 Explain why a compound cannot be formed by bonding together two cations or two anions.

Remember!
Electrons in atoms are grouped into layers called electron shells or energy levels.

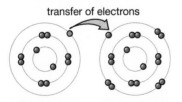

transfer of electrons

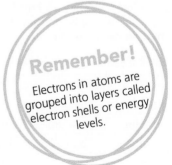

sodium atom, Na   chlorine atom, Cl   sodium ion, Na⁺   chloride ion, Cl⁻

FIGURE 5: Formation of sodium and chloride ions and ionic bonding.

Naming ionic compounds

You will find out:
> about naming some common ionic compounds
> why the names of some compounds end in -ide or -ate

Always read the label

In science as in life, it is essential to make sure you get details correct. Knowing the difference between sodium chloride solution and sodium hypochlorite (bleach) could avoid serious injury. The name tells us about the composition of the substance – what it contains.

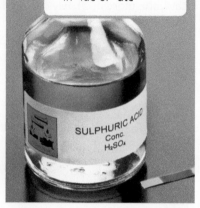

FIGURE 1: The contents of the two bottles look the same but one contains water; the other a strong acid! Careless labelling of the bottles could be fatal.

Writing the names of ionic compounds

There are many different ionic compounds. Each is made from bonding cations with anions.

Almost all of the ionic substances you will need to know have a two-word name. This is like a person having a first name and a second name.

cation + *anion* ⇒ *ionic substance*
sodium + chloride ⇒ sodium chloride
lithium + bromide ⇒ lithium bromide

Using Table 1 it is possible to combine the different cations and anions to make many ionic substances. Remember that the compound will be a cation bonded to an anion. You can make up any combination you wish. For example:

> lithium chloride

> potassium bromide

> ammonium sulfide.

You will have noticed that the name of some ions is sometimes slightly different from the name of the atom. For example, bromine becomes bromide and chlorine becomes chloride.

TABLE 1: Some common cations and anions.

Cations		Anions	
lithium	magnesium	chloride	oxide
sodium	calcium	bromide	sulfide
potassium	barium	iodide	sulfate
ammonium		nitrate	carbonate
hydrogen		hydroxide	

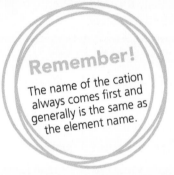

Remember!
The name of the cation always comes first and generally is the same as the element name.

QUESTIONS

1 a Draw a table with two columns – cation and anion. Put the following ions into the correct column: magnesium, aluminium, chloride, potassium, iodide, hydrogen, carbonate, sulfate, ammonium, hydroxide.

b What do you notice about the names of the cations compared to the names of the anions?

2 Name the ionic compounds formed when the following atoms bond:

a barium and oxygen

b calcium and chlorine

c iron and fluorine.

Q Ionic compounds   Polyatomic ions

Ions ending in '-ide'

The ending actually gives us an essential clue that the chemical is a compound. It is even possible to talk about groups of chemicals based on this. For example we talk about 'the **chlorides**' or 'the **sulfides**'.

The chlorides contain any chloride such as sodium chloride, lithium chloride, magnesium chloride and barium chloride. The different groupings may even act in similar ways. For instance, almost all chlorides are soluble in water. On the other hand, most nitrates are insoluble in water. The '-ide' ending at the end of an anion tells you that the anions contain atoms from one element only. Therefore, an oxide ion contains only oxygen, a sulfide contains only sulfur atoms, and so on.

FIGURE 2: Lapis lazuli, a rare, deep blue gemstone. The sulfide anion gives this gemstone its blue colour. Lapis lazuli was formerly used as the source of the blue pigment ultramarine in paint.

QUESTIONS

3 Explain what '-ide' at the end of an anion tells you. Provide some examples to support your answer.

4 Choose an '-ide' group and using your own research, list any properties that are shared by the chemicals in that group.

Ions ending in '-ate'

Sometimes the naming of ions is more complicated. This is especially true for ions containing more than one type of atom.

The '-ate' ending at the end of an anion tells you that the anion contains oxygen as well as the other elements in the name. Therefore, a sulfate ion contains sulfur and oxygen, a carbonate ion contains carbon and oxygen, and so on.

Some ionic compounds have similar names. Make sure you check carefully and use the correct name. This can prevent mistakes later on. This is very important when writing down chemical reactions as **word equations**.

For example, if we consider the reaction between silver nitrate and sodium sulfate we would have the following equation:

silver nitrate + sodium sulfate → silver sulfate + sodium nitrate

If we made a mistake and used sodium sulfide instead of sodium sulfate then this would be a completely different chemical reaction. Although only two letters are different in the name, the chemical compounds are very different.

Remember!
Most polyatomic ions are anions but some are cations, e.g. ammonium.

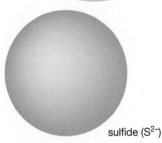
sulfide (S²⁻)

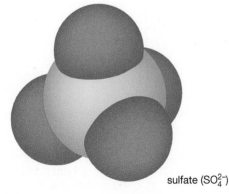
sulfate (SO₄²⁻)

FIGURE 3: Sulfide and sulfate are completely different ions. The sulfide ion contains just one sulfur atom; the sulfate ion contains one sulfur atom plus four oxygen atoms.

QUESTIONS

5 Describe the difference between a sulfide and a sulfate.

6 Write down the symbol equation for lead nitrate reacting with potassium iodide.

7 Explain how ions with very similar names can be significantly different.

Writing chemical formulae

You will find out:
> how to work out the formulae of ionic compounds
> about writing symbol equations

What's in a name?

You will be used to seeing shorthand symbols to represent objects or words. These can save us a lot of time and as long as we all use the same symbols it avoids confusion. Scientists also use symbols when writing about chemicals.

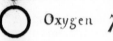

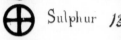

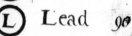

FIGURE 1: Some of Dalton's atomic symbols published around 200 years ago. Why do you think these didn't catch on?

Symbols for ions

Elements have a symbol as well as a name. For example, the symbol for sodium is Na and for potassium the symbol is K.

When ions are monoatomic, that is contain only atoms from the same element, the formula for the ion is the same as the symbol for the element with the addition of its charge. This is very helpful when you need to memorise them.

Cations usually keep the same name as the element, although anions change their endings to '-ide'.

Ions that contain atoms of two or more elements have formulae that show this. For example: ammonium NH_4^+, nitrate NO_3^-, carbonate CO_3^{2-} and sulfate SO_4^{2-}.

Table 1 shows the formulae for some common cations and anions.

Table 1 also shows the different charges that the ions have. When a cation and ion combine to make a compound, these charges must be balanced.

Remember!
'Halogen' refers to the elements in group 7 of the periodic table, but halide is the ionic form of halogens.

 QUESTIONS

1 Write down the symbols for carbonate, hydroxide, barium and sulfide.

2 Fluoride has a charge of –1. What does this tell you about fluoride?

3 Lithium has a charge of +1. Aluminium has a charge of +3. State why this is.

TABLE 1: Formulae and charges for some cations and anions.

Cations						Anions			
+1		+2		+3		−1		−2	
lithium	Li^+	magnesium	Mg^{2+}	aluminium	Al^{3+}	chloride	Cl^-	oxide	O^{2-}
sodium	Na^+	calcium	Ca^{2+}			bromide	Br^-	sulfide	S^{2-}
potassium	K^+	barium	Ba^{2+}			iodide	I^-	sulfite	SO_3^{2-}
ammonium	NH_4^+	iron (II)	Fe^{2+}			nitrate	NO_3^-	sulfate	SO_4^{2-}
hydrogen	H^+	copper	Cu^{2+}			hydroxide	OH^-	carbonate	CO_3^{2-}

Writing formulae for ionic compounds

When we write the name of an ionic compound in symbols it is called a **chemical formula**. The plural of formula is formulae. One advantage of using a formula is that it can save time and it also tells us exactly which types of atoms are present in a compound and in what ratio.

To write a chemical formula for an ionic compound you will need to know the formulae of the ions it contains. For example, magnesium has a charge of +2. This is shown as Mg^{2+}. Once you have found the correct formulae for the cation and anion in the compound the balanced formula can be found.

> Step 1: write down the correct name.

> Step 2: write down the correct formula for each ion including its charge.

> Step 3: balance the charges so that there are no extra positive or negative charges. You can only do this by adding more of a positive or negative ion. Never change the formula of an ion.

> Step 4: write down the final formula for the compound.

FIGURE 2: The universal language of chemistry means that it can be understood throughout the world.

Example 1: sodium sulfate

Formulae $\qquad$ Na^+ $\qquad$ SO_4^{2-}

Notice that the sodium ion has one positive charge and the sulfate ion has two negative charges. To balance this we need an additional sodium ion:

Balance $\qquad$ Na^+ $\qquad$ Na^+ $\qquad$ SO_4^{2-}

Final formula $\qquad$ $(Na^+)_2(SO_4^{2-})$ or Na_2SO_4

The small 2 after the symbol for sodium shows that there are two atoms of sodium.

Example 2: aluminium sulfate

Formulae $\qquad$ Al^{3+} $\qquad\qquad$ SO_4^{2-}
$\qquad\qquad\qquad$ Al^{3+} $\qquad\qquad$ SO_4^{2-}
Balance $\qquad$ Al^{3+} $\qquad\qquad$ SO_4^{2-}
charges $\qquad\qquad\qquad\qquad\qquad$ SO_4^{2-}

Final formula $\qquad$ $(Al^{3+})_2(SO_4^{2-})_3$ or $Al_2(SO_4)_3$

The brackets within the formula are to make it clear that there are three sulfate ions needed to balance the two aluminium ions. Without the brackets it might look as if the sulfur has 43 oxygen atoms attached to it.

QUESTIONS

4 Write down the chemical formulae for **a** lithium oxide, **b** magnesium hydroxide, **c** calcium carbonate and **d** ammonium nitrate.

5 Explain the advantages of using chemical formulae.

Balancing equations

The next logical step is to use symbols to describe chemical reactions. This means we are using chemical formulae in equations. This gives us a **symbol equation**.

For example, if we look at an equation you saw previously (on page 111):

$$\begin{array}{c}\text{silver}\\\text{nitrate}\end{array} + \begin{array}{c}\text{sodium}\\\text{sulfate}\end{array} \rightarrow \begin{array}{c}\text{silver}\\\text{sulfate}\end{array} + \begin{array}{c}\text{sodium}\\\text{nitrate}\end{array}$$

The first step is to make sure we have written the names properly. After that, work out the correct formula of each compound:

$$AgNO_3 + Na_2SO_4 \rightarrow Ag_2SO_4 + NaNO_3$$

The final step is to make sure there is the same number of each kind of atom on each side of the equation. You already know from the conservation of matter that atoms are neither created nor destroyed in a chemical reaction:

$$2AgNO_3 + Na_2SO_4 \rightarrow Ag_2SO_4 + 2NaNO_3$$

This is called balancing the equation.

QUESTIONS

6 Explain why the number 2 is written in front of the formulae for silver nitrate and sodium nitrate.

7 Balance the equation:

$$Na_2SO_4 + BaCl_2 \rightarrow NaCl + BaSO_4$$

8 Write the balanced symbol equation for the formation of sodium chloride. Remember first to work out the formula and then balance the equation.

9 Write the balanced symbol equation for ammonium hydroxide. Remember first to work out the formula and then balance the equation.

Looking into ionic compounds

Ionic compounds in your toothpaste

Sodium fluoride is an ionic compound that is added to toothpaste and some drinking water supplies.

FIGURE 1: Sodium fluoride is used in toothpaste to help strengthen teeth by the formation of fluorapatite, a naturally occurring component of tooth enamel.

You will find out:

> about the properties of ionic substances

> how ionic compounds have strong bonds

> about the lattice structure of ionic compounds

> how lattices are regular arrangements of ions

Substances made of ions

Ionic substances have similar properties:

> This is because ionic substances have similar structures.

> They often form crystals.

> Sodium chloride is an ionic substance that forms crystals (see Figures 2 and 3).

If you look at the lattice structure of sodium chloride (Figure 3) you will see why sodium chloride forms into cube-shaped crystals.

FIGURE 2: Crystals of table salt seen through a microscope.

FIGURE 3: A model of a small part of a crystal of sodium chloride. The green balls are chloride ions and the yellow balls are sodium ions.

QUESTIONS

1 Give the chemical formula of sodium chloride.

2 What are the names of the particles that make up sodium chloride?

Did you know?

Just 1 gram of table salt contains 10^{23} sodium ions and an equal number of chloride ions.

Properties of ionic compounds

Ionic substances have particular properties:

> They have high boiling and melting points (this can be seen in Table 1).

> They generally readily dissolve in water.

> They are poor conductors of electricity when they are solid.

> They are good conductors of electricity when they are molten or dissolved in water.

TABLE 1: Melting and boiling points of some common ionic substances. Can you identify any particularly interesting figures in the table?

Ionic compound	Melting point (°C)	Boiling point (°C)
sodium fluoride	992	1700
sodium chloride	808	1465
potassium fluoride	857	1505
magnesium oxide	2900	3600
magnesium chloride	714	1418

Q Crystal lattice   Electrostatic forces

FIGURE 4: Crystals of the ionic substance copper sulfate dissolve in the water and form a solution.

Did you know?

Magnesium oxide can be obtained by processing seawater.

QUESTIONS

3 Magnesium oxide is an ionic compound. Look up its boiling point and melting point in Table 1. Compare magnesium oxide to the other substances.

4 Using your own research, investigate the uses of magnesium oxide and relate them to its properties.

Structure of ionic compounds (Higher tier only)

Giant crystals

In an ionic compound, each positive ion is attracted to many negative ions. The ions form into a regular structure called a **crystal lattice**.

Each of the sodium ions is surrounded by six chloride ions and vice versa. This creates a very strong structure. This regular and repeating structure has many millions of ions strongly held together by very strong **electrostatic forces** (ionic bonds) between oppositely charged ions. The lattice structure explains many of the properties of ionic compounds.

There are not individual NaCl pairs within the sodium chloride structure. This is why it is best not to talk about sodium chloride molecules – no such thing exists. This is true for all ionic compounds.

Ionic substances: structure and properties

Many of the properties of ionic substances can be related to their structure.

> *High melting and boiling points.* This is as a result of the strong lattice structure of these compounds. It is unlikely that you would be able to melt any ionic compounds using a Bunsen burner. To break the positive and negative ions apart from a crystal lattice takes a great deal of energy. Magnesium oxide has a higher melting point than sodium chloride as the

magnesium and oxide ions have two charges each ($Mg^{2+}O^{2-}$) and so form stronger bonds than the sodium and chloride ions that have just one charge on each (Na^+Cl^-).

> *Solubility.* The positive and negative ions disperse in the water and the crystal lattice breaks down. This is in large part because of the special properties of water as a solvent. The water molecules are slightly charged themselves and this helps the dissolving process. Sodium chloride is soluble in water, but magnesium oxide is not.

> *Conductivity.* If you place an ionic crystal into an electrical circuit the current will not flow. The ions in the ionic lattice are not free to move. Ionic substances do not conduct electricity except when they are dissolved or molten.

By melting or dissolving the compound we allow the ions to move around freely. If electrodes are inserted into the liquid then the positive ions will move towards the negative electrode and the negative ions will move towards the positive electrode. Sodium chloride conducts electricity when it is molten or when it is dissolved in water. Magnesium oxide has such a high melting point that it would be difficult to get it to a molten state; also it is not soluble in water, therefore it does not conduct electricity.

QUESTIONS

5 Explain why the lattice structure of ionic compounds results in their having very high melting and boiling points.

6 Explain why solid ionic compounds do not conduct electricity but molten ionic compounds do. Use a diagram to help you.

7 Describe why the crystal lattice structure is so stable.

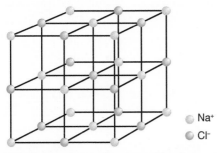

○ Na⁺
○ Cl⁻

FIGURE 5: The lattice structure of sodium chloride.

Solubility of ionic compounds

It's very salty

Not all ionic substances are as good at dissolving as others. Sodium chloride clearly dissolves well – it is a major part of the salt in the sea. However, limestone is also an ionic substance and it certainly does not dissolve easily.

You will find out:

> about general rules describing solubility

> how insoluble salts can be precipitates

> how to predict whether a precipitate will be formed

> how to name a precipitate

FIGURE 1: Lake Don Juan in Antarctica is thought to be the saltiest body of water on Earth with 413 g of calcium chloride and 29 g of sodium chloride per litre of water.

The most soluble ionic compounds

Most but not all ionic compounds are soluble. A simple experiment can be carried out to find out which ionic substances are soluble.

As shown in Figure 2, each compound is added to a test-tube of water and then the tube is shaken. Soluble substances seem to disappear.

If this solubility test is carried out on a wide range of ionic substances then some patterns emerge and some important **solubility rules** can be drawn up.

Did you know?

Differing solubilities can be used to separate substances.

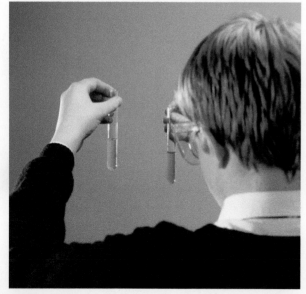

FIGURE 2: A simple solubility test.

Solubility rules

> All common sodium, potassium and ammonium salts are soluble.

> All nitrates are soluble.

> Common chlorides are soluble, except those of silver and lead.

> Common sulfates are soluble, except those of lead, barium and calcium.

> Common carbonates and hydroxides are insoluble, except those of sodium, potassium and ammonium.

Remember!

The solubility rules can be used to predict the solubility of products.

QUESTIONS

1 What do lead sulfate and lead chloride have in common?

2 State whether calcium chloride would be soluble or insoluble in water.

3 Describe what you would see if you added sodium carbonate to water and shook the test-tube.

4a Identify the risks in the experiment shown in Figure 2.

b Describe how you would manage these risks.

Q Displacement reactions   Precipitation reactions

Precipitates

If one of the products of a chemical reaction is insoluble then the chemical will come out of solution and settle out to form a solid deposit at the bottom of the tube called a **precipitate**. Reactions of this type are known as **precipitation reactions**. We can use these reactions to make insoluble salts.

If we react magnesium sulfate and sodium carbonate we make one soluble salt and one insoluble salt:

magnesium sulfate + sodium carbonate → magnesium carbonate + sodium sulfate

The magnesium carbonate is insoluble and will form a precipitate.

We show this in a chemical equation by adding **state symbols**. These tell us the state of the reactants and products in a reaction. The state symbols are:

> (s)   solid
> (l)   liquid
> (g)   gas
> (aq) aqueous (dissolved in water).

To show the precipitate in the reaction above we simply show the magnesium carbonate as a solid product:

magnesium sulfate + sodium carbonate → magnesium carbonate + sodium sulfate
$MgSO_4$ (aq) $NaCO_3$ (aq) $MgCO_3$ (s) Na_2SO_4 (aq)

FIGURE 3: A colourless solution of potassium iodide added to a colourless solution of lead nitrate, form an insoluble precipitate of lead iodide (cloudy yellow suspension). Write down the chemical equation including the state symbol for this reaction.

QUESTIONS

5 Describe what happens to the magnesium carbonate as it forms in the reaction between magnesium sulfate and sodium carbonate.

6 Describe the reaction between lead nitrate and sodium carbonate, giving products and reactants. Write the symbol equation with state symbols.

Predicting precipitates

We can use the solubility rules to help us to predict whether a precipitate will be produced or not. In almost every case the reaction will simply be a swapping over of the anions (negative ions) so that new chemicals are made. The solubility rules are used to check whether one of the new chemicals made is insoluble. If it is then a precipitate will form.

In the above reaction, the magnesium ions combine with the carbonate ions to form the new product magnesium carbonate. The solubility rules tell us that 'common carbonates and hydroxides are insoluble, except those of sodium, potassium and ammonium'. Magnesium carbonate is, therefore, insoluble.

FIGURE 4: The displacement reaction between magnesium sulfate and sodium carbonate.

QUESTIONS

7 Explain why a precipitate is seen when lead nitrate reacts with sodium sulfate.

8 For each of the following reactions, using aqueous solutions, predict whether a precipitate will be formed. If so, give its name:
a barium chloride and silver nitrate
b magnesium carbonate and hydrochloric acid
c lead nitrate and sodium carbonate.

Preparation of ionic compounds

Salts of silver

Silver nitrate is the starting material for film-based photography. It's not the silver nitrate that coats the film, but the silver halides that it produces. Silver nitrate is treated with sodium or potassium halide salts on the film to form the light-sensitive layer.

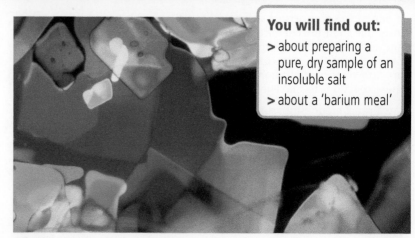

You will find out:

> about preparing a pure, dry sample of an insoluble salt
> about a 'barium meal'

FIGURE 1: Silver nitrate crystals seen under a microscope. This compound is still important in film-based photography.

Making an insoluble salt

The ionic compounds discussed in this unit are often called **salts**. Salts are very important chemicals and examples you have heard of already include sodium chloride, sodium sulfate, silver nitrate and magnesium chloride.

The important step in making an insoluble salt is to find two soluble salts that can react together. It is necessary that one of these salts contains the cation needed and the other the anion needed.

For example, if a sample of the insoluble salt lead chloride is needed we must:

> find a soluble salt containing lead ions

> find a soluble salt containing chloride ions.

Using our solubility rules we see that we could use lead nitrate and sodium chloride.

The process is straightforward. A solution of lead nitrate is added to a solution of sodium chloride and stirred or shaken. The soluble salts will react and a precipitate of lead chloride will form. The other salt produced, sodium nitrate, is soluble so stays in solution.

FIGURE 2: The formation of lead chloride from lead nitrate and sodium chloride.

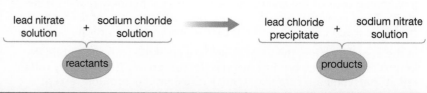

lead nitrate solution + sodium chloride solution → lead chloride precipitate + sodium nitrate solution

reactants → products

QUESTIONS

1 Suggest two salts you could react to allow you to prepare barium sulfate.

2 Write a plan to produce barium sulfate. Consider how you will use your equipment (using a diagram to help) and how you will minimise any risks.

Obtaining a pure salt sample

The lead chloride prepared above is not a pure sample. It is a precipitate but it is mixed with water, sodium nitrate and any unused lead nitrate and sodium chloride. In this form it is not very useful.

To obtain a pure, dry sample of lead chloride we must remove this salt from the other chemicals. The first step in this process is to filter the products through filter paper. Any soluble salts, and of course the water,

will pass through the filter paper. This is the **filtrate**. The solid precipitate of lead chloride will be trapped. This is known as the **residue**.

The residue in the filter paper can be washed by rinsing it with distilled water while it is still in the filter funnel. The residue can then be collected and dried – either in the air or in an oven.

Did you know?

Silver nitrate can be used to make the silver coating on mirrors.

QUESTIONS

3 Explain why it is important to wash the precipitate after filtering it.

4 Describe how you would make barium sulfate from barium nitrate and potassium sulfate. Include diagrams and symbol equations to illustrate the process and a risk assessment to identify potential problems.

Stage 1 Mix the solutions of the reactants

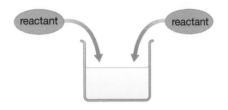

reactant   reactant

Stage 2 Filter the precipitate

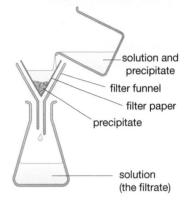

solution and precipitate
filter funnel
filter paper
precipitate

solution (the filtrate)

Stage 3 Wash the precipitate with distilled water

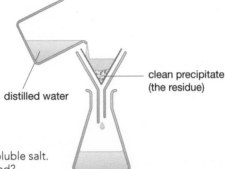

distilled water

clean precipitate (the residue)

Stage 4 Dry the precipitate

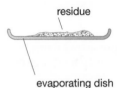

residue

evaporating dish

FIGURE 3: The experimental set-up for the preparation of a pure, dry sample of an insoluble salt. Why is it important that distilled water is used?

Using salts in X-rays

The properties of certain salts are very useful in medicine. For example, a barium salt, barium sulfate, is used to help doctors examine the upper digestive tract in patients who are experiencing problems and/or pain; this is called a **barium meal**.

Unlike bone, X-rays pass through soft tissue like the stomach or intestines. Barium salts are dense enough to stop X-rays passing through. Therefore if a barium sulfate suspension is swallowed by the patient, the white barium sulfate coats the gut and allows what is happening in the digestive tract to be seen on an X-ray.

From the X-ray, the doctor can obtain information about how the digestive tract is working and see whether there are any swellings, obstructions or irritations present.

Generally, the patient drinks about three cups of barium sulfate, which has often a fruity flavour added to make it taste less chalky. The procedure takes less than an hour.

Although barium compounds are toxic, the insolubility of the barium sulfate stops it from entering the blood. Therefore the patient is not poisoned by the treatment.

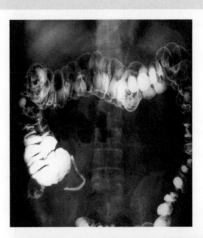

FIGURE 4: An X-ray of part of the abdominal region of a person who has swallowed a barium meal. What effect has the barium meal had?

QUESTIONS

5 Explain why silver nitrate is not used in place of barium sulfate when taking X-rays.

6 Insoluble salts are not only used in medicine. Silver nitrate is used to test water contamination in cargo ships. If the silver nitrate produces a precipitate, it indicates the presence of seawater. Explain how this works.

Testing for ions

You will find out:
> about tests for common cations and anions
> how chemists use spectroscopy

Distress signals

Why do flares and fireworks explode into so many different colours? The answer may surprise you. The colours are produced when metal ions are heated. Different metals produce different colours.

FIGURE 1: Distress flares can come in a range of colours. What ion could produce this flare?

Flame tests

When an ionic salt either as a solid or in solution is put into a flame, the heat of the flame causes the ions to emit a colour. The colour is specific to an element and the colour of the flame can help to identify the metal ions present in a sample.

To carry out a **flame test**:

> A nichrome wire is dipped into concentrated hydrochloric acid and held in a Bunsen burner flame until only a light orange colour is seen. This ensures that the wire is not contaminated.

> The clean wire is dipped into the concentrated acid again and then into a sample of the substance to be tested. A small amount of the substance will be picked up by the wire.

> The wire is held in the flame again and any change in colour noted.

Sometimes it can be difficult to identify an element as some elements have characteristic flames that are different shades of the same colour. For example:

> Strontium, lithium and calcium all give shades of red.

> This is when a comparative test must be done.

> Obtain known samples of these metal ions and then compare the colour of your unknown.

> You will soon see which shade of red it is.

Table 1 lists some metal ions and the colours that are produced in the flame test. Use this to find a match.

TABLE 1: The colours produced by some metal ions.

Metal ion	Flame colour
Calcium (Ca^{2+})	Brick red
Copper (Cu^{2+})	Blue/green (white flashes)
Potassium (K^+)	Lilac
Sodium (Na^+)	Yellow/orange

QUESTIONS

1 Suggest why it is important to clean the nichrome wire before carrying out a flame test.

2 Write down what you would see if you carried out a flame test using copper chloride.

3 If you saw a firework with a bright red colour, which metal ions might have been used in its manufacture?

nichrome wire dipped in solution

copper

sodium

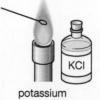
potassium

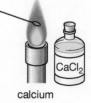
calcium

FIGURE 2: Carrying out a flame test. Note the colours of the flames.

Q Flame tests   Testing for ions   Inorganic tests

Testing for anions

Anions are the negatively charged ions in salts. We cannot use flame tests to identify these anions but there are some useful tests that we can use.

Carbonates

If dilute hydrochloric acid is added to a carbonate then **effervescence** or fizzing occurs. This is the result of the carbonate decomposing to give carbon dioxide gas. For example:

calcium carbonate + hydrochloric acid → calcium chloride + water + carbon dioxide

To confirm that the gas is carbon dioxide, it is bubbled through limewater. The limewater should turn milky.

Sulfates

Dilute hydrochloric acid and a few drops of barium chloride are added to a solution of the substance to be tested. If a white precipitate is formed, then the substance is a sulfate. For example, if the unknown substance is sodium sulfate then the reaction is:

sodium sulfate + barium chloride → sodium chloride + barium sulfate

All sulfate solutions give similar reactions to give a white precipitate of barium sulfate.

Chlorides

To test to see whether a substance contains chloride ions in solution, add dilute nitric acid and silver nitrate solution. A white precipitate of silver chloride is produced if chloride ions are present. For example:

sodium chloride solution + silver nitrate solution → sodium nitrate solution + silver chloride precipitate

QUESTIONS

4 Give the chemical formula for limewater.

5 Describe what would happen if you added dilute hydrochloric acid to a sample of copper carbonate. List the products.

6 A sample of a salt gives a lilac flame colour during a flame test. If dilute hydrochloric acid and barium chloride are added to a solution of the salt a white precipitate is formed. Name the salt.

Spectroscopy

Spectroscopy involves a sophisticated type of flame test. By heating the atoms in substances and measuring the light that comes off, chemists can find out a great deal about the elements present. When an element is heated it emits light at particular frequencies. This is why different metals give off different coloured light.

The spectroscope is the machine that detects and analyses specific substances. The result is an **emission spectrum**. This spectrum is unique for each substance.

The use of spectroscopy has also resulted in the discovery of new elements – such as caesium and rubidium.

Robert Bunsen and Gustav Kirchhoff pioneered work into the field of spectroscopy in the mid 19th century.

They discovered caesium and rubidium when they were heating samples, using Bunsen's famous 'burner', to investigate the colours in the line spectra of different materials. Each element has its own line spectrum, so when they found new line spectra, they knew they had found new elements.

Spectroscopy can be used to detect the presence of very small amounts of elements. This can be important in solving crimes, for example. Scientists can even look at emission spectra from space and work out the elements found in distant stars and galaxies.

FIGURE 3: These images are based on data collected on 18 January 2004 by Omega, the visible and infrared mineralogical mapping spectrometer, on board ESA's Mars Express orbiter. They show infra-red (left and centre) and visible (right) images of water and carbon dioxide ices at the southern pole of Mars. The polar ice cap is at the bottom of all three images. The pictures confirm the presence of water ice (dark blue, left image) and carbon dioxide ice (purple, centre image) on the planet. The ices appear turquoise in visible light.

QUESTIONS

7 Explain how a crime scene investigator could use spectroscopy to identify an unknown substance at a crime scene.

8 Using your own research, write a short report to explain how spectroscopy can be used to tell us more about our Universe.

Preparing for assessment: Applying your knowledge

To achieve a good grade in science, you not only have to know and understand scientific ideas, but you also need to be able to apply them to other situations. This task will support you in developing these skills.

✳ Unknown substances

Chemists are often called on to identify unknown substances. These could be something found at a crime scene or produced by a chemical reaction in a lab.

✳ Task 1

A chemist was given a light green powder and asked to identify it. When the powder was burned in a flame test, it produced a brilliant blue–green flame. The powder did not dissolve in water or alter the pH of the water when added.

> Name an element that produces a green flame in a flame test.

> List some common substances that are insoluble in water.

> Identify a test that would distinguish between a sulfate and a hydroxide.

Task 2

When the substance was mixed with hydrochloric acid and barium chloride was added a white precipitate formed.

> Deduce the identity of the unknown substance.

> Write out the name of the unknown substance.

> Write the formula of the unknown substance.

 ## Task 3

Dilute hydrochloric acid added to some small white chips of marble caused fizzing to occur. What does this tell you about the composition of marble and how might you confirm this?

> Write a word equation for this reaction.

> **Higher tier only:** Write balanced chemical equations for the reactions that occur.

 ## Task 4

Spectroscopy has developed considerably since Robert Bunsen and Gustav Kirchhoff's carried out their investigations in the 19th century and is now major branch of chemistry. One of Bunsen and Kirchhoff's great achievements was the discovery of the elements caesium and rubidium.

> Explain the role of spectroscopy in this discovery.

 ## Maximise your grade

These sentences show what you need to include in your work to achieve each grade. Use them to improve your work and be more successful.

E

For grade E, your answer should show that you can:
> state the results of flame tests for group 1 metals
> state the solubility rules for common substances
> write word equations for chemical reactions.

C

For grade D, C in addition show that you can:
> describe how flame tests can be used to distinguish between group 1 metals
> describe the tests to identify common anions
> write simple chemical equations for reactions.

A

For grade B, A, in addition show that you can:
> describe the changes in solubility of common substances
> write balanced chemical equations for reactions
> explain how chemists use spectroscopy.

Covalent bonds

You will find out:
> about covalent bonds
> about the formation of simple covalent molecules

Vital molecules

Water is the most common compound in the Universe, and it covers 70% of the Earth's surface. Humans are composed mostly of water: newborn babies are 78% water. Without water there would be no life on Earth. Without covalent bonds, there would be no water molecules.

FIGURE 1: . Water might be the most common compound in the Universe, but what is the most common molecule?

Covalent molecules

Molecules are groups of atoms held together by covalent bonds. Covalent bonding occurs when atoms share electrons to make them more stable.

Oxygen, water and methane are all bonded covalently. Figure 2 shows models of these molecules to explain how atoms are joined or bonded together.

Covalent bonding:

> occurs between atoms of non-metals

> involves sharing electrons between atoms

> forms molecules

> may form molecules that contain atoms of an single element or atoms from different elements.

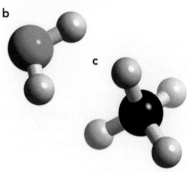

FIGURE 2: Molecular models showing **a** oxygen, **b** water and **c** methane. Oxygen atoms are coloured red, carbon atoms are coloured black and hydrogen are coloured white. Why is the same colour always used to show atoms of one element?

> ### QUESTIONS

1 State how many atoms of hydrogen there are in a molecule of water.

2 State which of the molecules shown in Figure 2 contains only one type of atom.

3 How many bonds does carbon make?

Sharing electrons

In Figure 2 you can notice that water is formed from two non-metallic elements – hydrogen and oxygen. Methane is also formed from two non-metallic elements – carbon and hydrogen. There are no metal atoms to act as donors of electrons and so **ionic bonds** cannot form. Something else must be happening to bond the atoms together.

In covalent bonding:

> electrons are not transferred from one to the other, as happens in ionic bonding

> the atoms share electrons instead

> the atoms want to achieve a full outer shell, as this is the most stable electronic configuration.

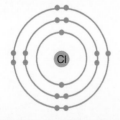

FIGURE 3: Electron configurations for hydrogen, chlorine and carbon.

Remember!
A full outer shell is the most stable electronic configuration for atoms. Bonding can achieve this.

Figure 4 shows a **covalent bond** forming between two hydrogen atoms. The covalent bond between the two atoms of hydrogen is shown by a pair of electrons (a cross for the electron from the first molecule and a dot for the electron from the second).

Notice:

> The covalent bond holds the two atoms together because the positively charged nuclei of the atoms are attracted to the negatively charged shared electrons between them.

QUESTIONS

4 Explain the overall electronic charge of a molecule of hydrogen.

5 Noble gases, such as argon and neon, have a full outer electron shell. Suggest why they do not react to form covalent bonds.

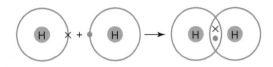

FIGURE 4: Comparing the formation of covalent bonds in a hydrogen molecule.

Stable configurations

Sharing electrons

Atoms have electrons in shells around the nucleus. If you look at the periodic table, the **group number** tells you the number of electrons in the outer shell. Only the noble gases – neon, argon, etc. – in group 0 have a full set of electrons in their outer shells. Other non-metal atoms get a full set by sharing electrons in a covalent bond.

> If an atom has seven electrons in its outer shell, like fluorine, it needs to share one more. It makes one covalent bond.

> If an atom has four electrons in its outer shell, like carbon, it needs to share four more. It makes four covalent bonds.

The number of bonds a non-metal atom makes is the number of electrons it needs to share to fill its outer shell.

The formula for methane is CH_4. Figure 5 shows the covalent bonds holding these five atoms together.

Count the electrons in each outer shell now. Remember that the first shell can hold only two electrons, so hydrogen forms only one bond.

> Two non-metal atoms can share electrons to make a covalent bond.

> The shared electrons are then counted as part of both of the outer shells.

When one bond is not enough

Whenever you see carbon in a compound, it makes four bonds in order to fill its outer shell. Those bonds could be four single bonds, or two **double bonds** … Can you think of other possibilities?

> A single covalent bond is a shared pair of electrons.

> A double bond is two shared pairs of electrons.

Some hydrocarbons contain double bonds, for example the alkenes (ethene, propene, etc.). So does oxygen gas, O_2.

The alkenes are more reactive than hydrocarbons with only single bonds (the alkanes) because the double bond is reactive. It can break open and form two new single bonds to other atoms.

Diatomic molecules

If a molecule is made up of two atoms we say it is a diatomic molecule; examples include chlorine (Cl_2), oxygen (O_2) and nitrogen (N_2). That is why oxygen molecules in the air are shown as O_2 in chemical equations.

QUESTIONS

6 Explain why it is easier for the atoms in covalent molecules to share the electrons in the bond, rather than try to steal electrons.

7 Explain why methane is often written down as CH_4.

8 Compare ionic bonding and covalent bonding.

9 Explain why the alkenes are more reactive than the alkanes.

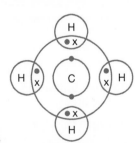

FIGURE 5: Dot and cross diagram of methane.

Drawing covalent compounds

Representing the world through models

In chemistry we cannot actually see what is happening when atoms bond together. We have to represent this using visual models. A model is something that tries to represent the world. You have used models for representing atomic structure and ionic bonding. In this section you will draw some models to show covalent bonding using dot and cross diagrams.

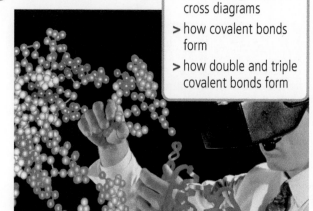

FIGURE 1: The future of chemistry? This chemist is using virtual reality to investigate molecular interactions in biochemistry.

 ## Drawing covalent bonds

Dot and cross diagrams are an easy way of showing the covalent bonds between atoms. They do this by representing the electron configuration in the highest energy level, or outer shell, of the atoms combining to form a molecule. Figure 2 shows a dot and cross diagram for hydrogen atoms bonding covalently to form a hydrogen molecule.

In the dot and cross diagram:

> the dot represents the electron in the outer shell of the left-hand atom. As a hydrogen atom has just one electron, Figure 2 shows only one dot

> the cross represents the electron in the outer shell of the other atom. As a hydrogen atom has just one electron, Figure 2 shows only one cross.

> the overlapping areas of the circles show the shared electrons. In the case of hydrogen this contains one dot and one cross.

To draw a dot and cross diagram, it is a good idea to ensure you have the correct tools:

> a sharp pencil for clear labelling

> a compass for drawing a neat circle

> a good eraser to ensure any errors can be tidily corrected.

When drawing diagrams, it is also useful to think about:

> planning how to use the space on the paper

> how big to make the circles

> ensuring that any symbols and lettering can be read easily.

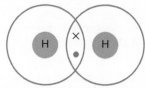

FIGURE 2: Two hydrogen atoms combining to form a hydrogen molecule (H_2).

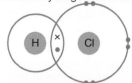

FIGURE 3: Bonding between hydrogen and chlorine atoms to form hydrogen chloride (HCl).

 ## QUESTIONS

1 a Draw a dot and cross diagram for a chlorine molecule. **b** State why the symbol for a molecule of chlorine is Cl_2.

2 State three features of dot and cross diagrams.

 ## Covalent bonds between different elements

Dot and cross diagrams can also be used to show:

> bonding taking place between atoms of different elements, such as hydrogen chloride

> bonding for a molecule containing more than two atoms, for example water and methane.

Hydrogen chloride (HCl)

Hydrogen chloride is a simple molecule containing one hydrogen atom and one chlorine atom.

The formation of the bond in hydrogen chloride is shown in Figure 3.

Water (H₂O)

Another very important covalent molecule is water. The formation of the bonds in a water molecule is shown in Figure 4.

Methane (CH₄)

In a methane molecule the carbon atom bonds with four hydrogen atoms. Notice that each bond is shown by a pair of electrons as in the diatomic molecules you have seen before. Also note that the molecule has no overall electrical charge. As with hydrogen molecules, all of the electric charges are balanced and methane exists as **discrete** molecules.

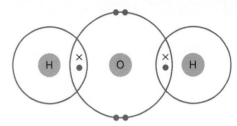

FIGURE 4: Bonding between hydrogen and oxygen in water.

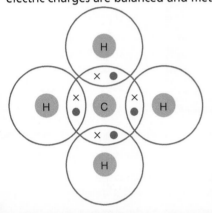

FIGURE 5: Bonding between carbon and hydrogen atoms to form methane (CH₄).

QUESTIONS

3 Explain why a molecule of methane has no overall electrical charge.

4 Describe one similarity and difference between the covalent bonds in hydrogen chloride and water.

5 Hydrogen atoms have one outer electron; fluorine atoms have seven outer electrons. Describe the formation of a simple molecule of hydrogen fluoride (HF). Use a dot and cross diagram.

More than one covalent bond (Higher tier only)

A single covalent bond occurs when two atoms share a pair of electrons. As you have seen, each atom shares one of its electrons to make the bond.

If two pairs of electrons are shared then a **double covalent bond** is made. Each atom shares two of its electrons. In a dot and cross diagram, this is shown by two electrons from each atom appearing in the 'shared' area of the diagram (see Figure 6). Each bond is shown by a pair of electrons.

It is also possible to have a **triple covalent bond**. Each atom shares three of its electrons in the bond. In this case the dot and cross diagram shows three electrons from each atom in the 'shared' area (see Figure 7).

Carbon forms very important covalent molecules. The main reason for this is that carbon can bond with other carbon atoms to form very long chains. These are the basis for the molecules needed for life, such as sugars and starches.

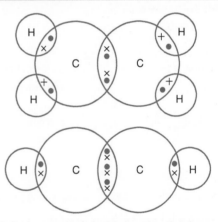

FIGURE 7: Carbon–carbon double bond and carbon–carbon triple bonds. What are these two molecules called?

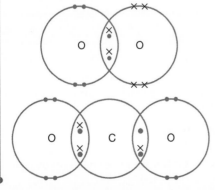

FIGURE 6: Covalent bonding in an oxygen molecule and a carbon dioxide molecule to show double bonds

QUESTIONS

6 Explain why hydrogen would never form double or triple covalent bonds with other hydrogen atoms or atoms of other elements.

7 Explain the difference between a single, a double and a triple covalent bond.

8 a Draw a dot and cross diagram to explain how four carbon atoms can be covalently bonded together in a chain. **b** How many possible bonds are still available?

Properties of elements and compounds

Melting moments

You will know that candle wax, a common covalent substance, melts easily. The temperature at which chemicals melt and boil is a very important way of identifying them.

FIGURE 1: List some of the very important properties of covalent molecules you can see.

> **You will find out:**
> > how to classify different elements and compounds
> > about the properties of simple covalent compounds
> > about the differences between simple and giant covalent compounds
> > about graphite and diamond

Classifying substances by their properties

The properties of covalent compounds are different to the properties of ionic compounds. This means that different elements and compounds can be classified as covalent or ionic by their 'properties'. These properties include:

> solubility in water
> **melting points** and **boiling points**
> electrical conductivity.

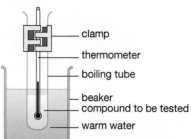

FIGURE 2: Apparatus for determining melting points and boiling points.

Labels: clamp, thermometer, boiling tube, beaker, compound to be tested, warm water

These properties can be investigated for different compounds by carrying out experiments:

> Solubility in water can be determined using the apparatus similar to that shown on page 116.

> Melting points and boiling points can be determined using the apparatus in Figure 2.

> Electrical conductivity can be determined using the apparatus in Figure 3.

By determining these properties for covalent substances, such as hexane, liquid paraffin and candle wax, and for ionic substances, such as copper sulfate, magnesium sulfate and sodium chloride, it is easy to build up information that can be used to classify elements and compounds.

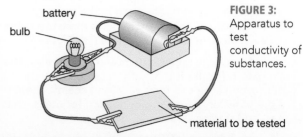

FIGURE 3: Apparatus to test conductivity of substances.

Labels: battery, bulb, material to be tested

● QUESTIONS

1 Choose an experiment from the three listed and prepare a plan for carrying it out.

2 List three different ways that you could present the results from your experiment.

Properties of compounds

Melting points and boiling points

Table 1 shows some melting points and boiling points. You will see that the covalent compounds have much lower melting and boiling points than ionic compounds. Many covalent compounds are gases at room temperature. This is because in covalent compounds, the forces between the molecules are generally very weak.

Solubility in water

Covalent substances are composed of discrete molecules with no overall electrical charge. They do not dissolve in water.

Electrical conductivity

Covalent substances do not conduct electricity; they act as insulators. This is because they have no overall electric charge.

Giant covalent substances

There are some exceptions to the rules about covalent compounds, these are when covalent molecules have giant covalent structures. The most well-known examples of giant covalent substances are diamond and graphite.

Unlike simple covalent compounds, both diamond and graphite are made from carbon and have extremely high melting points, over 3500 °C.

QUESTIONS

3 Using Table 1, identify which substance has the lowest melting point. Is this substance a covalent or an ionic substance?

4 Using Table 1, identify which substance has the lowest boiling point. Is this substance a covalent or an ionic substance?

5 Explain why covalent substances do not conduct electricity.

However, graphite is soft and in pencils can be rubbed off on to paper. Diamond is the hardest known naturally occurring material and can be used to drill through rock.

TABLE 1: Melting and boiling points of ionic and covalent compounds.

Substance	Melting point (°C)	Boiling point (°C)
Covalent substances		
hexane	−95	69
carbon dioxide	−78	−55
oxygen	−218	−182
methane	−183	−164
water	0	100
wax	45	300
Ionic substances		
magnesium chloride	714	1418
magnesium oxide	2900	3600
potassium chloride	772	1407
silver chloride	455	1557
sodium chloride	808	1465

Diamond and graphite (Higher tier only)

Graphite and diamond are both forms of pure carbon, so why do they have such different properties? The answer lies in their structures.

> Carbon always forms four bonds, as in CH_4, methane. In diamond, each carbon atom has four strong covalent bonds to other carbon atoms in a **tetrahedral** arrangement. (A tetrahedron is a regular triangular-based pyramid.)

> This 3-D network of strong bonds through the whole crystal makes the structure very rigid. This is why diamond is so hard.

> Graphite has a layered structure. Each carbon atom has three bonds to other carbon atoms, forming flat layers of hexagons, like honeycomb. These are strong covalent bonds.

> The fourth bond, between the layers, is much weaker. This is why the layers can slide easily over one another. Graphite can be used as a lubricant between two metal moving parts. It doesn't flow away like oil does.

> The bonding between the layers is made from freely moving delocalised electrons, similar to the 'sea of electrons' in metals. So, graphite is able to conduct electricity, and so it is used to make electrodes.

TABLE 2: Comparing the properties of diamond and graphite.

Diamond	Graphite
Atoms arranged tetrahedrally	Atoms in hexagonal layers
Strong bonding throughout structure	Weak forces between layers but strong forces within each layer
Extremely hard and rigid	Layers slide and rub off easily
Vaporises above 3550 °C	Vaporises above 3650 °C
Does not conduct electricity	Good electrical conductor

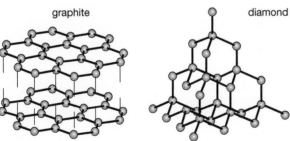
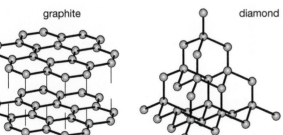
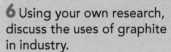

FIGURE 4: The structures of tiny sections of graphite and diamond lattices.

FIGURE 5: A tetrahedron – 'tetra-' means 'four' in chemistry.

QUESTIONS

6 Using your own research, discuss the uses of graphite in industry.

7 Explain why graphite conducts electricity, but diamond does not.

8 Do you think graphite conducts electricity well in all directions?

Separating solutions

You will find out:

> about using a separating funnel
> about using fractional distillation
> how nitrogen and oxygen are produced

Oil and water

You will have seen examples of pollution caused by oil leaks. The oil, which is made up of many different covalent compounds, does not dissolve in seawater. Instead it floats on top and causes a great deal of environmental damage.

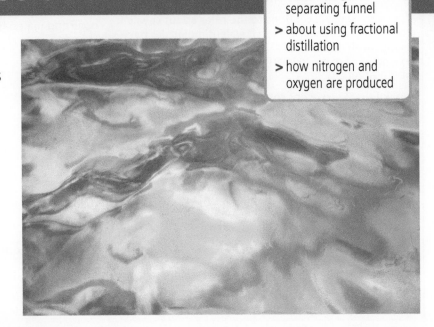

FIGURE 1: An oil slick on seawater. In what ways do oil slicks damage the environment?

Separating immiscible liquids

Two liquids that are almost completely insoluble in each other are described as **immiscible**. The liquids form two separate layers. The liquids do not interact with each other.

The two liquids can be separated by carefully using a separating funnel as shown in Figure 2.

The separating funnel is held firmly and the mixture added. The mixture is allowed to settle. The densest material will sink to the bottom. With an oil and water mixture, the water will be found at the bottom and the oil at the top.

The funnel tap is opened and the denser material collected in a beaker. When a small amount of the heavier liquid is left in the funnel the beaker is changed and the last bit of the heavier liquid and the first part of the lighter liquid is collected. The rest of the lighter liquid is collected in a third beaker. The middle beaker is waste as it is still a mixture.

QUESTIONS

1 Suggest why is it important to allow the mixture of liquids to settle before starting the separation process.

2 Research some examples, other than oil and water, of pairs of immiscible liquids.

3 Choose one of your pairs of immiscible liquids from question 2. Draw a labelled diagram to show how you would separate them.

Remember!

Some liquids mix, they are miscible. Some don't, they are immiscible.

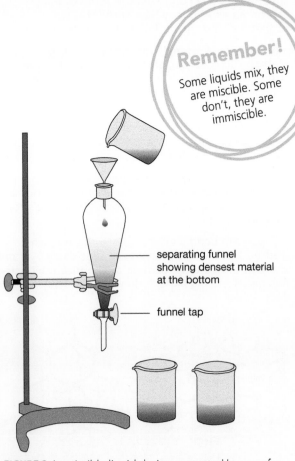

separating funnel showing densest material at the bottom

funnel tap

FIGURE 2: Immiscible liquids being separated by use of a separating funnel.

Separating miscible liquids

Miscible liquids can be separated by a process known as **fractional distillation**. This process is based on the fact that different liquids turn to vapour at different temperatures. This means that mixtures of liquids can be separated by heating them.

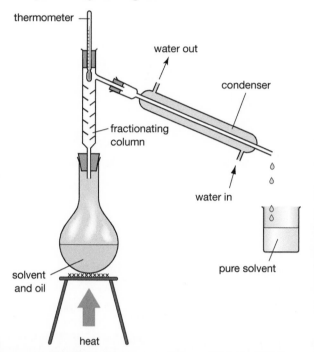

thermometer

water out

condenser

fractionating column

water in

pure solvent

solvent and oil

heat

An experimental set-up is shown in Figure 3.

Separating liquids by distillation depends on getting the temperatures exactly right; this is why the thermometer is included in the set-up. As the temperature reaches the boiling point of the liquid with the lowest boiling point it becomes a vapour and escapes from the other liquid. The vapour is collected as a liquid once it is cooled by the condenser.

You will recall that crude oil is fractionally distilled to obtain more useful products. The crude oil is boiled and the vapours enter a fractionating column. Here the vapours condense at appropriate temperatures to result in the specific fraction for that temperature. The smaller the covalent molecule the higher up the column it travels.

 QUESTIONS

4 What is the difference between fractional distillation and simple distillation?

5 If you were devising a fractional distillation experiment in the laboratory, identify potential risks and then explain how you might overcome them.

FIGURE 3: Laboratory fractional distillation apparatus.

Fractional distillation of air

One practical application of fractional distillation is to produce oxygen and nitrogen from liquid air.

At room temperature the constituents of air are gases. Before air can be fractionally distilled it must first be in the liquid state.

> The air is filtered to remove dust particles.

> Carbon dioxide and water are removed from the air.

> The clean, dry mixture of nitrogen and oxygen is liquefied by cooling it to about −200 °C.

> The liquid air is fractionally distilled.

> Nitrogen boils off at −196 °C and oxygen at −183 °C.

Gases are liquefied before they are stored and transported as they do not take up as much space as the gas would in the gaseous state.

FIGURE 4: A chemical plant for producing liquid oxygen.

 QUESTIONS

6 Draw a flow chart to show how liquid oxygen is obtained from air. At each stage of the process, describe the hazards involved and how the risk posed by the hazard can be minimised.

7 Prepare a short report on the uses of liquid oxygen and nitrogen.

 Fractionating column   Uses of nitrogen and oxygen

Chromatography

You will find out:
> how paper chromatography is used
> how to evaluate paper chromatograms

Colour coded

Chromatography (from the Greek words *chroma*, meaning colour, and *graphein*, meaning writing) was invented by a Russian botanist, M.S. Tsvet, in 1906. He used the technique to separate the pigments in a leaf. Today, chromatography is still an important method in chemical analysis.

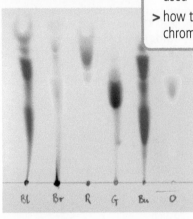

FIGURE 1: Paper chromatography of food colouring.

Paper chromatography

Chromatography can be used to separate mixtures into their components. It can be used to identify the substances that make up a mixture.

A typical set-up is shown in Figure 2. Note that the lid is needed to keep the air in the jar damp and to prevent the paper from drying out.

With paper chromatography:

> A spot of the mixture to be tested is put on the baseline of the chromatography paper. The baseline is shown as the pencil line in Figure 2.

> A solvent moves through the paper taking with it the chemicals to be separated.

> Possible solvents include water, ethanol and methanol. Sometimes a mixture of solvents may be used.

> As colours creep up the paper, this means that the chemicals are separated.

> Some chemicals travel through the paper a long way, do others not travel very far.

>The paper is known as the **stationary phase**. As the name implies, it does not move.

>The solvent, or liquid, the paper is dipped into is known as the **mobile phase**. As the name implies, it does move.

> Once the chromatography process has finished the paper is known as a **chromatogram**.

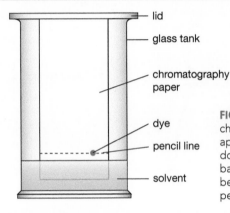

FIGURE 2: Paper chromatography apparatus. Why do you think the baseline should be drawn in pencil?

QUESTIONS

1 Suggest why the surface of the solvent must be below the spots of sample.

2 Explain why it is important to have all the spots of sample chemicals at exactly the same height on the chromatography paper.

3 Predict what would happen if the chromatography vessel wasn't covered by a lid.

Analysing and evaluating chromatograms

Chromatography is not just limited to investigating coloured materials. Forensic science makes use of chromatography to test for the presence of drugs, to analyse blood and other body fluid samples from crime scenes, and even to detect chemicals that may have been involved with explosives. Chromatography is also used to separate and identify many types of substances, such as medicines and drugs.

Q Uses of chromatography   Chromatography and food colourings

Investigating food colourings

Paper chromatography is also used in the food industry. It can show whether the colourings in a food are those listed on the label. This involves:

> extracting a sample of colour from the food

> drawing a baseline

> putting dots of the extracted colour and listed colourings along the line and labelling them

> standing the paper in a little solvent that dissolves the colourings.

The solvent rises up the paper, carrying the colours with it and separating them. The pattern produced forms the chromatogram.

To evaluate the results, look at the chromatogram in Figure 3. Compare the colours of the spots and their distances from the baseline. Three spots in the food sample means there were three dyes in the food. Two spots correspond with E102 and E133, therefore the food contained both these dyes.

The third spot corresponds with none of the known dyes: it is unidentified. It may be a colour naturally present in the food, an approved dye not listed on the label, or it could be an illegal dye. Further analysis is needed.

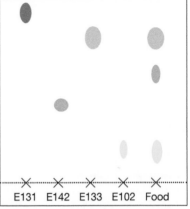

FIGURE 3: A chromatogram of food dyes. Which colouring in this food needs further investigation?

QUESTIONS

4 Explain what a chromatogram is and how it might be used.

5 A chromatogram has two spots the same shade of red but at different heights. What does this tell you?

6 Describe what sort of errors could occur during the chromatography process. How could they be avoided?

R$_f$ values and chromatography

As well as comparing how far the samples have travelled by using our eyes, we can take measurements. Measurements give us a more accurate figure for the distance travelled by each spot.

The distance travelled relative to the front edge of the solvent will be constant for each substance. Some will travel almost as far as the solvent. Others will not.

The distance travelled relative to the **solvent front** is called the **R$_f$ value**. It is calculated using the following equation:

$$R_f = \frac{\text{distance travelled by spot}}{\text{distance travelled by the solvent}}$$

If a substance travelled up from the baseline by 7 cm and the solvent front travelled 10 cm then the R$_f$ value would be:

$$R_f = \frac{7 \text{ cm}}{10 \text{ cm}} = 0.7$$

Note that the R$_f$ value has no units: it is just a number.

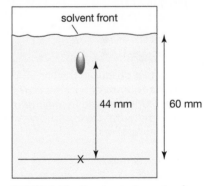

FIGURE 4: The R$_f$ value is the ratio of the distance travelled by the substance to the distance travelled by the solvent, which is constant for a given substance. What is the R$_f$ of the substance shown here?

QUESTIONS

7 If a solvent front has travelled 12 cm and the substance 6 cm from the baseline, what is the R$_f$ value?

8 Calculate the R$_f$ value if a substance travels 12 cm up the chromatography paper from the baseline and the solvent front has travelled 15 cm.

9 If the R$_f$ value of a substance is 0.75 and the solvent front has travelled 10 cm, what is the distance travelled by the compound?

Preparing for assessment: Analysis and conclusions

To achieve a good grade in science, you not only have to know and understand scientific ideas, but you also need to be able to apply them to other situations and investigations. This task will support you in developing these skills.

 Task

> Determine which soft drink is appropriate to sell children.

Context

Food and drink colourings are often used to enhance the appearance of food items.

A retailer was planning to import a new range of soft drinks aimed at children but wanted to make sure that the colourings used were safe. The retailer went to a research lab and asked them to test for a substance called carmoisine (E122), which is a colouring that is thought to cause hyperactivity in children.

Paper chromatography was used to separate the colourings in the soft drinks, allowing the chemists to identify which colourings they contain.

The drinks were spotted on a piece of chromatography paper and placed in a developing chamber containing a solvent. The solvent moved up the paper carrying the drink colouring with it. The different chemical properties of the colourings mean that they are not carried equally, so each drink has a distinctive distance it will move.

Results

The test produced the chromatograph here. Use a ruler to determine how far each spot for each drink moved in millimetres. Copy and complete the table to show your measurements.

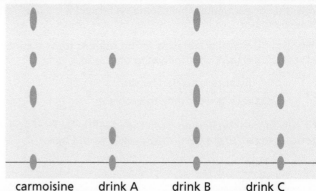

carmoisine sample   drink A   drink B   drink C

Substance	Distance spot 1 moved (mm)	Distance spot 2 moved (mm)	Distance spot 3 moved (mm)	Distance spot 4 moved (mm)	Distance spot 5 moved (mm)
Sample					
Drink A					
Drink B					
Drink C					

Processing the evidence

1. Construct another data table to record the R_f values.

2. Calculate the R_f value for each spot for each of the drinks and record them in your table.

> Remember, tables are supposed to make it easier to see the relevant information from an experiment, so think carefully about the organisation of your table.

> R_f values don't have units, so they only need to be labelled R_f value.

Stating conclusions

1. Compare the results for each of the drinks. Do any of the drinks have similar R_f values?

2. State your conclusion about which drink, if any, will be most suitable for selling to children.

3. Explain very clearly why you have reached the conclusion you reached.

4. Carry out secondary research into carmoisine (E122). How does your research support or change your conclusion?

> Be sure to use scientific language to gain Quality of Written Communication marks.

> Include data to support your decision. You could also include reasons why another interpretation is not valid.

> Choose your sources carefully – there are lots of myths about food colourings on the internet. Try to find sources of information that are backed up by scientific fact and that have a good reputation.

Evaluating the method and conclusions

1. Comment on the strengths and weaknesses of the research method.

2. Did the researchers obtain high-quality evidence?

3. How could the researchers improve the reliability of their results?

> Consider any potential problems with the method that might alter the results. For instance, placing the samples too close to the edge of the paper can alter the movement of the pigments as they travel up the paper.

> You should also discuss any possible errors that could happen during the interpretation of the data. Remember, sometimes the colourings are so similar in chemical properties that they do not separate completely. What problems could this cause?

> What does 'high quality' mean? Discuss this with a classmate before answering this question.

> Think about your primary evidence (your answer to question 1 will help) and secondary evidence (for example is there any bias in the sources?).

> Think about how to improve the accuracy and extent of the data.

Connections

How Science Works

> Collecting and analysing data.

> Interpreting data to provide evidence for testing ideas and developing theories.

> Working accurately and safely when collecting data

> Evaluating methods of data collection.

> Presenting information and developing an argument using appropriate language, conventions and symbols.

Maths in Science

> Understand and use direct proportion and simple ratios.

> Understand and use common measures and simple compound measures such as speed.

> Extract and interpret information from charts, graphs and tables.

C2 checklist (Topics 1–3)

To achieve your forecast grade in the exam you'll need to revise

Use this checklist to see what you can do now. Refer back to pages 102–35 if you're not sure.

Look across the rows to see how you could progress – **bold italic** means Higher tier only.

Remember you'll need to be able to use these ideas in various ways, such as:
> interpreting pictures, diagrams and graphs
> applying ideas to new situations
> explaining ethical implications
> suggesting some benefits and risks to society
> drawing conclusions from evidence you've been given.

Look at pages 264–86 for more information about exams and how you'll be assessed.

This checklist accompanies the exam-style questions and the worked examples. The content suggestions for specific grades are suggestions only and may not be replicated in your real examination. Remember, the checklists do not represent the complete content for any topic. Refer to the Specification for complete content details on any topic and any further information.

To aim for a grade E	To aim for a grade C	To aim for a grade A
recall the components and fundamental properties of an atom recall that the number of protons in the nucleus uniquely identifies the atom of an element	describe the nucleus of an atom as being very small compared to the overall size of an atom	
describe the periodic table as periods with elements arranged by increasing atomic number and groups arranged by elements of similar properties describe how Mendeleev used the periodic table to predict undiscovered elements explain how elements are classified as metals according to their position in the periodic table recall the meaning of the terms atomic number, mass number and relative atomic mass		***explain the existence of isotopes*** ***calculate relative atomic masses based on the atomic masses and relative abundances of an atom's isotopes***
recall that atoms contain equal numbers of protons and electrons	apply rules about filling of electron shells	explain the connection between the number of outer electrons and the position of an element in the periodic table
understand that atoms combine to form different compounds by forming new bonds recall that in ionic bonding electrons are transferred	describe how ionic bonds form by transferring electrons to produce cations and anions describe the use of -ide and -ate when naming compounds deduce the formulae of ionic compounds given the formulae of the constituent ions	

To aim for a grade E   To aim for a grade C   To aim for a grade A

describe some of the properties of ionic substances		*explain and describe the lattice structure of ionic compounds*
recall the general rules of solubility of common substances in water	describe how insoluble salts can form as precipitates	explain how solubility rules predict whether a precipitate will form
recall the method used to obtain an insoluble salt	apply the rules of solubility to the preparation a pure sample of an insoluble salt	explain why barium sulfate is used as a barium meal to X-ray internal organs
describe flame tests used to identify some common ions	describe tests used to identify some common anions	explain that chemists use spectroscopy to identify very small amounts of elements
describe a covalent bond as a pair of electrons shared between two atoms	describe the formation of simple molecular, covalent substances with dot and cross diagrams	explain how covalent bonding (**including double and triple bonds**) results in stable molecules using dot and cross diagrams
describe the properties of simple molecular covalent compounds	explain the properties of simple molecular covalent compounds	*explain how graphite and diamond as forms of carbon have such different properties*
recall that substances can be classified as covalent, ionic or giant covalent, according to their properties	describe the differences in the properties of simple molecular and giant molecular covalent substances.	
recall that a separation funnel can be used to separate two immiscible liquids	describe how miscible liquids can be separated using fractional distillation	describe the procedure for using factional distillation to separate oxygen and nitrogen from liquid air
recall that paper chromatography can be used to separate and identify components of mixtures	describe the procedure for using paper chromatography to separate and identify colouring agents in food	evaluate data from paper chromatography to identify components of a mixture, including R_f calculations

Exam-style questions: Foundation

AO1 **1 a** The number of protons in the nucleus of an atom is called the …

A ☐ atomic number

B ☐ mass number

C ☐ relative atomic mass

D ☐ formula mass. [1]

AO1 **b** Copy and complete the table below:

Particle	Relative charge
Proton	
Neutron	
Electron	

[3]

AO1 **c** Explain why atoms usually do not have a charge associated with them. [2]

AO2 **d** Copy and complete the diagram below to show the correct electron configuration for carbon. [2]

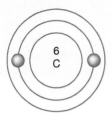

[Total: 8]

2 a Use the terms below to complete the following sentences.

ionic   positive   negative   electrons   protons

AO1 **i** Cations have a _____ charge. [1]

AO1 **ii** Anions have more _____ than _____. [2]

AO2 **b i** Jeevan was asked to make a label for a bottle of potassium sulfate. She knew that potassium's formula is K and that sulfate is SO_4. Write the formula Jeevan should put on the label. [2]

AO2 **ii** Describe a test that could be used to confirm that the compound contains sulfate. [2]

AO2 **c** State whether potassium sulfate is soluble or insoluble in water. [1]

[Total: 8]

3 Pat carried out an investigation into the melting point, solubility and conductivity when dissolved of two substances. One substance is ionic and the other covalent.

The following table shows his results.

Property	Substance A	Substance B
Melting point (°C)	801	186
Solubility in water	High	Low
Conductivity	Good	Poor

AO2 **a i** What type of compound is substance A? [1]

AO2 **ii** Use the information from the table to explain how you reached your decision. [2]

AO2 **b** Methane is a covalent compound with the formula CH_4. Draw a dot and cross diagram for methane. [2]

AO2 **c** Describe how covalent bonds form between carbon and hydrogen in a molecule of methane. [3]

[Total: 8]

4 Samantha was trying to determine which of four pigments was used to colour her favourite sweet. She got samples of the four possible pigments and a sample of the pigment from the sweet. She then used paper chromatography to compare her sweet to the four possible pigments.

The solvent front moved 9.5 cm. The table shows the results of her test.

Pigment	Distance travelled (cm)	R_f value
Sample 1	9.2	0.97
Sample 2	7.9	0.83
Sample 3	8.7	0.92
Sample 4	5.3	0.56
Sweet	7.8	

AO2 **a** Calculate the R_f value for Samantha's sweet. [2]

AO3 **b** Use evidence from the chromatogram to explain which is the most likely pigment used in Samantha's sweet. [2]

AO1 AO2 **c** Paper chromatography is used in the food industry to identify the food colourings that are in certain foods. Describe the stages needed to produce a paper chromatogram that can identify a particular food colouring in a fruit squash. [6]

[Total: 10]

Summary of Assessment Objectives

AO1 recall the science   AO2 apply your knowledge   AO3 evaluate and analyse the evidence

✳ Worked example

Sodium fluoride has the formula NaF. It is present in some toothpastes.

AO2 **a** **i** Sodium has 11 electrons. Draw the electronic structure of sodium. [2]

✔ ✔

AO2 **ii** Fluorine has nine electrons. Draw the electronic structure of fluorine [2]

✔ ✔

AO2 **iii** Calculate the relative formula mass of sodium fluoride (Na = 23, F = 19) [1]

23 + 19 = 42 ✔

AO2 **b** Sodium and fluorine both form ions when they make the compound sodium fluoride.

What happens to the electronic structures of each atom as they form ions? [2]

The sodium and fluorine each share an electron to form a bond. ✘ ✘

AO2 **c** Explain how sodium sulfate solution and barium fluoride solution could be used to make sodium fluoride. [3]

Mix them and then evaporation ✘ ✘ ✘

This candidate scored 5 marks out of a possible 10. The candidate could have improved their grade by fully revising ionic bonding and separation before the exam. They could also have given more time to parts **b** and **c** in the exam, ensuring that they had written enough points for the number of marks available.

How to raise your grade

Take note of the comments from examiners – these will help you to improve your grade.

The good, clear diagrams show the electrons as crosses on each shell. In this type of question it is a good idea to label the centre of each atom, so that there is no confusion as to which atom is which. This also applies to ions. Two marks would be awarded to each diagram.

The clear calculation shows the working out. If you have a more complex calculation and make a simple error, you will still get credit for showing that you know how to calculate the answer. A simple number is either full marks or no marks. This answer receives a mark.

The candidate has failed to realise that this is ionic bonding, transferring electrons, rather than sharing electrons. The answer should state that an electron is transferred from a sodium atom to a fluorine atom, forming a sodium ion and a fluoride ion. As a rule, if the compound contains a metal, then it is always ionic bonding. No mark would be given.

No marks are awarded. Sodium sulfate mixed with barium fluoride would produce barium sulfate precipitate. Sodium fluoride could be obtained by evaporation of the filtrate. Candidates should be aware of solubility rules and procedures for separating mixtures, as practical techniques are often assessed in the exam.

AO1 **1 a** Elements in the same group have the…

A ☐ same number of protons in the nucleus

B ☐ same number of neutrons in the nucleus

C ☐ same number of electrons in the outer shell

D ☐ same number of protons and neutrons. [1]

Two stable forms of carbon exist:

Atoms	Relative atomic mass	Abundance (%)
^{12}C	12	98.93
^{13}C	13	1.07

AO2 **b** Calculate the relative atomic mass for carbon using the information in the table. [2]

AO2 **c** Use the information in the table to explain what is meant by the term isotope. [2]

AO2 **d** Carbon is located in group 4 of the periodic table and has an electron configuration of 2.4. Oxygen is located in group 6 and has an atomic number of 8.

Draw the electron configuration for oxygen. [1]

AO1 **e** Oxygen is a diatomic element. Draw a dot and cross diagram for a molecule of O_2. Show the outer electrons only. [2]
[Total: 8]

2 Patients sometimes drink barium sulfate to allow X-rays to be taken of their digestive system. Barium chloride is highly toxic.

AO1 **a** What does the '-ide' at the end of 'chloride' tell you about this substance? [1]

AO2 **b** Explain why barium sulfate is safe to drink but barium chloride is not. [2]

AO2 **c** Barium chloride has a melting point of 962 °C. Explain why barium chloride has such a high melting point. [2]

AO2 **d** Describe a test to detect the chloride ions in a solution of barium chloride. [3]
[Total: 8]

3

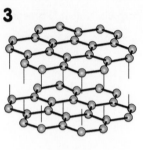 

graphite   diamond

AO1 **a** What type of bond joins the carbon atoms in these two substances? [1]

AO2 **b** Diamond and graphite are both giant molecular structures. What is meant by the term giant molecular structure? [3]

AO2 **c** Hexane has a simple covalent structure. Explain how the properties of hexane are different to the properties of diamond. [6]

AO1 **d** Explain why diamonds are hard enough to be
AO2   used as cutting tools but graphite is not, in terms of structure and bonding. [2]

AO1 **e** Graphite is often used as a lubricant. Explain why graphite makes a good lubricant. [2]
[Total: 14]

4 Lead chloride is used in glass making. Lead chloride ($PbCl_2$) can be produced by reacting lead nitrate ($Pb(NO_3)_2$) with sodium chloride (NaCl).

AO2 **a** Write the balanced chemical equation for this reaction. [2]

AO2 **b** Predict whether lead chloride is soluble or insoluble. [2]

AO2 **c** Explain how a sample of lead chloride could be produced in the laboratory. Include any necessary safety precautions. [6]
[Total: 10]

Summary of Assessment Objectives

| AO1 recall the science | AO2 apply your knowledge | AO3 evaluate and analyse the evidence |

Worked example

AO2 **a** Deuterium is also known as heavy hydrogen because it has an atomic mass of 2. Most hydrogen has an atomic mass of 1.

Explain the difference in atomic mass between the two substances. [2]

The most common form of hydrogen has one proton in its nucleus and therefore an atomic mass of 1. Deuterium is an isotope of hydrogen. It has one proton and one neutron in its nucleus which increases its atomic mass to 2. ✔ ✔

AO2 **b** ^1H makes up 99.985% of all hydrogen. Deuterium (^2H) accounts for 0.015%. Calculate the relative atomic mass of hydrogen. [2]

1 amu + 2 amu/2 = 1.5 amu ✘ ✘

AO2 **c** Hydrogen is a diatomic element and exists as H_2. Describe the bond that holds the two hydrogen atoms together. [2]

The two hydrogens share a pair of electrons between them in a covalent bond. ✔ ✔

AO1 **d** State two properties that identify hydrogen as a simple molecular, covalent substance. [2]

Weak attractive forces between molecules mean low boiling points. ✔ ✘

How to raise your grade

Take note of the comments from examiners – these will help you to improve your grade.

Full marks awarded. The answer is clear and explains where the extra mass comes from.

The correct answer is 1.00015. The candidate should have multiplied the mass of each of the two isotopes by their relative abundance to get the correct answer. Remember that there are mathematical formulae in chemistry too and you will need to know when and how to apply these in your exam.

The answer is clear and complete. It identifies the bond as a covalent bond and describes the arrangement of the electrons. However, it is more scientifically accurate to say 'hydrogen atoms' rather than 'hydrogens'. Be sure to use precise terms in your exam.

The answer only receives 1 mark because the answer only provides one property. The candidate could have also included low melting points or poor conductors. Be sure to answer the question completely.

This candidate scored 6 marks out of a possible 8. The candidate could have easily secured a grade A by learning and practising their Unit 2 calculations.

C2 Discovering chemistry (Topics 4–6)

What you should know

Groups in the periodic table

Substances have chemical and physical properties.

Metals have particular properties and distinct uses.

Elements are arranged in the periodic table with elements in the same group being similar to each other and metals on the left and non-metals on the right.

You can use the periodic table to make predictions.

 State two properties of metals.

Chemical reactions

Acids and bases react to form salts.

In displacement reactions, more reactive metals displace less reactive metals.

Reactions happen at different speeds.

The rate of reaction is faster with more concentrated acids.

 Describe the reaction of an acid with a base.

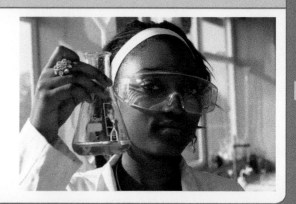

Quantitative chemistry

Chemical reactions can be represented as word and symbol equations (C1 – Topic 1).

When substances react they produce products that are different to the reagents.

 Write a word equation for the reaction of hydrochloric acid with sodium hydroxide.

You will find out about

> the classification of elements as alkali metals, halogens, noble gases and transition metals based on their position in the periodic table

> the structure and properties of metals

> the classification of substances as ionic, simple molecular covalent, giant molecular covalent and metallic based on their physical properties

> the physical properties of the alkali metals

> the reactivity of the alkali metals

> the chemical and physical properties of the halogens

> displacement reaction and the halogens

> the properties and uses of the noble gases

> chemical bonds breaking and producing a reaction that is endothermic

> chemical bonds being made and producing a reaction that is exothermic

> representing heat energy changes occurring in chemical reactions

> reaction rates and the factors that affect them

> chemical reactions as collisions of particles

> the effect of catalysts on reaction rates

> catalytic converters

> calculating relative formula mass, empirical formulas and percentage composition of simple compounds

> using balanced equations to calculate reacting masses

> theoretical yields and percentage yields

> the role of chemists in maximising yields in industrial chemistry

Structure and properties

You will find out:
> how elements and compounds are classified
> about the physical properties of different types of substances

Diamonds are for ever

In the *Pioneer* space probe to Venus, one of its windows was made from diamond as it was transparent to infrared light and could cope with both the low temperature and pressure of space as well as Venus' high temperature and pressure.

FIGURE 1: An artist's representation of a *Pioneer* probe on the surface of Venus.

Unique properties

All substances have a unique set of properties that allow scientists to distinguish them from all other substances. These properties are divided into two categories:

> **Chemical properties** describe how a substance reacts with other substances.

> **Physical properties** can be measured without chemically changing the substance.

Physical properties include:

> **Melting point**: the temperature at which a solid becomes a liquid.

> **Boiling point**: the temperature a liquid becomes a gas.

> **Solubility**: the amount of a substance that will dissolve in a fixed amount of solvent.

> **Electrical conductivity**: how well a substance conducts an electric current.

These properties can be used to identify the type of bonding present in a substance because the physical properties of a substance are a direct result of its bonding.

Elements and compounds can be classified as:

> **Ionic compounds**. They contain positively charged metal ions and negatively charged non-metal ions.

> **Simple molecular covalent compounds**. They are small molecules that consist of non-metalic atoms only.

> **Giant molecular covalent compounds**. They are very large structures (huge numbers of atoms) consisting of non-metallic atoms held together by covalent bonds.

> **Metallic compounds**. They are individual metal ions surrounded by a sea of electrons.

QUESTIONS

1 State what is meant by a physical property. Provide an example to support your answer.

Relative properties

Relative melting point
The melting point of a substance is directly related to the strength of the attractive forces holding the individual particles in place. In diamonds, the individual carbon atoms are held in place by covalent bonds. Extreme temperatures are required to break the bonds. In simple covalent molecules, the forces between the individual molecules are relatively weak and therefore the melting point is low.

Relative boiling point

As with melting point, the boiling point of a liquid depends on the strength of the forces between particles. The stronger the forces the more energy it will take to break the intermolecular forces and allow the individual particles to separate.

Solubility

While melting point and boiling point are totally dependent on the forces between the particles of the substance, solubility depends on the interaction between two different substances. The substance being dissolved is called the solute. The solvent is the liquid that the solute is being dissolved in.

As a general rule, covalent molecules are insoluble in water and ionic substances are soluble in water.

Electrical conductivity

Electrical conductivity is dependent on the ability of electrons to move. The sea of delocalised electrons found in all metals allows them to conduct electricity as solids or liquids. Metals are the only solids except graphite that can conduct electricity. Most ionic compounds will conduct when molten or in aqueous solution.

TABLE 1: Relationship of structure to physical properties.

Type of structure	Relative melting point	Relative boiling point	Relative solubility in water	Electrical conductivity
Ionic	High	High	Soluble	Good conductors in aqueous solutions or when molten
Simple molecular covalent	Low	Low	Insoluble	Non-conductors as solids, liquids and in solutions
Giant molecular covalent	Very high	Very high	Insoluble	Non-conductors (graphite is an exception)
Metallic	High	High	Insoluble	Good conductors as solids or liquids

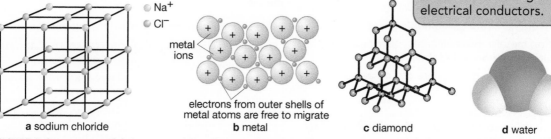

○ Na$^+$
○ Cl$^-$

metal ions

electrons from outer shells of metal atoms are free to migrate

a sodium chloride   b metal   c diamond   d water

FIGURE 2: Structure models (not to scale). **a** The ionic structure of sodium chloride. **b** A metal; showing the 'sea of electrons' – this means the electrons that surround the positively charged metal ions. **c** Diamond; a giant molecular covalent structure. **d** Water; a simple covalent structure.

QUESTIONS

2 A substance has a high melting point and is a good conductor as a solid. What type of structure does it have?

3 A compound is a non-conductor of electricity as a solid and insoluble in water.
a Name the two types of structure that the compound could be.
b How could you determine what type of structure the compound is?

4 Explain why quartz (silicon dioxide) has a very high relative melting point.

5 Suggest why simple covalent structures are not good electrical conductors.

Hydrogen bonding

One of the most important of forces that holds molecules together is hydrogen bonding. Hydrogen bonding is about 10 times weaker than covalent bonding and occurs whenever hydrogen is covalently bonded to elements with high attraction to electrons or **electronegativity**.

Elements such as oxygen, fluorine and chlorine have very high electronegativities. When hydrogen is covalently bonded to any of these elements the sharing of electrons is unequal. This means that the hydrogen atom is always deficient in electrons and the electronegative element always has an abundance of electrons. Therefore, hydrogen always has a slightly positive charge and the electronegative element has a slightly negative charge. These slightly negative charges and slightly positive charges can interact with other charged molecules allowing them to stick together like two magnets.

This will not be assessed in your GCSE Additional Science exam but it will be useful for further study in Unit 3 and at A level.

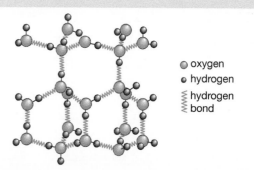

○ oxygen
○ hydrogen
≷ hydrogen bond

FIGURE 3: Hydrogen bonding between water molecules in an ice lattice.

QUESTIONS

6 Explain why water is often referred to as the universal solvent.

7 Describe the bond between hydrogen and fluorine.

Classifying elements into groups

Heavy metal

We live in a metal world. About 3% of the human body is made up of metal and metals are essential for our health. One of the most common metals in our bodies is iron, where it combines with a protein to form haemoglobin in our blood.

FIGURE 1: Can you think of some metals that are essential to human life?

You will find out:

> how to classify elements as alkali metals, halogens, noble gases and transition metals
> the properties of metals
> the properties of transition metals

Groups in the periodic table

The groups in the periodic table contain elements that have similar chemical properties. Some of these groups have been given names:

> group 1 elements are called **alkali metals**
> group 7 elements are called **halogens**
> group 0 elements are called **noble gases**
> **transition metals:** those elements between group 2 and group 3 in the periodic table.

We will explore these groups here and on pages 148–53.

What are metals?

Most of the elements in the periodic table are metals. All metals share certain properties:

> **Malleability**: they can be made into thin sheets. For example, aluminium for making drinks cans.

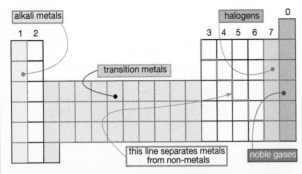

FIGURE 2: The periodic table, showing some of the named groups.

> **Electrical conductivity**: the ability to conduct an electric current. For example, copper is a useful metal for making electrical cables.

Both of these properties come from the structure of metals.

TABLE 1: Some element groups and their properties.

Group number	Name of element family	What is special about these elements?
1	Alkali metals	They react with water to make alkalis
2	Alkaline earth metals	They form alkalis, and many rocks in the Earth have a lot of these metals in them
7	Halogens	Halogens make salts – halogen means 'salt maker'
0	Noble gases	They are generally considered unreactive
Between groups 2 and 3	Transition metals	They can form coloured compounds

QUESTIONS

1 Classify the following elements as alkali metals, halogens, noble gases or transition metals: sodium, radon, bromine, titanium, francium, iodine, neon.

Metals

All metals have loosely held outer electrons, which means that atoms readily lose electrons and become positive ions. These outer electrons are so loosely held that they move freely from atom to atom. This is called delocalisation. Metals are often described as a regular arrangement of positively charged metal ions floating in a sea of delocalised electrons (see Figure 2b on page 145).

The strong attractions between ions and the delocalised electrons hold the metal atoms tightly together. This metallic bonding explains other properties associated with metals:

> Closely packed atoms give high density.

> The bonding makes metals difficult to break apart, so they are strong and hard.

> It takes lots of heat energy to separate the atoms to let them flow and vaporise. So metals have high melting and boiling points.

> The layers of ions can slide over each other, but still be held together by electrons. So metals bend and stretch without breaking. They are malleable and ductile.

> The delocalised electrons carry a charge or heat energy through the metal structure. So metals also conduct electricity and heat well.

Transition metals

The transition metals make up the largest collection of elements in the periodic table. They are particularly characterised by:

> high melting point (except mercury, the only metal that is liquid at room temperature)

> the formation of coloured compounds.

Most of them have the usual properties of metals. For example, they have high melting points, boiling points, densities and conductivities. They are also hard, shiny and malleable (can be beaten into shape).

You will know some transition metals already, such as iron, copper, zinc, gold and silver.

⊙ QUESTIONS

2 Explain what is meant by a 'sea of electrons'.

3 Draw a labelled diagram to show the arrangement of electrons in the transition metals.

4 Explain why transition metals conduct electricity well.

Trends across the period

The groups of the periodic table are made of elements that have similar chemical properties. As we investigate these groups we notice trends associated with the specific groups. There are also trends that occur across the periods of the periodic table. These include:

> increasing electronegativity

> decreasing atomic radius.

Increasing electronegativity

As we proceed across a period of the periodic table each step adds another proton to the nucleus and another electron to the outermost energy level. **Electronegativity** measures the attractive force between the nucleus and bonded electrons. When each electron shell is full a new one must be started. This new electron shell is slightly further away from the nucleus and therefore experiences less attractive force. This explains the decrease in electronegativity at the beginning of each new period.

Decreasing atomic radius

The increased pull on the outer electrons across a period means that as we move across a period the electrons are being pulled closer to the nucleus because of the greater attractive force. This causes the **atomic radius** to get smaller across a period.

This will not be assessed in your GCSE Additional Science exam but it will be useful for further study in Unit 3 and at A level.

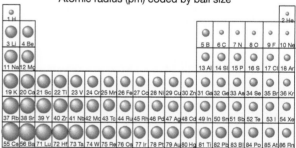

Atomic radius (pm) coded by ball size

FIGURE 4: A chart showing the trend in atomic radius in the periodic table.

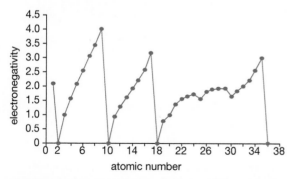

FIGURE 3: A graph showing the electronegativity trend for the first 36 elements.

⊙ QUESTIONS

5 Explain the trend between electronegativity, the periodic table and atomic radii.

Alkali metals

You will find out:

> about the properties of the alkali metals

> about the reactivity of alkali metals

Keep it covered

Sodium is so reactive that it needs to be stored under oil. Even though it is one of the most abundant metals on Earth, it is always found in minerals, and never in its elemental form.

FIGURE 1: This is what happens when water is dripped on to sodium metal. Can you write a word equation for the reaction?

Group 1 elements

The first three elements of group 1 of the periodic table are:

> lithium (Li)

> sodium (Na)

> potassium (K).

These metals are highly reactive and never found in their elemental forms. As members of the same group they share many characteristics:

> They are soft (they can be cut with a knife).

> They have low melting points (when compared to other metals).

> They react with water to form metal hydroxides and hydrogen gas.

> They have one electron in their outermost electron shell.

Softness

The attractive forces that hold the atoms in the metallic structure are weak and the metals are soft.

Low melting points

Lithium has the highest melting point of the group 1 elements (181 °C). Compare this to the transition metals, most of which have melting points above 1000 °C. The weak attractive forces that make these elements so soft also account for the low melting points.

TABLE 1: Some properties of group 1 elements.

Element	Atomic radius (m)	Melting point (°C)	Reactivity with water
Lithium	1.52×10^{-8}	181	Slow
Sodium	1.86×10^{-8}	98	High
Potassium	2.31×10^{-8}	64	Explosive

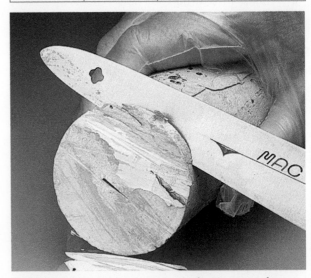

FIGURE 2: Sodium being cut with a knife. The cut surface soon goes from bright metal to a dull colour. Why is that?

Did you know?

Sodium and potassium can both be extracted from seawater which tastes salty because of the sodium and potassium ions dissolved in it.

QUESTIONS

1 Describe the electron configuration of the group 1 elements. Use a diagram to help you.

2 Give one reason why alkali metals are soft and have low melting points.

Reactivity

All alkali metals react with water (see Table 1) to produce soluble metal hydroxides, which are alkaline, and hydrogen gas:

alkali metal + water → metal hydroxide + hydrogen gas

For instance:

2Li (s) + 2H$_2$O (l) →   2LiOH (aq)   +   H$_2$ (g)
lithium + water   →   lithium hydroxide +   hydrogen gas

2Na (s) + 2H$_2$O (l) →   2NaOH (aq)   +   H$_2$ (g)
sodium   + water   →   sodium hydroxide   +   hydrogen gas

2K (s) + 2H$_2$O (l) →   2KOH (aq)   +   H$_2$ (g)
potassium + water   →   potassium hydroxide +   hydrogen gas

These reactions become more vigorous as we move down the group.

Trends

Moving down the group 1 elements, the outer shell electron is:

> further from the nucleus and so the **atomic radius** gets larger;

> shielded by an increasing number of inner electron shells.

The added distance of the outer shell electron from the nucleus and the increased shielding in each of the group 1 elements means that the attractive force holding the electron gets weaker as we move down the group. Therefore, as we move down the group the elements become more reactive because the attractive force holding the outer shell electron goes down, allowing ions to form more easily.

QUESTIONS

3 Predict how reactive the following metals would be in a reaction with water:
a rubidium compared to sodium
b caesium compared to rubidium.

4 Describe the trend in reactivity in the group 1 elements.

5 a Suggest two ways in which you would minimise the risks of reacting lithium and water.
b Suggest why you would take different safety precautions when reacting lithium and water, than when reacting francium and water.

Did you know?

Nearly all alkali metal compounds dissolve in water

Ionisation energy (Higher tier only)

The pattern of reactivity of the alkali metals can be explained by examining how easily the outer shell electron can be removed. In an attempt to better understand this process, scientists have developed methods to measure the energy required to remove electrons from atoms. This is referred to as the **ionisation energy**.

Table 2 shows the ionisation energy required to remove the outer shell electron from the first three elements of group 1. For comparison purposes, the ionisation energy for the second electron is also included. For the group 1 elements the second electron is from the next lower energy level, which is closer to the nucleus and therefore has a much stronger attachment. From this data it is easy to see why the reactivity of group 1 elements increases down the group.

TABLE 2: Ionisation energies of some group 1 elements.

Element	First ionisation energy (kJ/mol)	Second ionisation energy (kJ/mol)
Lithium	520	7300
Sodium	500	4600
Potassium	420	3100

QUESTIONS

6 Explain the trend in ionisation energies for the group 1 elements.

7 a Draw a graph of atomic mass and first ionisation energy for the elements listed in Table 2.

b Use this graph to predict the ionisation energy for the next element in group 1, rubidium (element 37).

This will not be assessed in your GCSE Additional Science exam but it will be useful for further study in Unit 3 and at A level.

Halogens

You will find out:
> about the properties of the halogens
> about the production of hydrogen halides
> about the reactivity of group 7 elements

Chemical warfare

The halogens include one of the first chemicals used in warfare – chlorine; and some that we still use every day in our war on bacteria – chlorine and iodine.

FIGURE 1: A British soldier wearing a gas mask.

Group 7 elements

The group 7 elements are called the halogens. They include fluorine (F), chlorine (Cl), bromine (Br), iodine (I) and astatine (As).

Properties

As members of group 7:

> they all have electron shells that are one electron from being full

> one electron is needed to make a full shell, so when two atoms share an electron they form a stable molecule

> therefore they exist as covalently bonded pairs of atoms, that is they are all **diatomic elements**.

Their physical properties are summarised in Table 1.

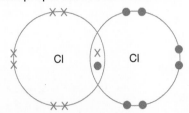

FIGURE 2: A dot and cross model of chlorine showing its diatomic structure.

Reactivity

All halogens react with hydrogen to produce hydrogen halides that are soluble in water:

halogen + hydrogen → hydrogen halide

These hydrogen halides form acid solutions.

The halogens become less reactive as you go down the group:

> This reactivity is dependent on the halogen's attraction to electrons.

> The attractive force on outer shell electrons goes down as each successive electron shell is added moving down the group.

> Therefore, the ability of the element to take an electron and form a negatively charged ion is reduced.

Did you know?

Fluorine is the most reactive element in the periodic table.

QUESTIONS

1 State what is meant by diatomic elements.

2 Describe the trends in physical properties that you notice as you move down Table 1.

TABLE 1: Some physical properties of the group 7 elements.

Element	Atomic radius ($\times 10^{-11}$ m)	Melting point (°C)	State (at 20 °C)	Colour
Fluorine	7.09	−219	Gas	Pale yellow
Chlorine	9.94	−101	Gas	Pale green
Bromine	1.14	−7	Liquid	Red–brown
Iodine	1.33	114	Solid	Grey
Astatine	1.43	302	Solid	Unknown

Hydrofluoric acid   Halogen lamps   Fluoridation

Metal halides

The attractive force of halogens on electrons allows them to take electrons from elements that do not have a tight hold on their outer shell electrons.

The reaction of halogens with metals produces ionic compounds as the halogens take electrons from the metal to form ions.

These ionic compounds are commonly called **salts**. The halogen becomes negatively charged due to the extra electrons while the metal becomes positively charged when it loses electrons to the halogen. These ions then form ionic bonds to form metal halides.

Table 2 summarises the reaction of halogens with metals.

Notice that each metal bonds with the number of halogens equal to the metal's group number.

> Group 1 elements like sodium bond with a single chlorine.

> Group 2 elements like calcium bond with two and so on.

> Transition metals like iron are more difficult to predict because some of them can produce ions with different charges.

TABLE 2: Summary of the formation of metal halides, where X represents one of the halogens.

2Na	+	X_2	$\rightarrow$	2NaX
sodium	+	halogen	$\rightarrow$	sodium halide
Ca	+	X_2	$\rightarrow$	CaX_2
calcium	+	halogen	$\rightarrow$	calcium halide
2Al	+	$3X_2$	$\rightarrow$	$2AlX_3$
aluminium	+	halogen	$\rightarrow$	aluminium halide
2Fe	+	$3X_2$	$\rightarrow$	$2FeX_3$
iron	+	halogen	$\rightarrow$	iron halide

 QUESTIONS

3 Explain why halogens form ionic compounds with metals.

4 Write balanced equations for the reaction of iodine with lithium, bromine with magnesium and chlorine with gallium.

Investigating the reactivity of halogens

The combination of reactivity and the colours of the halogen allow for an interesting investigation into their reactivity. Because the halogens get less reactive down the group, each halogen has the ability to displace the halogens below it in reactions. For example:

$$Cl_2 \text{ (aq)} + 2KBr \text{ (aq)} \rightarrow 2KCl \text{ (aq)} + Br_2 \text{ (aq)}$$

This reaction is called a **displacement reaction**; because of the higher reactivity, chlorine has the ability to displace bromine in solution. Table 3 summarises the results of displacement reactions within group 7. You will notice that chlorine has the ability to displace bromine in solution and iodine in solution, meaning that chlorine is more reactive than both of those elements. Bromine cannot displace chlorine in solution, but can displace iodine in solution. Bromine is less reactive than chlorine but more reactive than iodine. Iodine cannot displace either chlorine or bromine.

Remember!
This mnemonic can help you recall the common diatomic elements:
I Bring Clay For Our New House.

TABLE 3: Displacement reactions within group 7.

Halogen	Colour	Reaction with potassium chloride	Reaction with potassium bromide	Reaction with potassium iodide
Chlorine (aqueous)	Pale yellowish green	No reaction	Yellowish orange colour of bromine	Brown colour of iodine
Bromine (aqueous)	Yellowish orange	No reaction	No reaction	Brown colour of iodine
Iodine (aqueous)	Brown	No reaction	No reaction	No reaction

 QUESTIONS

5 Describe what happens in a displacement reaction.

6 Explain why halogens higher in the group can displace those below them in chemical reactions.

Noble gases

You will find out:
> about the properties of the noble gases
> about the discovery of the noble gases
> about the uses of noble gases

No reaction

Elements usually make themselves known by the way they react. It was the fact that they did not react that led to the discovery of the noble gases.

FIGURE 1: Brilliantly lit signs are produced using noble gases. Here is a selection.

 ## Completely full

The group numbers of the periodic table indicate the number of electrons in the outer shell.

The number of electrons in the outer shell affects how reactive an element is. Generally, the fewer electrons in an outer shell, the more reactive an element. (Helium is an exception.)

The elements of group 0:

> have eight electrons in their outer shell, which is a 'full set' (two for helium)

> as these elements have a 'full set' of electrons in their outer shell, they do not react with other elements

> are known as the **noble gases**.

The elements in group 0 are referred to as **inert**, meaning non-reactive.

Properties

By being familiar with the properties of the elements of the periodic table, chemists can pick just the right element to produce the reaction they want. Sometimes, however, chemists want elements that do not react and the noble gases come to the rescue. All noble gases share certain properties:

> *Inertness*: they do not react with other substances. This is useful in some types of welding where an inert atmosphere is required and in filament light bulbs.

> *Low density*: their low densities mean that they normally exist as gases. This is useful for filling balloons.

> *Non-flammability*: since they are non-reactive they do not combust. Along with their low density, this is why they are used to fill balloons.

These properties make the noble gases the elements of choice whenever a situation requires a non-reactive gas.

FIGURE 2: The *Spirit of Freedom* used a combination of helium and hot air to circumnavigate the world. Hydrogen is lighter than helium, so why didn't they use hydrogen in the balloon?

QUESTIONS

1 State three properties that all noble gases share.

2 a Draw the electron configurations of helium and neon.

  b Use your diagram to explain why the noble gases are inert.

Lord Rayleigh   William Ramsey

Discovering the noble gases

After the publication of Mendeleev's periodic table, chemists began searching for undiscovered elements.

In 1895 Lord Rayleigh noticed that nitrogen purified from the air had a different density than nitrogen produced by chemical reactions.

The nitrogen made from purified air was produced by chemical reactions to remove all of the other gases. By not reacting in the purifying process the noble gases revealed themselves.

This observation prompted Lord Rayleigh and William Ramsay to hypothesise that the nitrogen purified from air must be a mixture of gases.

To test the **hypothesis** they developed an experiment where liquefied air was separated using fractional distillation. The results of this experiment led to the isolation of the first samples of the gas that became known as argon.

By the end of the 19th century Ramsay had gone on to discover krypton, neon and xenon. The discovery of these gases and the analysis of their properties added a whole new group to the periodic table.

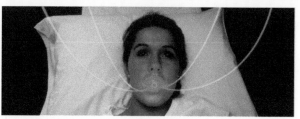

FIGURE 3: A low-power red argon laser passes through four optical fibre waveguides to treat a cancer in a woman's throat.

QUESTIONS

3 a Describe the process that led to the discovery of the noble gases.

b Note down the similarities between the basic scientific process that Rayleigh and Ramsay used to discover the noble gases, and the process that you used in your Science Controlled Assessment.

4 Explain why the noble gases formed a new group in the periodic table.

Predicting properties

One of the most amazing things about the periodic table is the regularity of trends that occur when you begin to examine it. For instance, if the densities of the first three noble gases are plotted on a graph with atomic masses a clear pattern is obvious (see Figure 4).

By examining the graph we can see that the points plotted are not perfectly straight, but very close. If we draw a **line of best fit** through the points that we have plotted we see that the line intersects atomic mass 84, the next noble gas, just above 3.5. The true value is 3.733, not a bad estimate.

It was observations like this that allowed chemists to predict the properties of elements that had not been discovered when Mendeleev formulated the periodic table.

TABLE 1: Boiling point data for the first three noble gases.

Element	Atomic mass	Boiling point (°C)
Helium	4.003	−269
Neon	20.179	−246
Argon	39.948	−186

QUESTIONS

5 Estimate the density of xenon. Remember, you can find xenon's atomic mass in the periodic table.

6 Use the data in Table 1 to plot a graph for boiling point against atomic mass.

7 a Estimate the boiling point for krypton, atomic number 36.

b Calculate the percentage error.

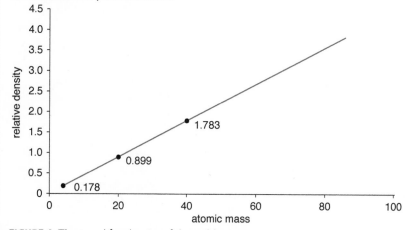

FIGURE 4: The trend for density of the noble gases.

Preparing for assessment: Applying your knowledge

To achieve a good grade in science, you not only have to know and understand scientific ideas, but you also need to be able to apply them to other situations. This task will support you in developing these skills.

✹ 'Dancing around and delirious with joy!'

What do you see when you look at the periodic table? You see a summary of hundreds of pieces of information about elements, brought together in one chart. This information has been discovered by many different scientists from all over the world, but a few people have made a major contribution and one of those was Cornishman Humphry Davy.

Around 1800 there were a number of scientists experimenting with using electricity to break down substances into their component elements. Davy was convinced he could do this to what were then

known as the alkali earths. At first he was unsuccessful – he tried passing current through solutions of alkali earths, but this simply released hydrogen. He then tried melting the compounds and passing a current through them. This worked much better and produced tiny beads of pure metal. When beads of one of these metals were dropped on to water they 'skimmed about excitedly with a hissing sound, and soon burned with a lovely lavender light' according to Humphry's brother John.

✹ Task 1

What was the metal that, when Davy added to water, 'skimmed about excitedly with a hissing sound, and soon burned with a lovely lavender light'?

> How could you use this test to distinguish between metals?

Humphrey 'danced around and was delirious with joy' when he saw this lavender light.

Task 2

Think about the reaction of the metal added to water.

> If a pH indicator such Universal Indicator solution was added to the water after the reaction, what would it show?

> What product from the reaction causes this result?

> How does this help to explain the general name given to the group 1 metals?

> Why is a safety screen necessary during the reaction?

 Task 3

> Write a word equation to summarise the reaction.

> **Higher tier only:** Write a balanced chemical equation for the reaction.

 Task 4

It is possible to predict how group 1 metals will bond with other groups of elements in the periodic table.

> Explain how a chemist would know that calcium would form a single ionic bond with chlorine.

 Task 5

A lab technician was preparing an experiment to investigate the reactivity of group 1 and group 7 elements. In the stock room, she discovered three bottles without labels and three labels that had fallen off. The labels read 'potassium chloride', 'potassium bromide' and 'potassium iodide'. The bottles each contained a clear liquid.

> Describe how the technician could decide which label went with which bottle.

> Describe the results that the technician should expect to see.

Maximise your grade

These sentences show what you need to include in your work to achieve each grade. Use them to improve your work and be more successful.

E
For grade E, your answer should show that you can:
> state the results of flame tests for alkali metals
> recall the position of the alkali metals in the periodic table and describe their properties
> write word equations for chemical reactions.

C
For grade D, C in addition show that you can:
> describe how flame test can be used to distinguish between group 1 metals
> describe the reactions of a group 1 metal in water
> describe the reactions of halogens with metals to form metal halides
> write simple chemical equations for reactions.

A
For grade B, A, in addition show that you can:
> describe and explain the pattern of reactivity of group 1 metals with water and use it to predict the reactivity of elements in the group
> write balanced chemical equations for reactions.

Exothermic and endothermic reactions

Hot and cold

All chemical reactions involve energy. Explosions are just one example of a reaction that gives out heat energy to its surroundings. There are also reactions that take energy from the surroundings, creating a cooling effect.

FIGURE 1: A chemical reaction inside this pack makes an instant cold compress. Why is this useful?

Energy changes

When you look around, there are chemical processes going on everywhere.

During most chemical reactions chemical bonds are broken and reformed between different substances.

Exothermic reactions

Reactions that give off heat energy are called **exothermic reactions**.

> For example, the combustion in a car's engine gives off heat energy so it is also an exothermic reaction.

When chemical bonds are formed energy is released, which makes the process exothermic:

> For example, when a hydrocarbon burns, some energy must be added to break the bonds of the reactants, but large amounts of energy are given off as the carbons and hydrogens are oxidised.

Endothermic reactions

Reactions that take in heat energy are called **endothermic reactions**:

> For example, when plants grow they use photosynthesis to take in heat energy.

Energy is required to break chemical bonds, which makes the process endothermic:

> For example, the chemical cold packs used in first-aid kits are ammonium chloride and water. The water capsule is broken and dissolves the ammonium chloride; an endothermic reaction takes place – the cold pack gets cold because when ammonium chloride dissolves it absorbs heat energy. Ammonium nitrate also dissolves in water endothermically.

QUESTIONS

1 Reactions that give off heat energy are _____, while reactions that absorb heat energy are _____.

2 State why an explosion is an exothermic reaction.

Measuring change

The energy changes that take place during chemical reactions can be measured in the lab using a set-up similar to Figure 2.

To measure the energy change in a neutralisation reaction:

> Place 50 cm^3 of 1.0 M hydrochloric acid into a foam cup.

> Place a thermometer in the cup and allow the temperature to stabilise by standing for 5 minutes.

> Add 50 cm^3 of 1.0 M sodium hydroxide and observe the thermometer.

> Record the temperature every minute for 5 minutes.

Remember!

Wear eye protection when using acids and alkalis.

Q Energy profile diagrams   Enthalpy

Notice the increase in temperature. The neutralisation of hydrochloric acid with sodium hydroxide is clearly exothermic.

Another reaction that can easily be measured in the lab involves dissolving ammonium chloride in water. This is an endothermic reaction:

> Place 50 cm³ of water into a foam cup.

> Place a thermometer in the water and allow it to stand for 5 minutes to stabilise the temperature.

> Add 2 g of ammonium chloride to the water and observe the thermometer.

> Record the temperature for 5 minutes.

Notice the temperature drop. The dissolution of ammonium chloride is an endothermic reaction.

QUESTIONS

3 Discuss the advantages of using a digital thermometer in these experiments.

4 Explain why a foam cup is used in these experiments.

5 Suggest ways of presenting your results for the experiments. Then, select what you consider to be the best one, giving reasons for your choice.

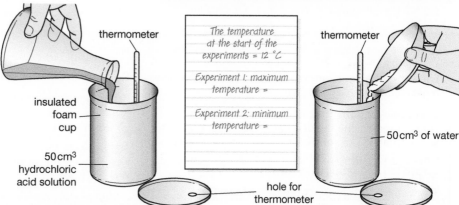

The temperature at the start of the experiments = 12 °C

Experiment 1: maximum temperature =

Experiment 2: minimum temperature =

thermometer

insulated foam cup

50 cm³ hydrochloric acid solution

thermometer

50 cm³ of water

hole for thermometer

FIGURE 2: A simple calorimeter set-up for two experiments to measure energy change.

Seeing energy changes (Higher tier only)

One way to understand the energy changes that happen during a chemical reaction is to use graphs called **energy profile diagrams**. Energy profile diagrams show the energy present in the reactants and the products. This allows us to determine whether a reaction is endothermic or exothermic.

In both diagrams in Figure 3 the energy of the reactants is increased. This is the energy required to break the bonds of the reactants. Breaking bonds is always endothermic. From the peak energy level the energy decreases down to the products. Making bonds is always exothermic.

In Figure 3a the energy of the products is less than the energy in the original reactants. Since energy can be neither created nor destroyed the energy must have been given off by the reaction. This reaction is exothermic.

In Figure 3b the energy of the products is higher than the energy in the original reactants. This means that the reaction has absorbed energy. This reaction is endothermic. In both cases, the energy given out is the difference between the energy needed to break the bonds and the energy released when the new bonds form.

Remember!
Breaking bonds is always endothermic.

QUESTIONS

6 a Draw energy profile diagrams for the two reactions carried out above: hydrochloric acid with sodium hydroxide and ammonium chloride with water.

b What do your energy profile diagrams show?

7 Explain why energy profile diagrams are useful.

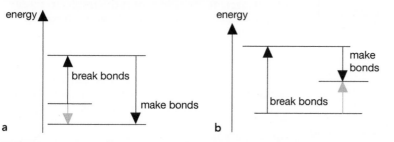

energy

break bonds

make bonds

a

energy

make bonds

break bonds

b

FIGURE 3: Energy profile diagrams for **a** exothermic and **b** endothermic reactions.

Reaction rates

You will find out:

> about the effects of temperature, concentration and surface area on reaction rates
> how to investigate reaction rates
> about collision theory

Fast or slow?

Imagine what would happen if metals corroded at the same speed as the combustion of gunpowder. Cars would rust to pieces before they could be painted.

FIGURE 1: Explosion caused by 23 kg of gunpowder.

Factors that affect reaction rates

For a chemical reaction to occur the reactant particles must collide with each other.

Chemical reactions happen at different speeds. Understanding the factors that affect reaction rates allows chemists to control chemical reactions and carry out potentially dangerous reactions in a controlled and productive way.

Three main factors affect the rate of reaction:

> temperature
> concentration
> surface area of a solid.

Temperature

The rate of reaction increases with an increase in temperature. As the temperature increases, the reactant particles move around more quickly. If the reactants move around more quickly there is greater likelihood that they will collide. More collisions mean more reactions.

Concentration

Because chemical reactions require the reactant particles to collide, increasing the concentration of the reactants increases the possibility of collisions. Increased collisions mean increased reaction rate.

Surface area of a solid

When one or more of the reactants are solid, surface area has the same effect as increasing the concentration.

Surface area increases as particle size gets smaller. Lots of little pieces of a solid react more quickly than one big piece.

QUESTIONS

1 State what must occur for a chemical reaction to happen.

2 Complete Table 1 on the factors that affect reaction rates, by stating high or low for each condition.

TABLE 1: Factors that affect the rate of reactions.

Factor	Increases	Decreases
Temperature		
Concentration		
Surface area		

Investigating reaction rates

When particles collide, and the collision has enough energy, then chemical reactions occur.

The reaction between hydrochloric acid and calcium carbonate makes a good system to investigate the factors that affect reaction rates. Figure 2 shows a possible set-up for such investigations.

Temperature

On a balance, place a flask and add 50 cm³ of hydrochloric acid at room temperature. Record the mass. Add 2 g of medium-sized marble chips (calcium carbonate) and start a timer. Record the mass every minute for 5 minutes. Repeat the experiment with hydrochloric acid that has been stored in the refrigerator. You would expect the results to show that the mass decreases more slowly with cooled hydrochloric acid.

Concentration

The same experiment can be carried out using two different concentrations of hydrochloric acid instead of two different temperatures. You will notice the mass reduces more quickly with a higher acid concentration.

Surface area

In a third investigation, two sizes of marble chips can be used. If small chips are compared to large chips the effect of surface area can be tested, since small chips will have a greater surface area than large chips. The mass will decrease more quickly with the smaller chips.

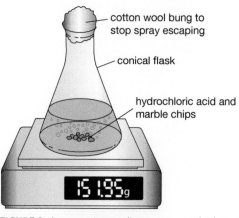

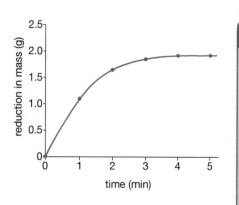

FIGURE 2: An experimental set-up to study the rate of reaction of hydrochloric acid and calcium carbonate.

QUESTIONS

3 Discuss the factors that need to be taken into account when planning the experiment.

4 Explain why you would expect the results for the experiments set out on pages 158–9.

Collision theory (Higher tier only)

Chemists use **collision theory** to explain how reactions happen at the atomic level. For reactants to be able to react they must collide. This seems quite obvious. However, there are some conditions that must be met during these collisions:

> First, the collision must occur with sufficient energy to allow the electron shells of the two reactants to penetrate each other so that the bonding electrons can be rearranged to form a chemical bond.

> Second, in most cases the reactants must have the correct orientation. In reactions like hydrogen reacting with chlorine orientation is not a problem, but in more complex reactions orientation is very important.

Figure 3 shows three possible results from a collision between two reactants:

> The first collision fails to lead to a reaction because of insufficient energy.

> The second collision fails to lead to a reaction because the orientation of the two reactants is incorrect.

> The third collision results in a reaction as the reactants have sufficient energy and are correctly orientated.

Anything that increases the frequency of collisions increases the probability of the reactants colliding with sufficient energy and the correct orientation. This in turn will increase the rate of reaction.

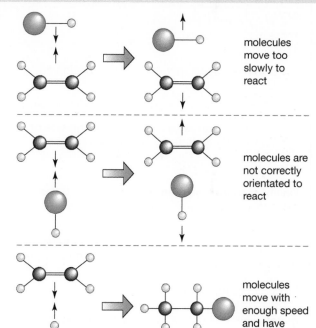

FIGURE 3: Three possible outcomes of a collision between two molecules.

Did you know?

A rule of thumb is reaction rate doubles with every 10 °C increase in temperature.

QUESTIONS

5 Explain why not all collisions between reactants result in a reaction.

6 Describe how increasing the temperature, concentration and surface area speeds up the rate of reaction.

Catalysts

You will find out:
> about the effect of catalysts on reactions
> about catalytic converters in cars

Whiter than white

When we wash clothes, washing powder is used to make sure that the clothes are as clean as possible.

Amazingly, dirty clothes can be cleaned at temperatures as low as 30 °C. This is because an enzyme has been added to the washing powder. Enzymes are catalysts that break down dirt and grease very quickly.

FIGURE 1: Washing powder can wash clothes at low temperatures – all because of enzymes!

Changing rates

Reaction rates:

> are affected by temperature, concentration and surface area

> **catalysts** can also have an effect on reaction rates

> catalysts are substances that increase the rate of reaction without being used up in the reaction.

Catalytic converters

One of the most common uses of catalysts is the catalytic converter in the exhaust system of all modern cars:

> The combustion that takes place in a car's engine always produces carbon monoxide and some unburnt fuel. Both are dangerous pollutants that should not be pumped into the environment.

> The catalytic converter contains a thin layer of metal, such as platinum, which aids the reaction between these pollutants and oxygen to convert them into carbon dioxide and water:

$$\text{carbon monoxide} + \text{unburnt fuel from exhaust gases} + \text{oxygen} \rightarrow \text{carbon dioxide} + \text{water}$$

FIGURE 2: A mechanic holding a catalytic converter before fitting to a car.

QUESTIONS

1 Define the term catalyst.

2 Design a leaflet explaining why catalytic converters are necessary in cars.

Catalytic converters

The catalytic converter is part of the exhaust system:

> Hot exhaust gases heat it.

> The catalytic converter works best at high temperatures, explains why the catalytic converter is installed as close to the engine as possible.

Figure 3 shows the internal construction of the catalytic converter. The extremely intricate design provides a large surface area. This large surface area makes the converter more efficient by providing a greater area for the chemical reaction to occur.

The surface of the packing inside a catalytic converter is covered with platinum or palladium. The reactants are the exhaust gases from the engine. Through the action of the catalyst, these harmful gases are converted to carbon dioxide and water. Anything that damages the surface of the catalytic converter reduces the efficiency of the catalytic reaction. This is why it is important that engines are tuned correctly so that oil and other solid pollutants do not cover the surfaces inside the catalytic converter.

QUESTIONS

3 Suggest why sports car manufacturers warn against driving their cars on dry grass.

4 Describe how the extensive surface area inside a catalytic converter makes it more efficient.

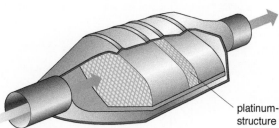

catalytic converter catalyses the reactants and produces carbon dioxide and water

hot exhaust gases from the engine contain carbon monoxide and some unburnt fuel

platinum-coated honeycomb structure has a large surface area

FIGURE 3: A car's catalytic converter.

Catalytic pathways

For chemical reactions to occur, several things must happen. The first of these events is the breaking of the bonds in the reactant particles. This requires energy. Chemists believe that a catalyst works by lowering the energy required to get the reaction started.

If you recall energy profile diagrams, the energy is added to the reactant particles to break the bonds that hold the reactants together. Catalysts allow for an alternative pathway from reactants to products. This new pathway requires less energy to break the bonds of the reactants, which means that a greater properties of collisions are effective and the reaction rate is faster.

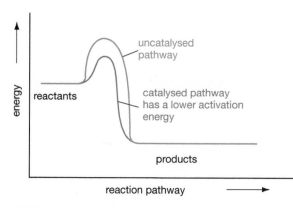

FIGURE 4: Energy profile diagram showing the effect of a catalyst.

QUESTIONS

5 Explain why catalysts cause an increase in the rate of reaction.

6 Explain why the reaction pathway levels off to a straight, steady line.

7 Using the internet, research the uses of catalysts in industry and prepare a short presentation to present your findings.

🔍 Metal catalysts   Activation energy

Preparing for assessment: Planning an investigation

To achieve a good grade in science, you not only have to know and understand scientific ideas, but you also need to be able to apply them to other situations and investigations. This task will support you in developing these skills.

✹ Investigating the effect of concentration on reaction rate

The rate of a reaction can be measured by determining the rate at which reactants are used up or the rate at which products are made.

When sodium thiosulfate solution is reacted with hydrochloric acid, sulfur is produced as a precipitate.

✹ Useful information

The sulfur produced by this reaction is insoluble and settles to the bottom of the beaker.

The dependent variable for this experiment will be the time it takes to make enough sulfur to obscure the 'X' under the beaker.

The concentration of the sodium thiosulfate can be reduced by mixing it with distilled water. For instance, if you mix 40 cm³ of sodium thiosulfate with 10 cm³ of distilled water the sodium thiosulfate will be only 80% as strong as the original solution of sodium thiosulfate.

Planning

1. Suggest a hypothesis that you could test.

2. Decide how many different concentrations of sodium thiosulfate you should use in this experiment.

3. Make a list of all of the equipment you will need to carry out this experiment.

4. Make a list of possible errors that could occur during the experiment and explain how you will prevent them.

5. Identify any hazards that you might encounter during this experiment. How you will reduce the risks associated with them?

6. Write out a plan for this experiment.

> This is the independent variable. Consider the range of concentrations (high, medium, low) that would be sensible to test and also the number of values you need to test in order to get sufficient data.

> Remember to explain your choice of equipment. Equipment needs to be suitable for the tests to be carried out. For example, taking time measurements to a tenth of a second will require an accurate stopwatch.

> Think about what errors can occur at each step of the experiment. How will those errors affect the results of the reaction? Remember to consider control variables.

> Hazards are anything that can cause harm. These can not always be avoided, so the important thing becomes reducing the risk of the hazard actually causing harm.

> Your plan should clearly describe how you will use your results to determine whether the hypothesis is correct or not. The plan should be clear and logical to gain Quality of Written Communication marks. Remember that others should be able to duplicate your experiment and see if they get the same results.

Processing the evidence

A student carried out this experiment and found that when 100% sodium thiosulfate was used the 'X' was obscured in 34.3 seconds. When the strength of the sodium thiosulfate was reduced to 80% it took 43.7 seconds to make enough sulfur to block out the 'X'. Sodium thiosulfate that was 60% of the original strength took 64.3 seconds to produce enough sulfur to block out the 'X' and 40% took 92 seconds.

1. Construct a results table to show this data.

2. Draw a graph of the results.

3. Describe the effect of reducing the concentration of the sodium thiosulfate on the rate of reaction.

4. Do the results of this experiment support your hypothesis?

> When constructing a data table include the units for each of the variables that you record in the headings of the table and not in the individual cells. Use headings that are clear and descriptive.
>
> The independent variable should always be the first column in the table.

> When constructing a graph, the independent variable is usually placed on the x-axis.

Connections

How science works

> Collecting and analysing data.

> Planning to solve a scientific problem.

> Collecting data from secondary sources.

> Working accurately and safely when collecting first-hand data.

> Presenting information using appropriate language, conventions, symbols and tools.

Maths in science

> Understand number size and scale and the quantitative relationship between units.

> Understand and use common measures.

> Translate information between graphical numeric forms.

> Extract and interpret information from tables.

Mass and formula

You will find out:

> how to calculate relative formula masses

> how to calculate percentage composition of compounds

> about calculating empirical formulae for simple compounds

Heavier or lighter?

Our galaxy, the Milky Way, is very large. It measures about 10 000 light-years across. The mass has been calculated as 10^{42} kg, that is about 2000 billion times the mass of the Sun.

FIGURE 1: The Milky Way is estimated to have 50 billion planets.

What is the mass?

It is often necessary to carry out chemical reactions on paper before carrying them out in the laboratory. To do that chemists must quantify elements and compounds.

Relative atomic masses

Atoms are extremely light. But we don't need to worry about the tiny masses of atoms in order to do calculations in chemistry.

What we do is we use *relative* atomic masses (A_r) where the mass of an element's atoms is compared to that of a hydrogen atom. Figure 2 shows that a carbon atom is as massive as 12 atoms of hydrogen:

> carbon has a relative atomic mass of 12

> similarly, 16 oxygen atoms weigh the same as a hydrogen atom

> so oxygen has an A_r of 16.

Some frequently used relative atomic masses are given in Table 1.

The periodic table includes the relative atomic masses for all of the elements. These can be used to calculate the **relative formula mass** (M_r) for compounds.

TABLE 1: Relative atomic masses of selected elements.

Element	A_r
Hydrogen	1
Carbon	12
Nitrogen	14
Oxygen	16
Sodium	21
Magnesium	24
Sulfur	32
Calcium	40

Relative formula masses

Compounds contain more than one element chemically bonded together.

> The relative formula mass of a compound is found by adding up the atomic masses of each of the atoms composing one molecule (or formula) of the compound.

> Remember that methane has the formula CH_4. This means it contains one carbon atom and four hydrogen atoms.

> Add up the individual masses of these (C = 12, H = 1).

So, the M_r for CH_4 = 12 + (4 × 1) = 16: the relative formula mass of methane is 16.

Similarly, for water (H_2O):

$$M_r = (2 \times A_r(H)) + (1 \times A_r(O)) = (2 \times 1) + (1 \times 16) = 18$$

and for nitric acid (HNO_3):

$$M_r = (1 \times A_r(H)) + (1 \times A_r(N)) + (3 \times A_r(O)) = (1 \times 1) + (1 \times 14) + (3 \times 16) = 63$$

FIGURE 2: A carbon atom is 12 times heavier than a hydrogen atom.

QUESTIONS

1 Define the term relative formula mass.

2 Calculate the relative formula masses of calcium carbonate ($CaCO_3$), sulfuric acid (H_2SO_4) and carbon dioxide (CO_2). Use Table 1 to help you.

Calculating the percentage composition of a compound

Sometimes chemists want to know how much of a compound's mass is made up of a specific element. The **percentage composition** is the percentage of a compound's mass that is accounted for by each of its constituents. For example, what percentage of the mass of water (H_2O) is made up of oxygen?

The mass of oxygen in water is 16. The total mass of water is 18. Therefore the percentage of oxygen in water is:

$$\frac{16}{18} \times 100 = 88.89\% \text{ oxygen}$$

QUESTIONS

3 Calculate the percentage of sulfur in sulfuric acid.

4 Calculate the percentage of oxygen in calcium carbonate.

Calculating empirical formulae

The **empirical formula** of a compound is the simplest formula that shows the numerical relationship of the elements present in the compound. Determining the empirical formula is usually the first step in identifying a new compound.

We can work out the formula of a compound such as magnesium oxide by finding its reacting masses in a simple experiment. For example, burning 10.00 g of magnesium to produce an oxide with a mass of 16.40 g allows the empirical formula to be calculated as follows:

> *Step 1*: find the mass of each element in a compound:

  Mg: 10.00 g   O: 16.40 g – 10.00 g = 6.40 g

> *Step 2*: Divide the mass of each element by its atomic number:

  Mg: $\dfrac{10.00 \text{ g}}{24} = 0.41$ O: $\dfrac{6.40 \text{ g}}{16} = 0.40$

> *Step 3*: divide your answers by the lowest answer. This gives you a ratio:

  Mg: $\dfrac{0.41}{0.40} = 1.02$ O: $\dfrac{0.40}{0.40} = 1.00$

> *Step 4*: relative number of atoms (rounded):

  Mg: 1   O: 1

In the case of magnesium oxide, the ratios indicate that the elements are in equal ratios in the compound. This means that for each magnesium atom there is an oxygen atom, producing an empirical formula for magnesium oxide of MgO, which also turns out to be the true formula.

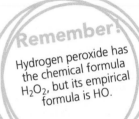

Remember!

Hydrogen peroxide has the chemical formula H_2O_2, but its empirical formula is HO.

QUESTIONS

5 Find the empirical formula for calcium hydroxide with 1.6 g of calcium, 1.28 g of oxygen and 0.08 g of hydrogen.

6 Calculate the empirical formula of a substance that contains 0.709 g of iron and 0.901 g of chlorine.

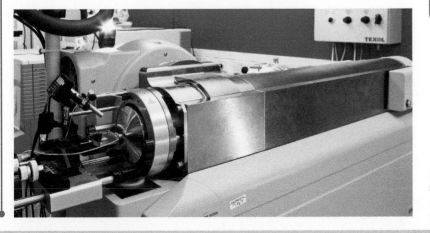

FIGURE 3: A high-resolution mass spectrometer can be used to measure relative atomic masses to several decimal places.

Calculating yields

You will find out:
> about the yield of chemical reactions
> why actual yield from a chemical reaction is usually less than predicted
> how to calculate theoretical yield and percentage yield

Where does it all go?

Strawberries, sugar and water heated together in the correct proportions, when cooled, will make jam. But the volume in jars does not match the volume of the raw ingredients. How much product will come out of a chemical reaction? Chemists can predict the yield of a reaction and then compare their actual results to the prediction.

FIGURE 1: How close is the actual yield to the predicted yield?

 Missing product

When chemists carry out chemical reactions in the lab they mix the reactants and then obtain the products. The mass of product obtained after the reaction is called the **yield**. In the lab, chemists often find that the actual yield is less than they predicted.

There are a number of reasons why the actual yield is almost always less than the predicted yield:

> *Incomplete reactions*: some of the reactants did not react. This can happen when not all of the reactants reach the proper temperature.

> *Losses during preparation*: some of the reactants do not make it into the reacting vessel. This can be due to spillage or evaporation.

> *Unwanted reactions*: other reactions occur alongside the primary reaction. Reactants can react in different ways producing different products.

All of these factors contribute to actual yields always being less than the predicted yield. **The predicted yield is also known as the theoretical yield.**

To compare the actual yield with the theoretical yield chemists calculate the **percentage yield**. This is the ratio of actual yield to the theoretical yield.

Remember!
The actual yield is always less than the theoretical yield.

QUESTIONS

1 State what is meant by the term yield.

2 Why is the actual yield usually less than the theoretical yield?

FIGURE 2: The incomplete combustion of methane produces carbon monoxide, which is a colourless, poisonous gas. Detectors are important safety devices in every home.

Theoretical and percentage yields

Theoretical yield

The theoretical yield is the predicted yield based on a chemical equation. To calculate the theoretical yield of calcium chloride ($CaCl_2$) formed when 2.0 g of calcium oxide (CaO) is reacted with an excess of hydrochloric acid (HCl) we begin with a balanced equation:

$$CaO \text{ (s)} + 2HCl \text{ (aq)} \rightarrow CaCl_2 \text{ (aq)} + H_2O \text{ (l)}$$

These are the steps of the calculation.

> *Step 1*: calculate the M_r of CaO: 40 + 16.00 = 56.

> *Step 2*: calculate the M_r of $CaCl_2$: 40 + (2 × 35) = 110.

> *Step 3*: this means that 56 g of CaO would yield 110 g of $CaCl_2$.

> *Step 4*: 2 g of CaO would theoretically yield x g of $CaCl_2$, then:

$$\frac{2}{56} = \frac{x}{110}$$

$$x = \frac{220}{56}$$

$$= 3.93 \text{ g of } CaCl_2$$

Percentage yield

From these calculations, the theoretical yield is 3.93 g of calcium chloride ($CaCl_2$). However, if we go to the lab and carry out this reaction and only produce 3.01 g of calcium chloride ($CaCl_2$), what is the percentage yield?

$$\text{percentage yield} = \frac{\text{actual yield}}{\text{theoretical yield}} \times 100 = \frac{3.01 \text{ g}}{3.93 \text{ g}} \times 100\% = 77\%$$

 QUESTIONS

3 Calculate the theoretical yield of sodium chloride (NaCl) when 3.0 g of sodium hydroxide (NaOH) is reacted with a excess of hydrochloric acid (HCl).

4 What is the percentage yield for this reaction if 3.51 g of sodium chloride is produced?

FIGURE 3: When magnesium burns, some magnesium oxide escapes as smoke.

Calculating masses of reactants and products (Higher tier only)

Chemists call the branch of chemistry that deals with the quantitative relationships between reactants and products **stoichiometry**.

If the mass of any of the reactants or products is known, any of the other values can be calculated from a balanced equation, for example:

$$2C_8H_{18} \text{ (l)} + 25O_2 \text{ (g)} \rightarrow 16CO_2 \text{ (g)} + 18H_2O \text{ (g)}$$

So, how much oxygen would be required to completely combust 100.0 g of octane (petrol)? The calculation for the theoretical yield of this reaction is as follows:

> *Step 1*: calculate the M_r of C_8H_{18}:
(8 × 12) + (18 × 1) = 114

> *Step 2*: calculate the M_r of O_2: (2 × 16) = 32

> *Step 3*: from the balanced equation we know that two molecules of octane react with 25 molecules of oxygen.

Therefore: 25 × 32 g of oxygen would completely combust 2 × 114 g of octane.

This equates to 800 g of oxygen and 228 g of octane.

> *Step 4*: therefore 100 g of octane would require $\frac{228x}{800}$ g of oxygen to completely combust.

To find the mass of oxygen, rearrange the calculation:

$$x = \frac{800 \times 100}{228}$$

$$= 350 \text{ g}$$

From these calculations, 350.0 g of oxygen is required to completely combust 100.0 g of octane.

Using stoichiometry, chemists can work out the quantities of reactants and products given one of the quantities in a chemical equation.

 QUESTIONS

5 How much LiOH would be required to remove 900.0 g of CO_2 given this reaction:
$2LiOH \text{ (s)} + CO_2 \text{ (g)} \rightarrow Li_2CO_3 \text{ (s)} + H_2O \text{ (g)}$?

Commercial chemistry

You will find out:
> about unwanted products of chemical reactions
> about finding the most economically favourable reactions
> about the role of industrial chemists

Increasing yields

Chemists are interested in yields. Their main interest is in maximising them, but there are other considerations too, such as avoiding damage to the environment and avoiding wasting expensive resources.

FIGURE 1: Slag is a by-product of smelting ores. When ground down, it is often used in the manufacture of cement. An example of minimising waste.

Unwanted products

All chemical reactions produce products. However, there are some chemical reactions that produce heat and unwanted products. These unwanted products are considered **waste**.

These waste products are not commercially useful. That is, they cannot be sold or used as raw materials to make useful products. They present a number of problems:

> *Economic*: waste products must be disposed of efficiently and cheaply. Any money spent on disposal has to be deducted from the profit created by the commercial product.

> *Environmental*: the environment should be damaged as little as possible. This may mean converting the waste products in another reaction to make them less harmful. Or, as in the case of sulfur dioxide, produced by burning hydrocarbons to produce electricity, converting them to useful compounds that can be sold.

> *Social*: disposal must be socially responsible. Improperly disposed of chemical waste can cause health-related problems. This can place an unnecessary strain on medical services. For example waste chemicals leaking into the water supply or leeching into soil can affect not only people's health, but cause disruption to farm animals and food crops.

FIGURE 2: Improperly treated waste products can cause environmental damage and health problems. A technician monitors the quality of groundwater.

Did you know?

More than 5 million tonnes of chemical waste was produced in the UK in 2009.

Remember!
Any products of chemical reactions that cannot be sold are considered waste.

QUESTIONS

1 State the meaning of waste with respect to chemistry.

2 Describe the problems associated with chemical waste.

3 Name two waste products and the processes that create them.

Q Chemical engineering   Rational drug design

Balancing act

Industrial chemists are involved in a very delicate balancing act. They need to balance all of the considerations. Sometimes there are conflicts. It is possible that one reactant gives a higher yield than another, but also produces a waste product that maybe difficult to dispose of. The conditions that produce the highest yield may be dangerous and require special equipment that drives up the cost. It may be more economical to reduce the yield and reduce the cost of the equipment required.

These are only a few of the considerations that chemists must balance to produce an economically viable product.

It is clear that industrial chemists do more than mix chemicals together to get the product they want. Only when all of these considerations have been dealt with can the chemist begin to relax.

 QUESTIONS

4 Discuss some of the conflicts that chemists must deal with in commercial chemistry.

Finding the best value reactions (Higher tier only)

The industrial chemist's job is to make the best value products. With a product in mind, the chemist will work long and hard to find the most economically suitable reaction. The main goals will be:

> a high percentage yield

> a reaction where as many of the products are commercially useful as possible

> a reaction that happens at a suitable speed.

High yield

To maximise yield, chemists will examine every step of the process. This will begin with the way reactants are handled before the reaction. Then attention will turn to reaction conditions. Chemists will want to ensure that as much of the reactants as possible reacts. This can include such things as the type of reaction vessel, mixing reactants and proper reacting conditions, including temperature.

Commercial products

Almost from the beginning, chemists will look at the other products that are produced during the reaction. They will look for reactants that produce multiple

commercial products or products that can easily be converted to useful products. The idea is to minimise waste at every step. For example, in a blast furnace for extracting iron, a major by-product is calcium silicate. Fortunately this can be made into breeze blocks which are used in the construction of houses.

Suitable speed

The speed of a reaction can be crucial. If the reaction goes too slowly, secondary unwanted reactions may occur, decreasing the percentage yield and producing more unwanted products. A good example is when producing food products: items can spoil or go stale if produced too slowly. The opposite extreme is an explosive reaction that may kill or injure workers and damage equipment.

Remember!
Industrial chemists must balance safety, economics and chemistry.

FIGURE 3: Industrial-sized reaction vessels.

 QUESTIONS

5 Explain why it is necessary to have a suitable reaction speed.

6 Imagine you are an industrial chemist. Prepare a marketing leaflet to show how well your company understands the main goals of commercial chemistry.

7 Using your own research, prepare a 200-word report on why maximising yields is important in industrial chemistry.

C2 checklist (Topics 4–6)

To achieve your forecast grade in the exam you'll need to revise

Use this checklist to see what you can do now. Refer back to pages 144–69 if you're not sure.

Look across the rows to see how you could progress – **_bold italic_** means Higher tier only.

Remember you'll need to be able to use these ideas in various ways, such as:
> interpreting pictures, diagrams and graphs
> applying ideas to new situations
> explaining ethical implications
> suggesting some benefits and risks to society
> drawing conclusions from evidence you've been given.

Look at pages 264–86 for more information about exams and how you'll be assessed.

This checklist accompanies the exam-style questions and the worked examples. The content suggestions for specific grades are suggestions only and may not be replicated in your real examination. Remember, the checklists do not represent the complete content for any topic. Refer to the Specification for complete content details on any topic and any further information.

To aim for a grade E	To aim for a grade C	To aim for a grade A
classify substances as ionic, simple and giant molecular covalent and metallic	describe the different properties of ionic, simple and giant molecular covalent and metallic substances	
classify elements as alkali metals, halogens, noble gases and transition elements based on their position in the periodic table	describe the structure and explain the properties of metals in terms of ions and electrons	
recall the position of the alkali metals in the periodic table and describe their properties	describe the reactions of lithium, sodium and potassium with water	describe **_and explain_** the pattern of reactivity of lithium, sodium and potassium with water and use it to predict the reactivity of other alkali metals
recall the position of the halogens in the periodic table, describe their properties and that they exist as diatomic molecules	describe the reactions of halogens with metals to form metal halides	describe the relative reactivity of halogens by their displacement reactions with halide ions in aqueous solutions
recall the position of the noble gases in the periodic table and describe them as being inert	describe the discovery of noble gases in terms of their inertness	use a known pattern in physical property of the noble gases to predict the value for another member of the group

To aim for a grade E

recall that when chemical bonds are made, heat energy is given out and so the reaction is exothermic

recall that when chemical bonds are broken, heat energy is taken in and so the reaction is endothermic

To aim for a grade C

describe the energy changes that occur during chemical reactions

To aim for a grade A

draw and analyse simple energy diagrams for the changes that occur during chemical reactions

---

describe how temperature, concentration and surface area affect the rates of chemical reactions

explain how reactions occur when particles collide

describe how rates of reaction are increased by increasing the frequency and/or energy of collisions

describe why not all collisions lead to a reaction

---

describe the effect of catalysts on chemical reactions

describe how catalytic converters in cars have a large surface area and work best at high temperatures

explain how catalysts reduce the energy required for a reaction

---

carry out calculations for relative formula masses for simple compounds

calculate the percentage composition of a compound

calculate the empirical formula of a compound

---

recall that the actual yield of a reaction is usually less than the theoretical yield and likely reasons for the difference

calculate the percentage yield of a reaction from the actual yield and the theoretical yield

use balanced equations to calculate masses of reactants and products

---

describe the problems associated with unwanted by-products of chemical reactions

describe why there are unwanted by-products of chemical reactions

explain how industrial chemist try to maximise production and eliminate unwanted by-products

AO1 **1** **a** Lithium is in the first column of the periodic table. Lithium is a

    A ☐ noble gas

    B ☐ halogen

    C ☐ alkali metal

    D ☐ transition metal. [1]

AO1 **b** Lithium reacts by fizzing on the surface of water. What compound is formed during this reaction? [1]

AO1 **c** Lithium is a group 1 metal. State two properties of group 1 metals. [2]

AO3 **d** When lithium metal is placed in water it floats on the surface and fizzes. When sodium is placed in water it whizzes around on the surface and melts. Predict the reaction of potassium. [1]

AO2 **e** Describe the reaction between potassium and water in terms of reactants and products? [3]

    [Total: 8]

2 Robert measured the temperature of 50 cm³ of water for 5 minutes and then added 1 gram of ammonium chloride to the water and recorded the temperature every minute for the next 5 minutes. The following graph shows his results.

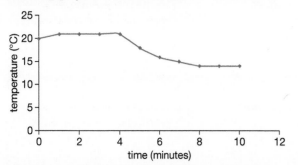

AO3 **a** What was the change in water temperature between 5 minutes and 10 minutes? [1]

AO2 **b** Draw a line on a copy of Robert's graph to show the temperature change that would occur if 2 grams of ammonium chloride were added to the water. [2]

AO3 **c** Using information from the graph state what type of reaction occurred between the water and ammonium chloride. [1]

AO2 **d** Using information from the graph, describe the reaction between ammonium chloride and water in terms of energy and bonds. [2]

    [Total: 6]

3 Potassium nitrate is widely used as a fertiliser. The formula for potassium nitrate is KNO_3.

AO2 **a** Calculate the relative formula mass of potassium nitrate. [2]

AO2 **b** What is the percentage composition of potassium in potassium nitrate? [2]

AO2 **c** Potassium nitrate can be prepared by the following reaction.

    NH_4NO_3 (aq) + KCl (aq) → NH_4Cl (aq) + KNO_3 (aq)

    Emma carried out this reaction and produced 2.3 grams of potassium nitrate. She calculated her theoretical yield as 2.8 grams of ammonium chloride. What is the percentage yield for Emma's reaction? [2]

AO2 **d** Suggest two reasons why Emma's yield was less than she predicted. [2]

    [Total: 8]

4 Matt investigated the effect of surface area on the rate of reaction. He placed marble chips in a beaker setting on a balance. He then added hydrochloric acid to the beaker and recorded the mass every minute. Matt produced this graph of his data.

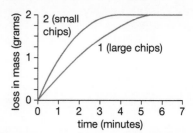

AO3 **a** Which reaction happened faster? [1]

AO2 **b** Explain why the loss in mass is constant for both small chips and large chips after 6 minutes. [2]

AO2 **c** Name one factor that Matt should have kept constant in his experiments. [1]

AO2 **d** In a third trial he used marble powder. Predict the rate of reaction for marble powder compared to the small chips and large chips. [2]

AO1 **e** Describe the factors that affect reaction rate. [6]

    [Total: 12]

Worked example

a Metals are malleable and good conductors.

AO1 i Describe the structure of metals. [2]

Atoms floating in electrons. ✘ ✔

AO1 ii How does the structure of metals allow them to conduct electricity? [1]

The free-floating electrons can easily move with the flow of electrical current. ✔

AO1 iii Most metals are transition metals. State two properties of transition metals. [2]

Hard and high melting points. ✔ ✘

AO1 b i The alkali metals are a particular group of metals. In which group in the periodic table are alkali metals found? [1]

A ☐ Group 0

B ☒ Group 1 ✔

C ☒ Group 2

D ☐ Group 7

AO2 ii Sodium is an alkali metal. How many electrons does sodium have in its outer shell? [1]

1 electron. ✔

AO2 iii Sodium reacts violently with water. The reaction produces hydrogen gas. Copy and complete the balanced equation for the reaction. [2]

$$2Na + \_\_\, H_2O \longrightarrow \_\_\, NaOH \_\_\_\_ + H_2$$

✔ ✘

AO2 iv Suggest whether the reaction between sodium and water is exothermic or endothermic. [1]

It is exothermic. ✔

The candidate scored 7 out of a possible 10. The candidate could have improved their grade by carefully reading the question and checking their answer in parts **aiii** and **biii** to ensure that they had fully answered the question.

How to raise your grade

Take note of the comments from examiners – these will help you to improve your grade.

This answer earns 1 mark. The atoms are positively charged ions surrounded by delocalised electrons. It is important to use the correct scientific terminology.

The answer clearly describes what allows metals to conduct electricity.

Transition metals all have relatively high melting points. However, they are not all hard. The correct answer is they form coloured compounds. It is important to be familiar with the properties of the major groups of elements in the periodic table.

Correct. Notice that the student originally marked answer C, but realised their mistake and clearly crossed it out. If they had not crossed out the incorrect answer, they would have gained no marks for their answer. An examiner can't give credit where the intention is not clear.

The candidate make the link between group number and electron configuration in the periodic table.

The correct answer is 2Na + 2H$_2$O → 2NaOH + H$_2$. The candidate gains 1 mark for writing the correct formulae for the reactants and products. However, they have forgotten to balance the equation.

A correct answer. Energy is given out in the reaction.

AO1 **1a** Neon is a noble gas. How many electrons does neon have in its outer shell?

A ☐ 0   C ☐ 8

B ☐ 1   D ☐ 10   [1]

AO1 **b** Noble gases are not reactive. Explain why the noble gases do not react. [2]

AO2 **c** Explain how the properties of helium make it suitable for use in balloons. [2]

AO1 **d** What did Lord Rayleigh notice about nitrogen purified from air when compared to nitrogen produced by chemical reactions that lead to the discovery of the first noble gas? [2]

AO3 **e** Use the information in the table to predict the boiling point of the missing element.

Element	Boiling point (°C)
helium	−269
neon	−246
argon	
krypton	−153

[1]
[Total: 8]

2 Charlie was investigating the temperature changes associated with reactions. He placed 50 cm³ of 1.0 M sodium hydroxide (NaOH) in a beaker and measured the temperature for 5 minutes. After 5 minutes Charlie added 50 cm³ of 1.0 M hydrochloric acid (HCl) to the beaker and recorded temperature for next 5 minutes. He collected the following data.

Time (minutes)	Temperature (°C)
1	21.0
2	21.0
3	21.0
4	21.0
5	21.0
6	26.0
7	26.5
8	26.0
9	25.5
10	25.0

AO2 **a** Write the balanced equation for this chemical reaction. [2]

AO3 **b** What type of reaction is this? [1]

AO2 **c** Draw a simple diagram to represent the energy changes that occurred during this reaction. [2]

AO2 **d** Explain how the reaction occurs between sodium hydroxide and hydrochloric acid, in terms of bonds between particles. [7]
[Total: 12]

3 A compound contains 4.151 grams of aluminium and 3.692 grams of oxygen.

AO2 **a** Calculate the empirical formula of aluminium oxide. [3]

AO2 **b** Iron (III) oxide (Fe_2O_3) is used in the thermite reaction. What is the percentage composition of Fe_2O_3? [2]

c The relative atomic mass of iron is 55.85. The relative formula mass of iron (III) oxide is 159.7.

AO2 **i** Write a balanced equation for the thermite reaction between iron oxide and aluminium. [1]

AO2 **ii** What mass of iron would be produced by 80 grams of iron (III) oxide? [2]

AO1 **d** The thermite reaction is used to weld railway
AO2 lines. The reaction produces a by-product called slag. Describe the factors that chemists would consider when deciding how economically favourable the thermite reaction is. [4]
[Total: 12]

4 The reactivity of halogens can be seen by reactions within the group. The table indicates when a reaction will occur.

	Potassium chloride solution	Potassium bromide solution	Potassium iodide solution
Chlorine water	No reaction	Reaction	Reaction
Bromine water	No reaction	No reaction	Reaction
Iodine water	No reaction	No reaction	No reaction

AO1 **a** What is the name given to this type of reaction? [1]

AO3 **b** Use this information to describe reactivity of chlorine. [2]

AO1 **c** Explain the trend in reactivity of the halogens in terms of electron configuration? [4]
[Total: 7]

Worked example

Lithium hydroxide (LiOH) is used to remove carbon dioxide from the air on the International Space Station.

AO2 **a** Using the periodic table calculate the relative formula mass of lithium hydroxide. [2]

6.941 amu + 16.00 amu + 1.008 amu = 23.95 amu. ✔ ✔

AO2 **b** The relative formula mass of CO_2 is 44.01 amu. What percentage of the mass of CO_2 is made up of oxygen? [2]

16.00/44.01 × 100 = 36.4%. ✘

AO2 **c** The balanced equation for the reaction between lithium hydroxide and carbon dioxide is

$$2LiOH + CO_2 \rightarrow Li_2CO_3 + 3H_2O$$

Calculate the amount of carbon dioxide that could be absorbed by 500 grams of lithium hydroxide. [3]

The M_r for 2LiOH is 2(7 + 16 + 1) = 2(24) = 48

The M_r for CO_2 is 12 + 2(16) = 12 + 32 = 48

Therefore, 48 grams of carbon dioxide would be absorbed by

48 grams of lithium hydroxide. ✔ ✘ ✔

AO2 **d** Explain why the amount of carbon dioxide absorbed by lithium hydroxide is never as much as calculated. [4]

Competing reactions and incomplete reactions. ✔ ✔ ✘ ✘

This candidate scored 6 marks out of a possible 11. The candidate could have improved their grade by practising these calculations and ensuring that they fully explained their answer in part **d**.

How to raise your grade

Take note of the comments from examiners – these will help you to improve your grade.

Full marks awarded. The candidate has calculated the answer correctly and shown all their workings.

The candidate has identified the correct calculation to find the percentage composition but has not taken into account that there are 2 oxygen atoms in the O_2 molecule. The candidate should have multiplied 16.00 by 2. To give a correct answer of 72.7%.

The candidate made a good start by calculating the relative mass of both compounds and equating them to the masses of the reactants. Unfortunately, the next step should have been to calculate the amount of CO_2 absorbed by 500 g of LiOH, and this missing step means an incorrect answer.

The candidate received 2 marks for correctly identifying reasons why actual yield is always less than theoretical yield. However, they have not provided any explanation for either of the reasons. Always answer questions completely.

P2 Physics for your future (Topics 1–3)

What you should know

Static and current electricity

Matter is made up of atoms.

Current is the rate of flow charge (P1 – Topic 5).

A generator supplies an alternating current (P1 – Topic 5).

The directions of conventional current and electron flow are opposite (P1 – Topic 5)

 Explain what is meant by electric current.

Controlling and using electric currents

Resistance has an effect on the size of current in a circuit.

Electrical current can be controlled in electrical circuits.

Electrical symbols can be used to represent components and circuits (P1 – Topic 5).

Potential difference (voltage) is energy transferred per unit charge (P1 – Topic 5).

Power is defined as the rate of energy transfer (P1 – Topic 5).

Electrical power = current × potential difference (P1 – Topic 5).

 What is the difference between electrical power and energy?

Motion and forces

Forces arise from interactions between objects.

The motion of an object is affected by forces and if they don't balance there is an overall resulting force.

Friction, air resistance, upthrust and weight are all forces.

Speed = distance/time.

 State the principle of conservation of energy.

You will find out about

> the nuclear structure of atoms

> how insulators get charged by transfer of electrons

> the uses and dangers of electrostatic charges

> how current is related to the flow of charges

> the equation $Q = I \times t$

> direct and alternating currents

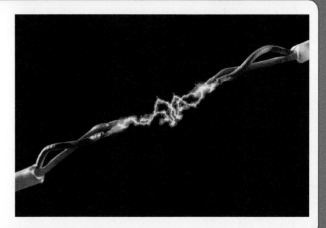

> simple series and parallel circuits

> how potential difference is defined in terms of energy transfer

> the equation $V = I \times R$

> current–potential difference graphs for filament lamps, diodes and resistors

> how resistance in a light-dependent resistor and a thermistor change

> the heating effect of electric current

> the heating in resistors as the result of collisions between electrons and atoms

> the equations $P = V \times I$ and $E = I \times V \times t$

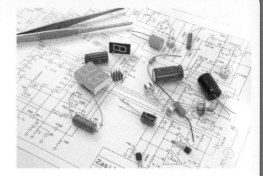

> scalar and vector quantities

> how to interpret distance–time graphs

> how to determine acceleration and distance travelled from velocity–time graphs

> the equation $a = \dfrac{v - u}{t}$

> the effect of forces on the motion of objects

> how to add forces to find the resulting force

> the equations $F = ma$ and $W = mg$

> air resistance and the motion of objects falling in air

Electrostatics

You will find out:
> about the structure of the atom
> how to charge insulators
> about forces between charged objects

Atoms are everywhere

All matter is made up of atoms. Atoms are tiny; about 0.000 000 2 mm in diameter. Modern scientists can use powerful microscopes to see individual atoms but their internal structure cannot be seen.

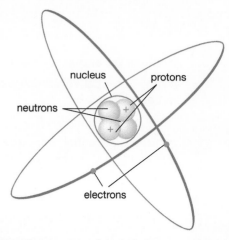

FIGURE 1: Gold atoms (yellow, red and brown) deposited on carbon atoms (green). What is the shape of the carbon atoms and how big are they?

The structure of atoms

Scientists believe in the nuclear model of the **atom**:

> The central core or **nucleus** of the atom has a positive charge.

> The nucleus has particles called **protons** and **neutrons**.

> The proton has a positive charge and the neutron has no charge.

> Negative **electrons** occupy the space around the nucleus.

> The diameter of the nucleus is about 100 000 times smaller than the diameter of the atom.

Table 1 summarises some important information on the particles of the atom.

An uncharged (neutral) atom has an equal number of electrons and protons. Removing electrons from the atom makes the atom have an overall positive charge and adding electrons to the atom makes it have a negative charge. A charged atom is called an **ion**.

Did you know?

Most of matter is empty space. For the Earth, all of its nuclei and electrons would fit inside a small school hall.

FIGURE 2: The structure of the helium atom. What is the net charge of this atom?

QUESTIONS

1 Name the particles inside the nucleus.

2 A particle is found inside the nucleus and has a positive charge. Name the particle

3 Explain why a nucleus has a positive charge.

TABLE 1: Atomic particles and their properties.

Particle	Where is it found?		Relative mass*	Relative charge*
	Inside the nucleus	Outside the nucleus		
Neutron	✓		1	0
Proton	✓		1	+1
Electron		✓	0	−1

*Mass and charge relative to that of the proton.

Static electricity

Charging insulators

Take a plastic ruler and rub it against your hair or jumper. The ruler becomes electrically charged. It will attract tiny pieces of paper or bend a thin stream of water from a tap. The charge on the ruler is on its *surface* and it does not move (**static**) as it does in current electricity. The charge is referred to as electro**static** charge.

You can charge an **insulator** by rubbing it against another insulator. Consider a polythene rod rubbed with a dry woollen duster. The **friction**, caused by the rubbing, strips off some of the outer electrons of the atoms in the duster and transfers them to the polythene rod. The duster is left with fewer electrons and becomes positively charged. The polythene has gained electrons and therefore becomes negatively charged.

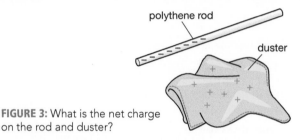

FIGURE 3: What is the net charge on the rod and duster?

It is not always easy to predict the charge on insulators. For example, rubbing a glass rod with wool makes the glass positive and the wool negative.

> All insulators can be charged by friction through the transfer of electrons. Metals cannot be charged by friction.

> The positive protons cannot move because they are stuck within the nuclei of the insulators.

> Each insulator acquires an equal but opposite charge.

Forces between charged objects

Charged objects exert a force on each other. There are two basic rules for the force between charged objects:

> Like charges repel.

> Unlike charges attract.

Figure 4 shows how you can demonstrate the repulsion and attraction between charged objects. The force is greater when the charged objects are closer.

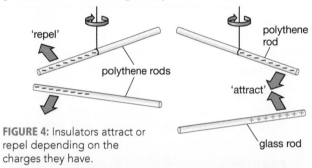

FIGURE 4: Insulators attract or repel depending on the charges they have.

QUESTIONS

4 Explain in terms of transfer of electrons how a woollen jumper and a balloon become charged.

5 Two charged rubber balloons repel each other. Deduce the possible charges on the balloons.

Gold-leaf electroscope

A gold-leaf electroscope is an instrument used to determine whether an insulator has a positive or a negative charge.

The electroscope has a metal cap, a metal rod and a gold leaf. The electroscope can be negatively charged by momentarily touching the metal cap to a negative terminal of a high-voltage supply. Note: for safety reasons, this must be done by your teacher.

Bringing a negatively charged rod close to the cap will repel the electrons on the cap towards the gold leaf. The gold leaf and the metal rod repel each other as they both have the same charge. Greater negative charge on the leaf and the bottom of the rod increases the divergence of the leaf.

negatively charged rod

metal cap

insulator

electrons repelled

metal rod

gold leaf

FIGURE 5: The gold-leaf electroscope.

QUESTIONS

6 Describe how you can use an electroscope to show that a woollen duster and a glass rod have opposite charges.

Uses of electrostatics

You will find out:
> about attraction by induction
> about uses of electrostatic charges

Killing all bugs

How can an electrostatic charge kill off the majority of harmful bugs on plants? Spraying insecticides from above would not attack bugs hiding under leaves. The solution is to use an electrostatically charged insecticide spread as this makes the insecticide coat the whole plant. This technique is quick, uses fewer chemicals and kills all hiding bugs.

FIGURE 1: The insecticide spray from this tractor is electrically charged.

 ## Electrostatic induction

Try this simple experiment. Rub a balloon against your clothes and then hold it against the wall. When you let go of the balloon it sticks to the wall. How can we explain this?

> The friction between your clothes and the balloon transfers electrons to the balloon.

> The surface of the balloon becomes negatively charged.

> The charged balloon repels some of the electrons away from the surface of the wall. This leaves the surface of the wall closer to the balloon with a positive charge.

> Opposite charges attract; hence the balloon is attracted to the wall.

The separated charges in the wall are called *induced charges*. **Electrostatic induction** is a redistribution of electrical charge in an object caused by another charged object.

Other examples of attraction by induction are:

> Small pieces of paper are attracted to a charged ruler or a comb.

> Dust sticks to the negatively charged screen of a television.

> A stream of water from a tap can be bent towards a charged insulator.

Remember!
Insulators become oppositely charged when rubbed together.

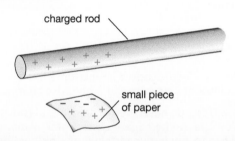
charged rod

small piece of paper

FIGURE 3: A charged rod can be used to pick up paper.

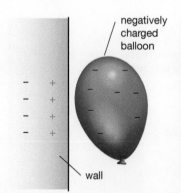
negatively charged balloon

wall

FIGURE 2: Why does the balloon stick to the wall?

QUESTIONS

1 State the overall charge on the wall in Figure 2.

2 Describe how the positively charged rod in Figure 3 attracts a small piece of paper.

3 Give two examples (other than those given on this page) of attraction by induction.

Uses of electrostatics

Electrostatic paint sprayers are used to give metal objects, such as car bodies and bicycle frames, an even coating of paint. The object to be sprayed is connected to a negative supply. The nozzle of the sprayer is charged positive; this makes the tiny droplets of paint emerging from the nozzle positively charged. The charged droplets of paint repel each other and form a dispersed cloud. The droplets are attracted to the object being sprayed. This technique uses less paint and coats even the underside of the object.

The same technique is used to spray plants with **insecticides**. The insecticide is given a positive charge and the plants acquire a negative charge by induction.

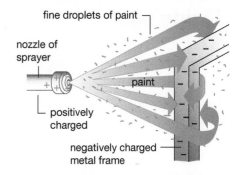

FIGURE 4: Electrostatic paint spraying.

QUESTIONS

4 Describe in terms of transfer of electrons how the paint droplets acquire a positive charge from the positively charged nozzle of the sprayer.

5 Explain why the paint droplets from a positively charged sprayer form a diffuse cloud.

6 Explain how electrostatics are used to apply insecticides.

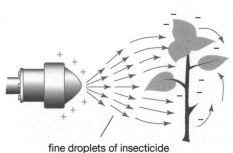

FIGURE 5: Spraying plants.

Electric force field

Why are charged droplets of paint attracted to objects of opposite charge?

Figure 6 shows a positively charged droplet close to a negatively charged metal sphere. The sphere creates an **electric force field** around it. Any charged object in this electric field will experience a force. This force field is represented by the purple lines known as electric field lines. The electric field lines are similar to magnetic field lines, except they are created by charges and not magnets. The closeness of the field lines indicates the strength of the field. The electric field is strongest at the surface of the sphere. The arrows in the field lines show the direction of the field. This is the direction along which a positive charge would tend to move.

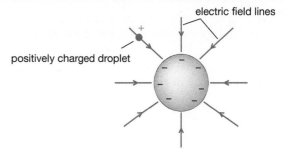

FIGURE 6: A charged sphere is surrounded by an electric force field.

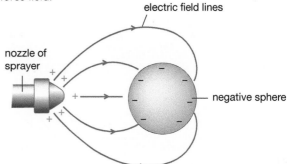

FIGURE 7: The electric field lines between the positive nozzle of a paint sprayer and a negatively charged sphere.

QUESTIONS

7 Figure 7 shows the electric field lines between the positive nozzle of a paint sprayer and a negatively charged sphere. Explain how the spray paint gives the sphere an even coating of paint.

Dangers of electrostatics

You will find out:
> about examples of electrostatic phenomena
> about earthing
> about the dangers of electrostatic charges

Lightning

You might have noticed a crackling noise when clothes rub together when you undress. The noise comes from tiny electrical sparks between the clothing caused by movement of charge. You can see these tiny sparks of lightning in the dark. These tiny flashes are safe, unlike lightning during a thunderstorm which can destroy buildings and start forest fires.

FIGURE 1: Lightning strikes can be dangerous.

Electrical shocks

Imagine an insulator with a large amount of negative charge and you bring your finger very close to this insulator. Electrons on the surface of the insulator will jump the tiny distance of air and travel through your finger to the Earth. These tiny sparks can be very unpleasant. The sparks give a sensation similar to being poked by a sharp pin! If the insulator is positively charged, the electrons will travel from the Earth to the insulator through your finger but the experience will still be unpleasant.

Here are some examples of electrical shocks from everyday objects:

> Walking on a synthetic (nylon) carpet will charge the carpet and you. You will get a shock when you are about to touch a metal tap or radiator.

> Your clothing gets electrically charged when rubbing against the synthetic material of the car seat. You will get a shock as you get out of the car.

> Some anaesthetics used in hospitals are explosive. This is why the floors of some operating theatres have tiles made of conducting material.

Remember!
Only negatively charged electrons can be transferred between objects.

Did you know?
A tiny spark can transfer 1000 billion electrons every second.

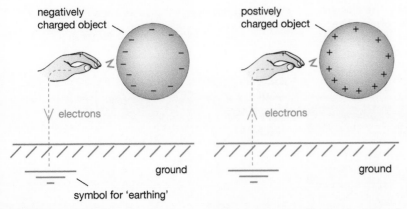

FIGURE 2: Like charges repel and unlike charges attract. Describe the direction of flow of the electrons.

QUESTIONS

1 A person walking on synthetic carpets becomes negatively charged. State what this means in terms of electrons.

2 Complete this sentence: When a charged object is discharged, electrons move from the _____ to the object or from the object to the _____.

Earthing

Electrical sparks create high temperatures and this makes them dangerous, especially when close to explosive materials. Most objects can be made safe by **earthing** them. This involves having a metal conductor secured between the object and the Earth. This helps to transfer electrons from the object to the Earth, where they are dispersed, or vice versa, and therefore reduce the dangers of sparking.

Here are some examples of earthing:

> *Fuelling aircraft and tankers*: the friction between the fuel and the rubber pipe makes each of them acquire opposite charges. The charges can build up and create a spark with devastating consequences. This is why aircraft and tankers are earthed with an earthing line when fuelling.

QUESTIONS

3 Explain why workers on an oil tanker wear shoes with metal soles rather than rubber soles.

4 Suggest why road-tankers often have a length of metal chain hanging down to the ground.

> *Tall buildings*: a lightning conductor is secured on the tops of very tall buildings to channel the charges during a thunderstorm safely to the Earth where they are dispersed.

FIGURE 3: How is fuelling this plane made safer?

Lightning

A lightning conductor is installed on top of tall buildings to protect them from the dangers of lightning strikes. This conductor is often a thick strip of copper secured to the outside of the building. The top of the conductor has pointed a spike and the bottom end is embedded in the ground.

Clouds rub against each other and become charged with electrons. When a negatively charged cloud passes overhead, it induces positive charges at the top of the lightning conductor. The spike repels positive ions in the air towards the cloud to neutralise its charge so there is no lightning. During a severe thunderstorm, this neutralisation process is too slow. Charges discharge between the cloud and the Earth to produce an electric current big enough to heat up

the air and produce light. Lightning strikes can cause fires, especially if they strike something that is potentially explosive.

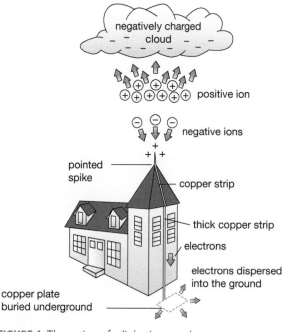

FIGURE 4: The action of a lightning conductor.

QUESTIONS

5 In the GCSE Science Physics Unit 1 you learnt about conventional electric current. In Figure 4, deduce the direction of conventional current:

a between the cloud and pointed spikes

b in the thick copper strip.

Charge and current

You will find out:
> about electric current
> how current and charge are related to each other
> about direct current

Lemon battery

Your mobile phone has a battery that supplies electric current to make it work. Batteries are quite expensive. You can make your own battery from a fresh lemon. Just insert copper and zinc electrodes into the lemon and away you go. The voltage across the electrodes is about 1 volt. The lemon battery is not practical for your mobile phone.

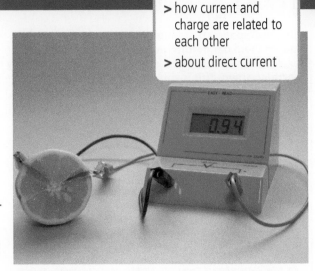

FIGURE 1: It is easy to make your own battery, but it might be a bit messy! Why would a lemon battery be inappropriate for your mobile phone?

 ## Simple circuits

Electric current

Figure 2 shows a cell connected to a filament lamp.

The cell helps to push the **electrons** round the circuit. The negative electrons are repelled by the negative (–) terminal of the cell and are attracted to the positive (+) terminal of the cell.

> **Electric current** is the rate of *flow* of charge.

> In metals, current is due to the flow of electrons.

> The unit for electric current is **amperes** or 'amps' for short.

The first scientists who worked with circuits thought that the charges moving in a circuit were positive and they drew arrows to show this. Physicists have kept this convention.

> **Conventional current** is the flow of positive charges.

Cells and batteries

The words *cell* and *battery* are often used interchangeably in everyday life, but not in physics. A cell is an individual chemical device with its own positive and negative terminals. A battery is a *collection* of cells, often joined together in a **series**.

Figure 3 shows two circuits with different numbers of cells. It is easier to represent a number of cells by the battery symbol shown.

Direct current

A cell or a battery connected to a lamp will provide a **direct current** (d.c.). This means that the direction of the conventional current in the component remains the same. Hence, the electrons travel in one direction only.

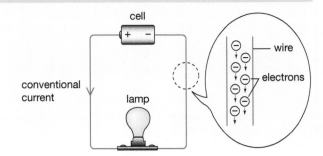

FIGURE 2: A simple circuit. Which way do the electrons travel?

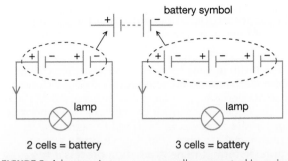

FIGURE 3: A battery is two or more cells connected in series.

QUESTIONS

1 State the missing words in the sentence below: Electrons move towards the _____ terminal of the cell because they have _____ charge.

2 In a lamp, the conventional current is from left to right. State the direction of the flow of electrons.

Q Cells and batteries   Conventional current   Direct current

Charge and current

Charge is measured in **coulombs** (C). An electron has a tiny negative charge of -1.6×10^{-19} C.

There is a link between the amount of charge passing through a point in a circuit and the current. The current is 1 ampere when the rate of flow of charge is 1 coulombs per second. The current is 2 amperes when the rate of flow of charge is 2 coulombs per second, and so on ... .

> Electric current is defined as the rate of flow of charge in a particular direction.

Current and charge are linked by the equations below:

$$\text{current (ampere, A)} = \frac{\text{charge (coulomb, C)}}{\text{time (second, s)}}$$

and

$$\text{charge (coulomb, C)} = \text{current (ampere, A)} \times \text{time (second, s)}$$

Using Q for charge, I for current and t for time, the equation above can be written as:

$$Q = I \times t$$

> **Did you know?**
>
> A current of only a few hundredths of an amp is sufficient to stop your heart and kill you.

Remember!
You can measure current with an ammeter.

QUESTIONS

3 The current in a lamp is 1.5 A. Calculate the charge in a time of 1.0 s, 2.0 s, 10 s and 1 hour.

4 In a time of 20 s, the charge passing through a lamp is 1.2 C. Calculate the current in the lamp.

5 Calculate the number of electrons responsible for a charge of 1.5 C.

Current in liquids

The electrons in metals are loosely bound to the atoms. When a metal wire is connected to a cell, these electrons move and produce a current in the circuit.

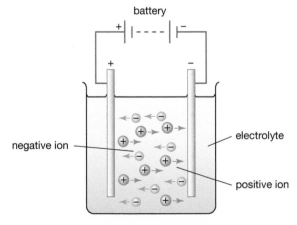

FIGURE 4: What particles are responsible for electric current in an electrolyte?

Figure 4 shows a conducting solution (an *electrolyte*) connected to a battery. What charges are responsible for the current in the solution? The solution has positive and negative ions. The current in the solution is due to the movement of these ions. The directions in which the ions move are shown in Figure 4.

QUESTIONS

6 Use Figure 4 to describe the direction of conventional current in the connecting wires and in the solution.

7 According to a student, the current in the liquid must be zero because an equal number of positive and negative ions travel in opposite directions. Explain whether or not you agree with this statement.

Q Charges in electrolytes   Flow of electrons

Current, voltage and resistance

Resistance

Did you know that you change the resistance of a circuit when adjusting the level of sound on a TV set? Figure 1 shows a collection of resistors. These components have different resistances and can be used to control the size of the current in circuits.

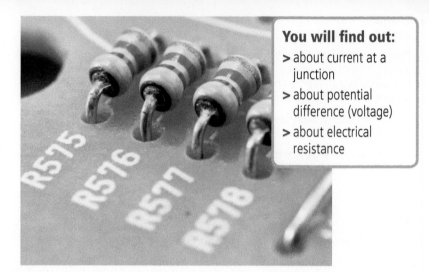

You will find out:
> about current at a junction
> about potential difference (voltage)
> about electrical resistance

FIGURE 1: Resistors. What is the purpose of the coloured stripes?

Electric current in circuits

Series circuit

The current in a circuit can be measured using an **ammeter**. It is always connected in **series** with a component.

Figure 2 shows components (lamps) connected in series. The ammeters X and Y show the same reading. The current will be larger when more cells are used, but the ammeters will still show the same current at all points around the circuit.

> The current in a series circuit is the *same* all the way round.

Parallel circuit

Figure 3 shows components connected in **parallel**. The current splits at the junction J. The sum of the currents shown by ammeters Y and Z is always equal to the current shown by ammeter X.

> Electric current is always conserved at a junction.

Current is conserved at a junction because the total number of electrons *entering* a junction must be equal to the total number of electrons *leaving* the junction. The electrons cannot just appear or disappear at the junction.

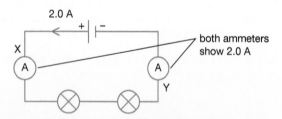

FIGURE 2: The current in each lamp is the same.

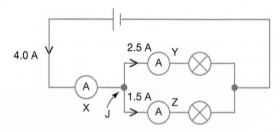

FIGURE 3: The current splits at J.

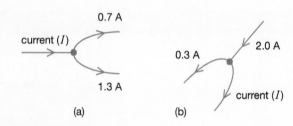

(a) (b)

FIGURE 4: Determine the current.

QUESTIONS

1 Three lamps are connected in series to a power supply providing a constant current of 3.0 A. State the value of the current in each lamp. Explain your answer.

2 Determine the current *I* in Figure 4.

Series circuits   Parallel circuits   Conservation of current

Determining resistance

The **voltmeter** in the circuit shown in Figure 5 measures the **potential difference** (p.d.) V in volts (V) across the component. It is connected in parallel with the component.

The ammeter measures the current I in amperes in the component.

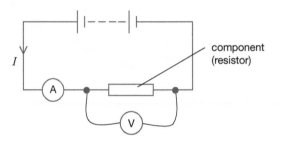

FIGURE 5: A circuit used to determine the resistance of a component.

The **resistance** of the component can be determined from the ammeter and voltmeter readings. The resistance R in ohms (Ω) of a component is given by the equation:

$$\text{resistance (ohm, } \Omega\text{)} = \frac{\text{potential difference (volt, V)}}{\text{current (ampere, A)}}$$

This may be written as:

$$R = \frac{V}{I}$$

Worked example

The current in a lamp with a p.d. of 6.0 V is 0.050 A. Calculate the resistance of the lamp.

$V = 6.0$ V, $I = 0.05$ A

$$R = \frac{V}{I} = \frac{6.0V}{0.05} = 120\ \Omega$$

An important equation $V = I\,R$

If you know the resistance of a component and the current in it, then you can use the following equation to calculate the potential difference across it:

$$\begin{array}{ccc} \text{potential difference} & = & \text{current} \quad\times\quad \text{resistance} \\ \text{(volt, V)} & & \text{(ampere, A)} \qquad \text{(ohm, } \Omega\text{)} \end{array}$$

or

$$V = I\,R$$

Hence the current in a series circuit is determined by the potential difference across the cell and the total resistance of the components of the circuit.

QUESTIONS

3 Calculate the resistance of a component with a p.d. of 5.0 V when carrying a current of 0.12 A.

4 Calculate the p.d. across a resistor of resistance 47 Ω carrying a current of 0.20 A.

Understanding potential difference (Higher tier only)

As electrons travel round a circuit, they transfer some of their electrical energy to other forms (heat and light). Potential difference is related to the energy transferred in this way.

Potential difference across a component is defined as the energy transferred per unit charge. That is:

$$\begin{array}{cc} \text{potential difference} & = \dfrac{\text{energy (joule, J)}}{\text{charge (coulomb, C)}} \\ \text{(volt, V)} & \end{array}$$

QUESTIONS

5 A charge of 80 C transfers 720 J of energy in a lamp. Calculate the potential difference across the lamp.

6 Determine the p.d. across the cell in the circuit shown in Figure 6.

> A potential difference of 1 volt is defined as 1 J of energy transferred per coulomb.

A voltmeter is an instrument that simply measures 'joules per coulomb'. In Figure 6, a charge of 1 C going round the circuit will transfer 1.2 J of its electrical energy into heat in the resistor and 0.3 J of its electrical energy into heat and light in the lamp.

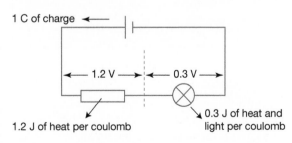

FIGURE 6: Potential difference is energy transferred per unit charge.

Lamps, resistors and diodes

You will find out:
> how a variable resistor changes current
> about lamps, diodes and fixed resistors

Identifying components

Experienced electrical engineers can identify components from their shapes and markings. In the laboratory, you can identify a component from the unique shape of its current against potential difference graph.

FIGURE 1: How can you identify a component?

Changing current in circuits

Resistance and length

Figure 2 shows a circuit that may be used to investigate how the resistance of a wire is affected by its length. The potential difference V across the wire and the current I in the wire can be used to determine its resistance. Table 1 shows the results for different lengths L of the wire.

> The resistance of the wire is directly proportional to its length – the resistance doubles when the length is doubled.

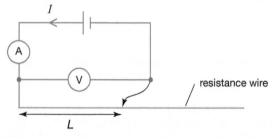

FIGURE 2: The meters help you to determine the resistance of the wire.

TABLE 1: Electrical properties for a length of a wire.

L (cm)	V (volts)	I (amps)	R (ohms)
10	1.6	3.2	0.5
20	1.6	1.6	1.0
40	1.6	0.8	2.0
80	1.6	0.4	4.0

Variable resistor

A variable resistor is a useful device for changing the current in a circuit. Its resistance can be changed manually. One particular variable resistor is known as a **rheostat**. Most rheostats are a wire-wound type that has a long length of wire coiled into a tight spiral. A slider is used to alter the length of the wire in the circuit and this is how its resistance is altered.

Figure 3 shows a rheostat used in a circuit to change the brightness of a lamp.

When the resistance of the variable resistor is set:

> to its maximum value, the current in the circuit is low and the lamp is dimly lit

> to its lowest value (often zero), the current in the circuit is high and the lamp is fully lit.

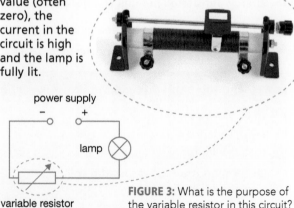

FIGURE 3: What is the purpose of the variable resistor in this circuit?

QUESTIONS

1 Use Table 1 to describe how the current is affected by the length of the resistance wire.

2 Use the Table 1 to sketch a graph of resistance against length of the wire. Describe the shape of this graph.

3 A variable resistor is adjusted so that current in a circuit decreases. Explain how the resistance of the variable resistor is changing.

Current against potential difference graphs

Figure 4 shows a circuit that can be used to investigate how the current *I* varies with potential difference *V* for devices such as a **filament lamp**, a **diode** and a **fixed resistor**. The current in the circuit is altered using the variable resistor.

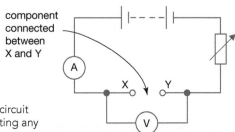

FIGURE 4: A circuit for investigating any component.

Figure 5 shows the *I* against *V* graphs for a filament lamp, a 100 Ω fixed resistor and a diode (made from the semiconductor material silicon).

Note how you can identify the device from the shape of the graph.

Filament lamp

> The current increases with p.d.

> The resistance of the filament increases as current is increased and it gets hotter.

Fixed resistor ——[ ]——

> The current is directly proportional to the p.d.

> The resistance of the resistor is constant.

Diode (silicon) —▷|—

> The diode is a device that only conducts in one direction.

> The diode has an infinite resistance when the current is zero.

> The diode has low resistance when it conducts.

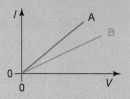

QUESTIONS

4 The *I* against *V* graphs of two resistors A and B are shown in Figure 6. State which resistor has the higher resistance. Explain your answer.

5 a Use the *I* against *V* graphs in Figure 5 to determine the resistance of the filament lamp and fixed resistor at 3.0 V and 6.0 V. **b** Discuss how p.d. affects the resistance of each device.

FIGURE 6: *I* against *V* graphs of two resistors A and B.

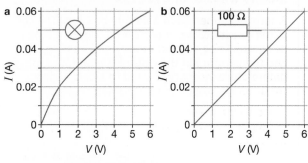

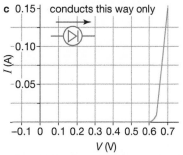

FIGURE 5: Current against voltage graphs for **a** a filament lamp, **b** a fixed resistor and **c** a (silicon) diode.

Practical application of a diode

A diode conducts only in one direction; this is when its anode is connected to a positive terminal and the cathode is connected to a negative terminal. Figure 7 shows how a diode and a lamp can be used to determine the polarities of an unmarked cell (or power supply).

QUESTIONS

6 Use the *I* against *V* graph for the diode in Figure 5 to describe how the resistance of the diode is affected by the p.d. across it.

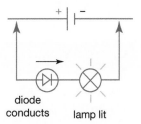

diode conducts   lamp lit

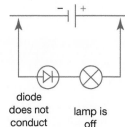

diode does not conduct   lamp is off

FIGURE 7: Determining the polarities of an unmarked cell using a diode and a lamp.

Heating effect of electric current

Cool computer

Computers and laptops get very hot when in use. The electric current passing through the components produces lots of heat. A fan is used to transfer heat away from the laptop so that it does not overheat and cause a fire.

FIGURE 1: Why do you need a fan inside your laptop?

You will find out:
> about the heating effect of electric current
> about electrical power
> how to determine electrical power and energy transfer

Heating caused by a current

Energy transfer in a resistor

A resistor connected to a battery gets hot. The current in the resistor causes it to heat up. Figure 2 shows a circuit that may be used to show this heating effect. The temperature of the resistor is monitored using a temperature sensor connected to a data-logger.

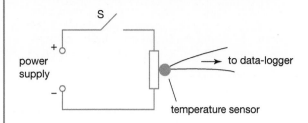

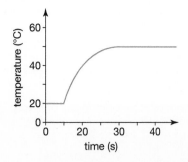

FIGURE 2: When the switch S is closed, the current in the resistor makes it hotter.

Advantages and disadvantages of the heating effect of a current

There are many electrical devices that we rely on to produce heat. For example, an electric heater, the heating element of an electric kettle and an immersion heater for a hot water tank.

However, excessive heat produced in electrical devices can potentially cause fires if there are no safety features. This is why you need a cooling fan in a laptop. Figure 3 shows a potential hazard which you must avoid in your home. It shows an overloaded mains socket. The socket is going to get very hot when all appliances connected to it are used simultaneously. It is a potential fire hazard.

FIGURE 3: An overloaded socket. Why is this dangerous?

QUESTIONS

1 State the missing words from the sentence:
A c_____ in a resistor will make it transfer h_____ energy.

2 Name two domestic appliances, not listed here, that rely on the heating effect of an electric current.

Q Power of electrical devices   Calculating electrical power

Electrical power

It would be helpful to know how to determine the **electrical power** of a device. From its power value, you can calculate how much electrical energy it will transfer and how much it would cost to use the device.

The power of a device is related to the current it carries and the potential difference (p.d.) across it:

$$\text{electrical power (watt, W)} = \text{current (ampere, A)} \times \text{potential difference (volt, V)}$$

You can also write this equation as:

$$P = I \times V$$

where P is the power, I is the current and V is the p.d.

Energy transfer

The energy transferred by any component can be found by multiplying the power by the time. Therefore:

$$\text{energy transferred (joule, J)} = \text{power (watt, W)} \times \text{time (second, s)}$$

or

$$\text{energy transferred (joule, J)} = \text{current (ampere, A)} \times \text{potential difference (volt, V)} \times \text{time (second, s)}$$

You can also write this equation as:

$$E = I \times V \times t$$

where E is the energy transfer, I is the current, V is the p.d. and t is the time.

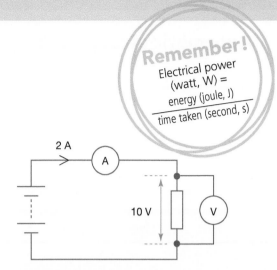

Remember! Electrical power (watt, W) = $\dfrac{\text{energy (joule, J)}}{\text{time taken (second, s)}}$

FIGURE 4: The ammeter and voltmeter readings are all you need to calculate the electrical power transferred by the resistor. Can you show that this power is 20 W?

 QUESTIONS

3 Calculate the power of a resistor carrying 0.050 A when connected to a 9.0 V battery.

4 A heater connected to a 12 V supply draws a current of 5.0 A. Calculate the power of the heater and the energy it transfers in a time of 1.0 minutes.

5 A resistor of resistance 4.7 Ω is connected to a 12 V supply. Calculate the power of the resistor.

Electrons and ions in the lattice (Higher tier only)

A current causes heating in a resistor. How can we explain this heating in terms of the electrons moving within the resistor?

Figure 5 shows electrons travelling through the **lattice** of a metal. When the current is switched on, the fast-moving electrons collide with the ions and transfer some of their kinetic energy to the ions. This increases the vibrational energy of the ions and they jiggle about their fixed points with greater amplitudes. This increased vibration of the ions is what we mean by heat energy.

> Electric current causes heating; the heating is the result of collisions between electrons and the ions in the lattice.

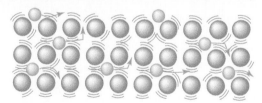

○ ions in the lattice
○ electrons collide with the ions

FIGURE 5: Heating is the result of electrons (green) colliding with the ions (red) of a material.

 QUESTIONS

6 Explain the shape of the graph in Figure 2 in terms of collisions of electrons and ions and heat lost from the surface of the resistor.

LDRs and thermistors

You will find out:
> about light-dependent resistors (LDRs)
> about thermistors
> about uses of LDRs and thermistors

Automatic street lights

Street lights are not manually switched on when it goes dark in your town. They are switched on automatically by circuits that have light-dependent resistors (LDRs).

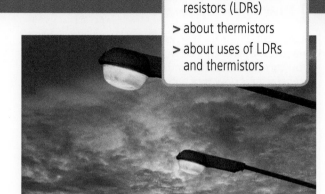

FIGURE 1: LDRs are used to switch on street lights at dusk.

LDRs and thermistors

Light-dependent resistor

A **light-dependent resistor** (LDR) is a special type of resistor made from a **semiconductor** material such as cadmium sulfide. The resistance of the LDR depends on the amount of light shining on it.

> The resistance of an LDR decreases as the intensity of light incident on it increases.

> More light → less resistance.

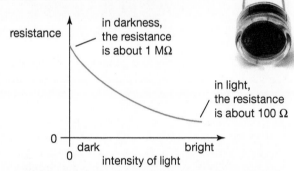

FIGURE 2: A photograph of an LDR and a graph showing how intensity of light affects the resistance of an LDR. Is the correlation between resistance and light intensity positive or negative?

Thermistor

A **thermistor** is a special type of resistor; its resistance depends on its temperature. The word **thermistor** is derived from 'thermally sensitive resistor'. Most commercial thermistors are made from various compositions of the oxides of manganese, nickel, cobalt, copper and iron. Thermistors are also made from semiconductors.

> The resistance of a thermistor decreases as its temperature increases.

> Greater temperature → less resistance.

A thermistor whose resistance decreases with temperature is referred to as a *negative temperature coefficient* (NTC) type.

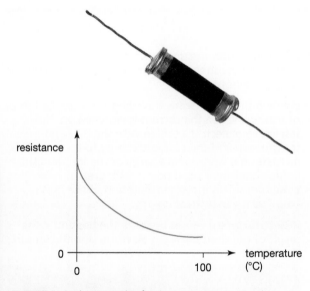

FIGURE 3: A photograph of a thermistor and a graph showing how temperature affects the resistance of an NTC thermistor. Is the correlation between resistance and temperature positive or negative?

QUESTIONS

1 A light-dependent resistor is placed under the light from a table lamp. Choose a word from the list below that best describes how its resistance changes when the light is switched off: increases, decreases, doesn't change.

2 A thermistor is removed from a hot oven and placed in a cold fridge. Describe how its resistance changes.

Practical circuits

Uses of LDRs

Circuits with LDRs can be used to detect changes in light **intensity**. Here are some examples of where LDRs are used:

> A simple light-meter, see Figure 4.

> A light-sensitive circuit for a burglar alarm.

> A circuit for automatically controlling how much light enters a camera.

> A circuit for automatically controlling street lights. At dusk, the street lights are switched on and when there is sufficient light in the morning, the street lights are switched off.

Uses of thermistors

Circuits with thermistors can be used to detect changes in temperature. Here are some examples of where thermistors are used:

> A simple electrical thermometer, see Figure 5.

> A circuit to switch on a fan inside your laptop when it overheats.

> A central heating controller that senses the temperature using a thermistor.

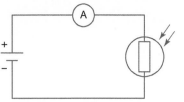

FIGURE 4: A simple light-meter.

FIGURE 5: A simple electrical thermometer.

QUESTIONS

3 Describe what would happen to the current when you:

a cover the LDR with your hand in the circuit shown in Figure 4

b warm up the thermistor in the circuit shown in Figure 5.

Explaining the variation of resistance

Thermistors

Metals are good electrical conductors compared to both semiconductors and insulators because they have a greater number of conducting electrons per unit volume. Increasing the temperature of a metal does not significantly change the number of conduction electrons.

Thermistors are made from either metal oxides or semiconductors. These materials respond very differently to changes in temperature. In a semiconductor or a metal oxide an increase in temperature frees up more electrons from the atoms and this causes the resistance to decrease.

LDRs

LDRs are made from semiconductors that are responsive to light. As the intensity of light falling on an LDR increases it frees up more electrons from the atoms and this causes the resistance to decrease.

Did you know?
Copper has about 10^{28} conduction electrons per cubic metre.

QUESTIONS

4 Figure 6 shows a circuit for switching on a fan inside a laptop. The device X gives an output of 0 V when its input voltage is 'low' and an output of 6.0 V when its input voltage is 'high'. Explain the behaviour of this circuit as the temperature increases.

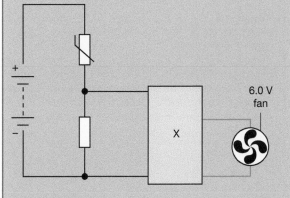

FIGURE 6: A circuit for switching on a fan inside a laptop.

Preparing for assessment: Applying your knowledge

To achieve a good grade in science, you not only have to know and understand scientific ideas, but you also need to be able to apply them to other situations. This task will support you in developing these skills.

 Shocking!

Many people experience electrostatic shocks when they get out of a car. Tina has often experienced these shocks when being driven to school by her father. Tina's father reckons that the car is electrically charged, but Tina, who does GCSE Science, thinks this is not the case.

Tina blames the synthetic fabric of her school uniform for the electrostatic shocks. Electrostatic charges are generated on the car seat and on a person's clothes. When a person leaves the car, they become positively charged and the seat is left with a negative charge. The magnitude of the positive and negative charges is the same. The positive charges on the person create a potential difference of about

10 000 V between the person and the ground. When the person reaches out to touch the metal door, electrical discharge and shock occurs. The discharging current is small; about 1 microampere in size, but you can definitely feel it.

Tina knows when she is going to experience these electrostatic shocks because the hairs on her head stand on their ends. Tina has a simple trick to avoid the electrostatic shocks. During the journey to school, she touches the car door several times to discharge herself. She remembered her science teacher calling this process *earthing*. Tina has happily spread this good news to her friends who are also driven to school.

 Task 1

Name the particle that is transferred between Tina's uniform and the car seat as they become charged.

 Task 2

Tina's hair becomes negatively charged on the journey to school. Explain why her hairs stand up.

 Task 3

Explain why the car seat becomes negatively charged.

 Task 4

Describe in terms of transfer of particles how Tina's jumper and the car seat acquire equal and opposite charges.

 Task 5

Explain how Tina 'earths' herself in terms of transfer of electrons. You can illustrate your answer using suitable diagrams.

 Task 6

The magnitude of the charge e on a single electron is -1.6×10^{-19} C. Estimate the number of electrons transferred per second when the discharge current is 1 µA (1 microampere = 10^{-6} A).

 Maximise your grade

These sentences show what you need to include in your work to achieve each grade. Use them to improve your work and be more successful.

E

For grade E, your answers should show that you can:
> explain why two insulators acquire equal but opposite charges
> recall how like charges behave.

C

For grade D, C, in addition show that you can:
> describe why an insulator is charged negatively
> state how insulators are charged.

A

For grades B, A, in addition show that you can:
> describe the process of earthing
> calculate the charge Q transferred using $Q = I \times t$ and the number N of electrons per second using $N = Q/e$.

Scalar and vector quantities

You will find out:

> about scalar and vector quantities

> about displacement, speed, velocity, acceleration and force

Direction matters

Calculating the total mass of 2 kg and 3 kg toy cars is simple; you just add them together. But what is the total of the two forces shown in Figure 1? This is not straightforward because it depends on the *directions* of the two forces. The answer is 5 N if the forces are in the same direction and 1 N if they are in opposite directions. The directions of the forces matter when you add forces together.

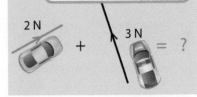

FIGURE 1: What is the answer?

Scalars and vectors

Two important types of quantity

All quantities in physics can be divided into two groups called **scalars** and **vectors**:

> A scalar quantity only has size (or magnitude). Examples include distance, mass, volume, temperature, speed and energy.

> A vector quantity has both magnitude and direction. Examples include displacement, velocity, acceleration and force.

Distance and displacement

Displacement is a vector quantity. Displacement has a size that is equal to the distance from a specified point and it also has direction.

Figure 2 shows the journey of an aeroplane from the airport A to place B. The aeroplane:

> has travelled a distance of 40 km

> has a displacement of 28 km (its size) at a bearing of 45° (its direction) from A.

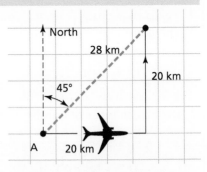

FIGURE 2: Can you see the difference between *distance* and *displacement*?

Speed

A train travels much more quickly than a bicycle. The train covers a greater distance in a given time. It has greater **speed** than the bicycle. It is helpful to know the speed of a train when planning a journey:

> Speed is defined as the rate of change of distance.

> As a word equation, speed is given by:

$$\text{speed (metre per second, m/s)} = \frac{\text{distance (metre, m)}}{\text{time taken (second, s)}}$$

> As an equation, the speed v is related to the distance x travelled and time t as follows:

$$v = \frac{x}{t}$$

> Most journeys are not covered at a constant speed. You can calculate the *average speed* using the speed equation above.

Velocity

> The **velocity** of an object is its 'speed in a specified direction', see Figure 3. It is a vector quantity.

> Velocity is also defined as the rate of change of displacement.

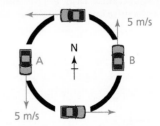

FIGURE 3: A car going round a roundabout at a constant speed of 5 m/s. Its velocity is different at all points. The velocity at A is *5 m/s due south* and at B the velocity is *5 m/s due north*.

QUESTIONS

1 State the difference between distance and displacement.

2 State one difference and one similarity between speed and velocity.

3 Calculate the speed of an athlete who takes 70 s to run round a 400 m track.

Scalars and vectors   Speed and velocity

Acceleration

An object is accelerating if its velocity is *changing*. Figure 4 shows a car whose velocity increases by 5 m/s every second. It has an acceleration of 5 m/s^2.

An object whose velocity *decreases* with time is said to have a **deceleration**. Deceleration means 'slowing down':

> **Acceleration** is defined as the rate of change of velocity.

> As a word equation, acceleration is given by:

$$\text{acceleration (metre per second squared, m/s}^2) = \frac{\text{changing velocity (metre per second, m/s)}}{\text{time taken (second, s)}}$$

> Acceleration a may be written as:

$$a = \frac{v - u}{t}$$

where u is the initial velocity, v is the final velocity and t is the time taken.

> For a decelerating object, the acceleration a will be *negative*.

FIGURE 5: This space shuttle has an acceleration of about 20 m/s^2 during lift-off.

Time (s)	0	1	2	3	4
Velocity of car (m/s)	0	5	10	15	20

FIGURE 4: Data for an accelerating car. What could you find out using this data?

QUESTIONS

4 A cheetah has greater acceleration than a car. This animal can reach a top velocity of 25 m/s from standstill in just 3.0 s. Calculate its acceleration.

5 A car slows down from 30 m/s to 5 m/s in 4.0 s. Calculate the magnitude of its deceleration.

More on acceleration

If you know the acceleration a of an object, then you can calculate other quantities relating to its motion – see Table 1.

TABLE 1: Equations relating to the motion of an object.

Quantity	Equation
Time t taken	$t = \dfrac{v - u}{a}$
Final velocity v	$v = u + at$
Initial velocity u	$u = v - at$
Average velocity v_{av}	$v_{av} = \dfrac{u + v}{2}$
Displacement s	$s = \left(\dfrac{u + v}{2}\right)t$

Did you know?

To escape from the Earth's atmosphere, a space rocket has to have a speed in excess of 10.5 km/s.

QUESTIONS

6 Determine the upward velocity of the space shuttle shown in Figure 5 after 3.0 s.

7 A motorbike has an acceleration of 5.0 m/s^2. Its velocity changes from 10 m/s to 30 m/s. Calculate:

   a the time taken for the acceleration

   b the distance travelled during the acceleration.

 Finding acceleration   Finding speed

Distance–time graphs

You will find out:
> how to interpret distance–time graphs
> how to determine speed and acceleration from a distance–time graph

Analysing motion

Figure 1 shows stroboscopic, or multi-flash, images of a falling apple. The images are taken at regular intervals of time. You can use the images to analyse the motion of this apple. The apple's velocity increases as it falls. Another technique for investigating the motion of the apple would be to plot a distance–time graph.

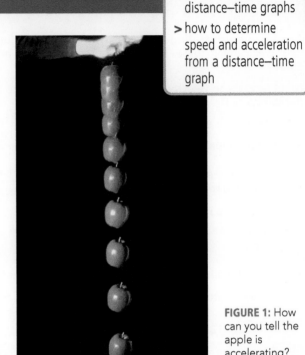

FIGURE 1: How can you tell the apple is accelerating?

Understanding distance against time graphs

Gradient

Graphs are very helpful in interpreting the motion of objects. Before you can do this, you need to know what is meant by the **gradient** of a line. Figure 2 shows a straight-line graph. The gradient, also known as the *slope*, can be determined by drawing a large triangle and doing the calculation below:

$$\text{gradient} = \frac{\text{change in } y}{\text{change in } x} \quad \text{or} \quad \text{gradient} = \frac{\Delta y}{\Delta x}$$

The gradient of this line is:

$$\text{gradient} = \frac{3-1}{6-2} = 0.5$$

The symbol Δ (Greek delta) used in Figure 2 means 'change in'.

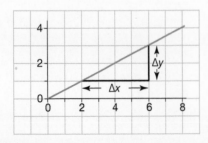

: Does the gradient of this line depend on the size
ᵣle?

Distance–time graphs

You can draw a distance against time graph for an object by recording the distance it travels at regular time intervals. In the laboratory, you simply need a ruler and a stopwatch to do this. What information can you get from a distance–time graph for an object?

> The gradient is equal to the *speed* of the object.

Figures 3 and 4 show the distance–time graphs for a car and the corresponding tables of results.

time(s)	0	1	2	3	4	5
distance (m)	40	40	40	40	40	40

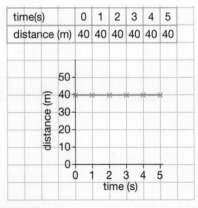

FIGURE 3: Stationary car. What is the gradient of the line?

ding the gradient of a line and curve   Distance–time graphs

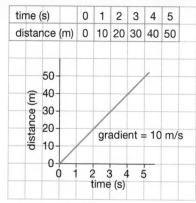

time (s)	0	1	2	3	4	5
distance (m)	0	10	20	30	40	50

gradient = 10 m/s

FIGURE 4: Car travelling at a constant speed of 10 m/s. What is the car's constant speed?

QUESTIONS

1 Complete this sentence: The g_____ of a distance–time graph is equal to s_____. This is because speed is equal to d_____ divided by t_____.

2 Explain how the graph shown in Figure 4 would be different if the speed of the car is 20 m/s.

3 Sketch a distance–time graph for an object that starts from zero distance, travels at constant speed of 2 m/s for 3 s and then remains stationary for a further 2 s.

Acceleration

Table 1 shows the data collected for the falling apple in Figure 1.

TABLE 1: Distance–time results for a falling apple.

Time (s)	0	0.1	0.2	0.3	0.4
Distance fallen (m)	0	0.05	0.20	0.45	0.80

QUESTIONS

4 The acceleration of an object falling on the Moon is smaller than that on the Earth. Describe how the distance–time graph would differ from that shown in Figure 5.

Figure 5 shows the distance–time graph for this falling apple. The graph is not a straight line but a curve. It shows that the apple falls longer distances in each subsequent 0.1 s.

> The apple is accelerating.

> The gradient of the graph increases with time.

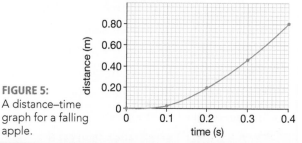

FIGURE 5: A distance–time graph for a falling apple.

Determining acceleration

In order to determine the acceleration of an object, you need to know its speed or velocity at different times.

How can you find the speed of an object from its distance–time graph when the graph is a curve? The speed can be calculated by determining the gradient of a **tangent** drawn to the curve.

Figure 6 shows a distance–time graph for a ball rolling down a straight slope.

> The speed at the start is zero.

> The speed of the ball at 0.2 s can be found from the tangent drawn.

> The speed of the ball at 0.2 s is 0.80 m/s.

> Since the ball is moving in a straight line, its final velocity at 0.2 s is 0.80 m/s.

> The acceleration a of the ball is:

$$a = \frac{v - u}{t} = \frac{0.80 - 0}{0.2} = 4.0 \text{ m/s}^2$$

FIGURE 6: How can you determine the speed from the graph?

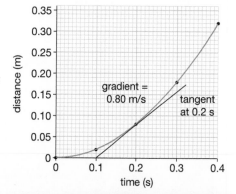

gradient = 0.80 m/s

tangent at 0.2 s

QUESTIONS

5 Use Table 1 to draw a distance–time graph for the falling apple. Interpret the shape of the graph and use it to determine the acceleration of the apple.

Q Finding speed

Velocity–time graphs

You will find out:
> how to interpret velocity–time graphs

Helpful graphs

Re-run in your mind the journey you took to school today. If you travelled in a car or by bus, the journey was definitely not done at a constant speed. The journey would have changing speed, stopping at junctions and so on. It would be easier to picture such a complicated journey by drawing a velocity–time graph.

FIGURE 1: What is the velocity–time graph for any of these cars?

Interpreting velocity against time graphs

Imagine a car travelling along a straight road. The velocity of the car at any time in its journey is shown by its speedometer. You can use this to plot a velocity–time graph for the car.

Figures 2–4 show different types of motion of a car.

> Figure 2 shows a velocity–time graph for a car travelling at a *constant velocity*.

– The velocity of the car is 20 m/s.

– The line is horizontal and has zero gradient.

> Figure 3 shows velocity–time graphs for *two accelerating* cars A and B.

– A straight line shows constant (or uniform) acceleration.

– The line has a positive gradient or slope.

– The steeper the line, the greater the acceleration.

– Car A has greater acceleration than car B.

> Figure 4 shows a velocity–time graph for a *decelerating* (slowing down) car.

– A straight line shows constant deceleration.

– The line has a negative gradient or slope.

FIGURE 2: A velocity–time graph showing constant velocity.

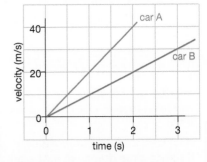

FIGURE 3: Two velocity–time graphs showing constant acceleration.

QUESTIONS

1 State which of the lines shows greater acceleration. Explain your answer.

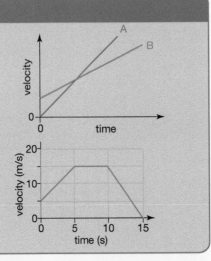

2 Describe the motion of an object with the velocity–time graph shown here.

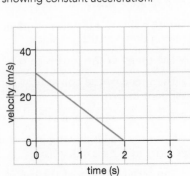

FIGURE 4: A velocity–time graph showing constant deceleration.

Q Velocity–time graphs   Finding distance from velocity–time graphs

Analysing velocity–time graphs

What further information can you get from a velocity–time graph? You can determine the acceleration and distance travelled from a velocity–time graph.

> Acceleration is equal to the gradient of the graph.

QUESTIONS

3 Calculate the acceleration of the car with the velocity–time graphs shown in Figures 2, 3 and 4.

Remember!

$$\text{Acceleration} = \frac{\text{change in velocity}}{\text{time taken}}$$

Solving problems (Higher tier only)

The area under a velocity–time graph is equal to the distance travelled (see Figure 5).

Figure 6 shows a velocity–time graph for a motorbike travelling along a straight road. It is travelling at a constant velocity for 5.0 s and then decelerates uniformly to a halt.

Calculate the deceleration of the motorbike and the total distance travelled:

deceleration time, $t = 8 - 5 = 3$ s

acceleration = gradient

Therefore, acceleration $= \dfrac{v - u}{t} = \dfrac{0 - 30}{3} = -10$ m/s^2

The minus sign indicates deceleration. The magnitude (size) of the deceleration is 10 m/s^2:

distance = area under graph

= area of rectangle + area of triangle

$= (30 \times 5.0) + \left(\dfrac{1}{2} \times 3 \times 30\right) = 195$ m

The total distance travelled by the motorbike is 195 m.

FIGURE 5: The information you can get from a velocity–time graph.

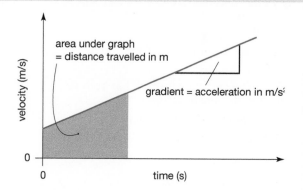

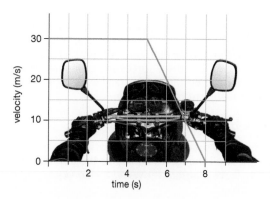

FIGURE 6: A graph for a decelerating motorbike.

QUESTIONS

4 Use Figure 3 to calculate the distance travelled by car A in a time of 2.0 s.

5 A car accelerates from 5 m/s to 25 m/s in a time of 6.0 s. Calculate the distance travelled by the car in this time.

6 A rocket accelerates uniformly from rest. In a time of 10 s it travels a distance of 1.5 km. Calculate the acceleration of the rocket.

Did you know?

A car airbag inflates when the deceleration of the car exceeds 60 m/s^2.

Understanding forces

You will find out:
> about free-body force diagrams
> about resultant forces
> about action and reaction
> about Newton's first and third laws

What is force?

Imagine trying to push a car; they're heavier than they look. Figure 1 shows the forces acting on the person and on the car. To analyse the motion of the car, you just need to know the forces acting on the car. The forces acting on the person are irrelevant.

FIGURE 1: Can you analyse the motion of this car?

The basics about forces

Forces

> A force is a push or a pull exerted by one object on another.

> Force is a **vector** quantity; it has both size (magnitude) and direction.

> The unit of force is the newton, N.

20 N
20 N
resultant force = 40 N

20 N   20 N
resultant force = 0

FIGURE 2: Why are the resultant forces different?

> When adding forces, you need to take their directions into account. For example, two 20 N forces acting in the same direction will give a resultant (net) force of 40 N. If these forces are acting in opposite directions, then they will cancel each other out and give a resultant force of zero.

Free-body force diagrams

In order to predict the motion of an object you need to know all the forces acting on the object. **A free-body force diagram** shows *all* the forces acting on one object.

Figure 3 shows examples of free-body force diagrams and includes the names of the forces.

Did you know?

The booster rockets of the space shuttle provide a force of about 12 million newtons.

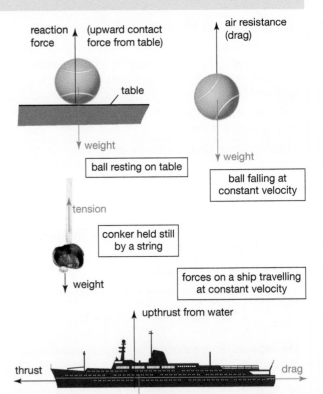

reaction force (upward contact force from table)

table

weight

ball resting on table

air resistance (drag)

weight

ball falling at constant velocity

tension

weight

conker held still by a string

forces on a ship travelling at constant velocity

upthrust from water

thrust   drag

weight

FIGURE 3: Free-body force diagrams.

QUESTIONS

1 List all the different names of forces from Figure 3.

2 Draw and interpret a labelled free-body force diagram for a swimmer floating still on water.

Newton's first and third laws

Newton's first law

A book left on a table will remain motionless unless you apply a force by moving the book or picking it up. An ice puck will keep moving at a constant velocity on the ice and it requires no force to keep it moving in this state.

Sir Isaac Newton in 1687 stated his first law of motion as follows. If there is no resultant force acting on an object, then:

> if stationary, it will remain at rest

> if moving, it will keep moving at a constant speed in a straight line.

All the examples shown in Figure 3 experience a resultant force equal to zero. The forces in each case balance out. They cancel each other out.

If there is a resultant force, then an object will have acceleration. This idea, expressed by Newton's second law, is discussed on pages 204–5.

Newton's third law

What happens when two cars collide or two magnets interact? The amazing fact is that each object exerts an equal force on the other object and the forces are always opposite. The forces on two interacting objects always come in pairs. This idea was summarised by Newton's third law as follows:

> When two objects interact, each object exerts an equal but opposite force on the other.

We know these equal and opposite forces as action and reaction forces.

Figure 4 shows some examples of interacting objects.

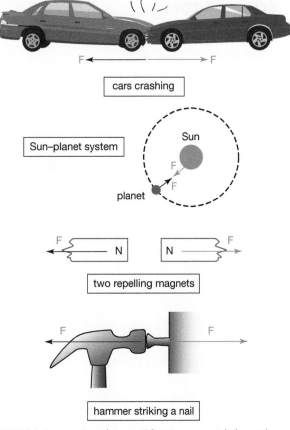

cars crashing

Sun–planet system

two repelling magnets

hammer striking a nail

FIGURE 4: Interacting objects. What is so special about the size and direction of the forces?

QUESTIONS

3 Explain why the conker shown in Figure 3 is at rest.

4 Explain why the ball falling in Figure 3 has a constant velocity.

Action at a distance

Gravitational force is a *fundamental* force that exists between all objects that have mass. The gravitational force between the interacting Sun and the Earth acts over a long distance. There is action at a distance. According to Newton's third law, the force provided by the Sun on the Earth is equal in size but opposite in direction to the force provided by the Earth on the Sun.

The gravitational force acting on an object on the Earth is called its weight. Every object around you has **weight**, including you. The Earth and you are interacting with each other. You are pulling the Earth towards you with a force equal to your weight!

QUESTIONS

5 Two magnets with opposing poles are placed close to each other. Explain the size of the *resultant force* on the two magnets.

Force, mass and acceleration

Speedy cars

It is easy to control and move a car when it is empty. However, when fully loaded, it is more difficult to make it go or stop. How quickly a car changes its velocity depends on its mass and the forces acting on it.

FIGURE 1: Driving this car around is not safe! Why?

You will find out:

> how acceleration is affected by force and mass

> about $F = ma$

Unbalanced forces

Resultant force

The motion of an object depends on the resultant force acting on it.

A car travelling along a straight road at a constant velocity has the following forces acting on it:

> the total forward force F between the tyres and the road

> fractional forces D, including the air resistance or drag opposing the motion of the car

> the weight W of the car

> the total upward contact force N provided by the road.

Since the car is not moving vertically up or down, N is equal to W.

The resultant force on the car in the horizontal direction is zero. The forces F and D are balanced. The car has no acceleration.

What will happen if the force F is suddenly increased? There will be an unbalanced force in the horizontal direction. The car's velocity will increase – it will accelerate in the direction of the resultant force.

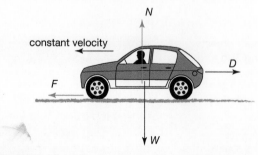

FIGURE 2: All the forces acting on a car moving at a constant velocity.

Factors affecting acceleration

The acceleration of the car depends on:

> the size of the resultant force

> the mass of the car.

Remember!
Force is a vector quantity. It has size and direction.

Did you know?

When a flea jumps, it can have an acceleration of 1400 m/s². This is 140 times greater than the acceleration due to gravity.

◉ QUESTIONS

1 The table below refers to forces F and D acting on the moving car shown in Figure 2. In each case, **a** calculate the resultant force and **b** state whether the car has acceleration, deceleration or a constant velocity.

	(a)	(b)	(c)
F (N)	200	300	0
D (N)	200	200	200

Q Investigating Newton's second law   Applications of Newton's second law

Force, mass and acceleration

Experiments show that acceleration a of an object is greater when the resultant force F is greater and when its mass m is smaller. In fact:

> acceleration is directly proportional to the resultant force ($a \propto F$)

> and acceleration is inversely proportional to the mass $\left(a \propto \dfrac{1}{m} \right)$

The resultant force F, mass m and acceleration a are linked together by the equation:

force (newton, N)	=	mass (kilogram, kg)	×	acceleration (metre per second squared, m/s²)

or

$$F = ma$$

This relationship is also known as **Newton's second law** of motion. It is a fundamental equation that can explain the motion of cars, rockets, atoms, planets, etc.

The equation $F = ma$ is used to define the unit of force, the newton.

> A resultant force of 1 N acting on a 1 kg object will cause it to accelerate at 1 m/s².

In order to determine the acceleration a of the lift shown in Figure 3, you must use the resultant force in the vertical direction.

resultant force = tension – weight

$$F = 8000 - 7000 = 1000 \text{ N m/s}^2$$

$$a = \frac{F}{m} = \frac{1000}{700} = 1.43 \text{ m/s}^2$$

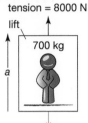

FIGURE 3: Finding the acceleration of a lift.

QUESTIONS

2 Calculate the resultant force on a 0.20 kg object with an acceleration of 6.5 m/s².

3 The table in question 1 refers to a car of mass 1200 kg. Calculate the acceleration of the car in each case $\left(\text{hint: } a = \dfrac{F}{m} \right)$.

Investigating $F = ma$

The link between resultant force, mass and acceleration can be investigated in the laboratory using trolleys and a motion sensor connected to a computer.

The motion sensor works by sending out pulses of ultrasound. The computer software analyses the reflected pulses to calculate the acceleration of the trolley. The force on the trolley is changed by using different numbers of elastic bands. Each elastic band is stretched by the same amount. The mass of the trolley is altered by loading masses on it.

To investigate the relationship between:

> force and acceleration – keep the mass of the trolley constant

> acceleration and mass – keep the force on the trolley constant.

QUESTIONS

4 Here are some results from a laboratory experiment.

m (kg)	0.8	1.6	2.4
a (m/s²)	1.5	0.75	0.5

a Explain what is controlled in this experiment.

b Use the data from the table to deduce the relationship between mass and acceleration.

Remember!

An object will only change its velocity if there is a net force acting on it.

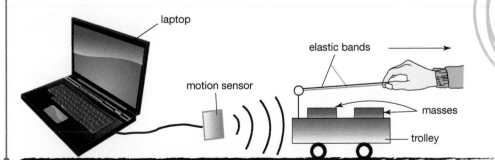

laptop

elastic bands

motion sensor

masses

trolley

FIGURE 4: Investigating $F = ma$ in the laboratory. What is the advantage of using an electronic motion sensor?

Falling objects

You will find out:
> about weight of an object
> about the acceleration of objects in a vacuum
> about the motion of an object in air

The Moon experiment

The *Apollo* missions took people to the Moon. Astronaut David Scott carried out a classic experiment on the Moon. He simultaneously dropped a 1.3 kg hammer and a 0.03 kg feather. Both hit the ground at the same time. In the absence of air resistance (the Moon is almost in a vacuum), the objects had the same acceleration of free-fall.

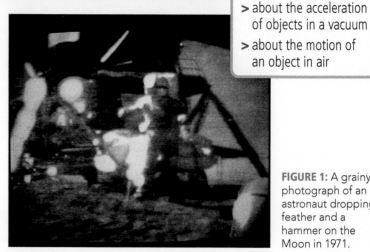

FIGURE 1: A grainy photograph of an astronaut dropping a feather and a hammer on the Moon in 1971.

Weight

The terms weight and mass are often used interchangeably, but in physics they are very different:

> **Mass** of an object is the amount of matter it contains. It is measured in kilograms (kg). The mass of an object remains a constant. Mass is a scalar property.

> **Weight** of an object is the Earth's gravitational force acting on it. It is measured in newtons (N). The weight of an object depends on where it is. Weight is a vector quantity.

A newton-meter can be used to measure the weight of an object. On the Earth, a 1 kg mass has a weight of 9.8 N or about 10 N. The Earth's **gravitational field strength** g is 10 newtons per kilogram. The weight W of an object is equal to its mass m multiplied by the gravitational field strength g:

weight (newton, N) = mass (kilogram, kg) × gravitational field strength (newton per kilogram, N/kg)

or $W = m \times g$ ($g = 10$ N/kg)

	mass	weight
on moon's surface	100 kg	160 N
on Earth's surface	100 kg	1000 N

FIGURE 3: Mass is constant, but weight can be different.

Remember!
In a vacuum all falling bodies accelerate at the same rate.

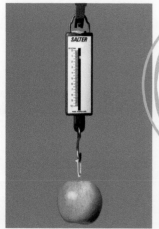

FIGURE 2: What is a newton-meter is used to measure?

QUESTIONS

1 State one difference between mass and weight.

2 Calculate the weight on Earth of:

   a a person of mass 60 kg

   b an apple of mass 120 g.

Q Video of feather–hammer experiment on the Moon   Motion of a skydiver

Objects falling

Free-fall

You would expect a heavier object to fall more quickly than a lighter object. Amazing as it may seem, as you have already seen in the introduction, this is not the case. Experiments carried out on falling objects in a vacuum on the Earth's surface show that all objects:

> have the same acceleration of free-fall of 9.8 m/s^2 (about 10 m/s^2)

> have an acceleration that is independent of their mass.

Drag

All objects moving in air experience air resistance. The shape of a car is streamlined to reduce the air resistance or drag. This saves on fuel and helps the car to reach greater speeds. The drag on an object also depends on its speed and area. The drag increases as the speed increases or the area at 90° to the direction of motion increases.

Falling in air

Figure 4 shows the journey of an 80 kg skydiver from the moment he jumps out of a helicopter.

QUESTIONS

3 Use $F = ma$ to determine the *acceleration* at each stage shown in Figure 5.

4 Explain what is meant by terminal velocity.

5 Explain why acceleration of free-fall is the same as gravitational field strength g.

Stage 1	At the start, the only force on the skydiver is his weight. The acceleration of the skydiver is 10 m/s^2.	
Stage 2	As he travels faster, the drag increases. The resultant force is less than the weight. The skydiver's acceleration is less than 10 m/s^2.	
Stage 3	Eventually the drag is equal to the weight. These two forces are balanced. The resultant force is zero. The skydiver has a constant velocity known as **terminal velocity**.	
Stage 4	The drag suddenly increases when the skydiver opens his parachute. The drag is greater than the weight. The resultant force is upwards. The skydiver decelerates.	
Stage 5	Eventually the drag is equal to the weight. The skydiver has a constant terminal velocity, which is much smaller than before.	

FIGURE 4: A falling skydiver.

A helpful graph

Figure 5 shows a typical velocity against time graph for a skydiver who has jumped off a stationary helicopter.

Use this graph to answer the questions.

QUESTIONS

6 Explain the shape of the graph in terms of the forces acting on the skydiver at A–B, B–C, C–D and D–E.

7 Suggest how the skydiver could decrease his terminal velocity before opening his parachute. Explain your answer.

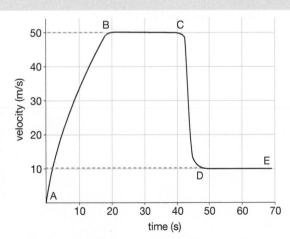

FIGURE 5: A velocity–time graph for a skydiver. How would this graph be useful for a skydiver preparing for a similar jump?

Preparing for assessment: Planning an investigation

To achieve a good grade in science, you not only have to know and understand scientific ideas, but you also need to be able to apply them to other situations and investigations. This task will support you in developing these skills.

✳ Looking into terminal velocity

When an object falls in a vacuum, the only force acting on it is its weight. However, when the same object is falling through a fluid, it experiences a resistive force called drag. Drag opposes the motion of the falling object. When the weight of the object is equal to its weight, the object travels at a constant velocity called *terminal velocity*.

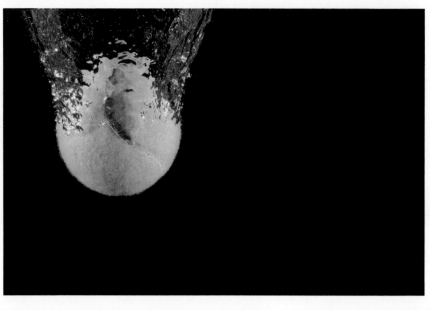

✳ Task

Plan an investigation to find out how the mass of a marble affects its terminal velocity when falling through oil.

✳ Resources available in the laboratory

Variety of marbles, a tall measuring cylinder with oil at room temperature, a metre rule and a stopwatch.

Planning

1. Suggest a hypothesis to investigate.

2. State the equipment you will need to carry out your investigation.

3. State the independent and dependent variables that you will measure. Decide on a suitable range of values for the independent variable.

4. List the things that you need to keep the same in order to ensure that a fair test.

5. Write a detailed method of how exactly you plan to carry out the investigation.

6. Think carefully about the method you have described. List all significant hazards in your investigation and state how each one can be controlled so that you can conduct the task safely.

Remember to justify your hypothesis using appropriate scientific terms.

Carefully explain the choice of your equipment.

The independent variable is what you will change to test the hypothesis. The dependent variable is what you will measure to find the results.

You should be able to explain why you have chosen the range for the independent variable.

In order to carry out a fair test, you can only change one thing at a time and you must control certain factors. Explain how you will control your chosen factors and why.

Consider your Quality of Written Communication. Make sure that your method is a logical sequence of steps. You can number the steps or use bullet points to communicate your method clearly.

Hazards are things which could cause harm. Significant hazards are ones where there is a reasonable chance of them occurring and causing injury or damage.

Processing evidence

1. Construct a results table with suitable columns for the independent and dependent variables.

2. Decide how you will analyse your results by indicating what form of graph will be most suitable. How will you label each of the axes?

3. How will you interpret your graphs so that you can describe the trends shown by your results?

4. What might you expect your results to show?

Remember to use the names and units of each variable.

Each axis will need the name and the unit; this should be the same as the headings used in the table of results.

Consider the correlation shown, whether the line is straight or curved, what type of proportionality is shown, etc.

Think back to your hypothesis.

Connections

How Science Works

> Planning to test a scientific idea.

> Planning an experiment and answering a scientific problem.

> Collecting and analysing scientific data.

> Collecting data accurately and safely, taking into account potential hazards.

> Presenting information and making conclusions and stating the results in a scientific fashion.

Maths in Science

> Understanding direct proportionality and simple ratios.

> Selecting the most appropriate type of graph for the experiment and appropriate scales for the axes.

P2 checklist (Topics 1–3)

To achieve your forecast grade in the exam you'll need to revise

Use this checklist to see what you can do now. Refer back to pages 178–210 if you're not sure.

Look across the rows to see how you could progress – **bold italic** means Higher tier only.

Remember you'll need to be able to use these ideas in various ways, such as:
> interpreting pictures, diagrams and graphs
> applying ideas to new situations
> explaining ethical implications
> suggesting some benefits and risks to society
> drawing conclusions from evidence you've been given.

Look at pages 264–86 for more information about exams and how you'll be assessed.

This checklist accompanies the exam-style questions and the worked examples. The content suggestions for specific grades are suggestions only and may not be replicated in your real examination. Remember, the checklists do not represent the complete content for any topic. Refer to the Specification for complete content details on any topic and any further information.

To aim for a grade E	To aim for a grade C	To aim for a grade A
describe the structure of the atom	explain how an insulator can be charged by friction explain electrostatic charging in terms of transfers of electrons	
recall that like charges repel and unlike charges attract	demonstrate an understanding of common electrostatic phenomena in terms of movement of electrons explain the uses of electrostatic charges, including paint and insecticide sprayers	
demonstrate an understanding of attraction by electrostatic induction		
demonstrate an understanding of the dangers of electrostatic charges	explain how earthing safely removes excess charges	
recall current is the rate of flow of charge	use the equation: $Q = It$	
recall that cells and batteries supply direct current	describe direct current explain that current is conserved at a junction	
describe how an ammeter is connected in series and measures current in amperes	describe how a voltmeter is connected in parallel and measures potential difference in volts use the equation: $V = IR$	*explain that potential difference is energy transferred per unit charge*

210

To aim for a grade E   To aim for a grade C   To aim for a grade A

understand that the current in a circuit can be changed using a variable resistor

demonstrate an understanding of how current varies with potential difference for filament lamps, diodes and fixed resistors

distinguish between the advantages and disadvantages of heating effect of an electric current

use the equations: $P = VI$ and $E = IVt$

explain the transfer of heat in components in terms of collision between electrons and atoms in the lattice

describe how the resistance of an LDR changes with light intensity and how the resistance of a thermistor changes with temperature

demonstrate an understanding of displacement and velocity

recall velocity is speed in a stated direction and is a vector quantity

use the equation speed = distance/time

interpret distance–time graphs

demonstrate an understanding of acceleration

use the equation: $a = \dfrac{v - u}{t}$

interpret velocity–time graphs

calculate acceleration from gradient of velocity–time graph

calculate distance travelled from the area under the velocity–time graph

draw and interpret free body diagrams

demonstrate an understanding of action and reaction forces

explain how resultant forces affect the motion of objects

calculate resultant forces

demonstrate an understanding of how a body accelerates in the direction of a resultant force

use the equation: $F = ma$

use the equation: $W = mg$

describe how bodies fall at the same acceleration in vacuum

understand the relationship between weight and mass

describe the motion of objects falling in air

211

AO1 **1 a** Neetu rubs a balloon on her jumper. The balloon becomes positively charged.

AO1 **i** The jumper has …

A ☐ a positive charge

B ☐ a negative charge

C ☐ no charge

D ☐ gained electrons. [1]

AO1 **ii** The balloon will …

A ☐ repel positive charges

B ☐ attract positive charges

C ☐ repel negative charges

B ☐ not be affected by any other charges. [1]

b The diagram below shows a charged balloon picking up a small piece of paper.

AO1 **i** Explain why the top end of the paper becomes negatively charged. [2]

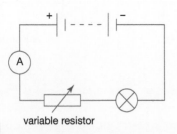

AO1 **ii** Explain why the net charge on the piece of paper is zero. [1]

AO1 **c** An electric spark is created between two
AO2 objects. The sparks lasts for a time of 30 seconds and carries a current of 0.006 A. Calculate the charge flow. State the unit. [3]

[Total: 8]

2 The diagram below shows an electrical circuit.

AO1 **a** On a copy of the diagram, show how you can connect a voltmeter to measure the potential difference across the lamp. [1]

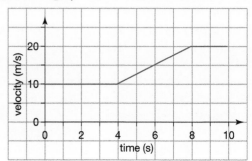

variable resistor

AO1 **b** Name one electrical quantity that remains the same throughout the circuit. [1]

AO2 **c** Explain what would happen to the brightness of the lamp as resistance of the variable resistor is slowly decreased. [2]

AO2 **d** Use a copy of the axes below to sketch a suitable graph for a filament lamp. [2]

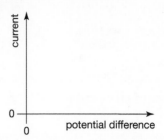

AO2 **e** The current in the variable resistor set at 120 Ω is 0.03 A. Calculate the potential difference across the variable resistor. [2]

[Total: 8]

AO1 **3 a** The graph below shows the motion of a car.

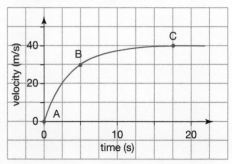

Describe the motion of the car during the time from 0 to 4.0 s. [1]

AO2 **b** Use the graph to calculate the acceleration of the car from 4.0 s to 6.0 s. State the unit. [3]

AO3 **c** The graph below shows the velocity against time graph for a skydiver.

The terminal velocity of the skydiver is 40 m/s. The weight of the skydiver is 800 N. Use the information above to explain the shape of the graph at A, B and C in terms of forces. [6]

[Total: 10]

✳ Worked example

a The graph below shows the motion of a motorcyclist

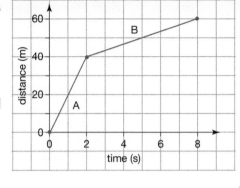

AO1 i In which section, A or B, does the motorcyclist have the greatest speed? [1]

The greatest speed is when the gradient of the line is the greatest.

This happens in section A. ✔

AO2 ii Calculate the average speed of the motorcyclist in the time of 8 s. State the unit. [3]

speed = distance/time

speed = 40/2 ✘

speed = 20 m/s ✘ ✔

b The diagram below shows the horizontal forces acting on the motorcyclist.

AO2 i Calculate the size of the resultant horizontal force acting on the motorcyclist. State the direction of the force. [2]

direction of motion

600 N   700 N

net force = 700 – 600

net force = 100 N ✔

The direction of the force is in the direction of motion. ✘

AO2 ii Describe how this resultant force would affect the speed of the motorcyclist. [2]

The net force would make the motorcyclist travel faster. ✘

[Total: 8]

How to raise your grade

Take note of the comments from examiners – these will help you to improve your grade.

> Correct. The candidate has given an explanation that is correct, but not required by the question.

> The candidate has quoted the correct equation for speed, but sadly has worked out the constant speed during section A. The correct answer would have been the total distance of 60 m divided by the total time taken of 8.0 s. The correct answer is 7.5 m/s. The examiner has awarded a mark for the correct unit.

> The candidate has the correct size of the force, but the direction is incorrect. There is a net force of 100 N *against* the direction of travel. Always look at the details of the diagram carefully.

> The candidate's answer is incorrect because it carries over the error from part i. The net force is against the direction of motion, therefore the motorcyclist will decelerate. The speed of the motorcyclist will decrease. The answer is also for brief for 2 marks.

This candidate scored 4 marks out of a possible 8. The candidate could have lifted their performance by interpreting calculations carefully and providing greater depth in the answers.

AO1 **1** **a** The figure shows a diagram of a helium nucleus.

proton
neutron

i A neutral atom of helium has …

A ☐ 4 electrons

B ☐ 3 electrons

C ☐ 2 electrons

D ☐ 1 electron. [1]

AO1 **ii** The charge of a single electron is -1.6×10^{-19} C. The charge on the helium nucleus is …

A ☐ -1.6×10^{-19} C

B ☐ -3.2×10^{-19} C

C ☐ $+3.2 \times 10^{-19}$ C

D ☐ $+6.4 \times 10^{-19}$ C. [1]

b The diagram shows a thundercloud above a tall building with an earthed lightning conductor.

During a lightning flash, a current of 2000 A travels through the earthed conductor for a time of 0.020 s.

AO1 **i** State the direction of the flow of electrons between the cloud and earthed conductor. [1]

AO1 **ii** Explain the purpose of the earthed lightning conductor. [1]

AO2 **iii** Calculate the number of electrons transferred to the conductor. The charge on a single electron is -1.6×10^{-19} C. [4]

[Total: 8]

AO1 **2** A filament lamp is rated as '6 V, 24 W'.

a 6 V is the same as …

A ☐ 6 J/C

B ☐ 6 J/s

C ☐ 6 J C

D ☐ 6 J s. [1]

AO2 **b** Draw an electrical circuit with a filament and a diode connected in series to a 6 V battery. [2]

AO2 **c** Explain whether or not the lamp connected in your circuit in **ii** is lit. [2]

AO2 **d** Calculate the current in the filament lamp when it is connected to a 6 V power supply. State the unit. [3]

[Total: 8]

3 **a** The diagram shows two positive ions.

B   A

AO1 **i** On a copy of the diagram draw the forces experienced by the ions. [2]

AO2 **ii** The mass of A is larger than the mass of B. Explain which ion will have greater acceleration. [2]

b The figure shows the velocity against time graph for a car.

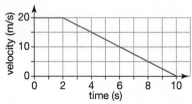

AO2 **i** Describe the car's motion from 0 to 10 s. [2]

AO2 **ii** Calculate the distance travelled by the car during deceleration. State the unit. [3]

[Total: 9]

AO3 **4** **a** The graph below shows the variation of resistance of a metal wire with temperature.

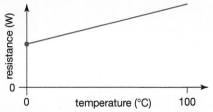

Describe how temperature affects the wire's resistance in terms of electrons and the metal ions. [2]

b A thermistor is connected to a 10 V battery. The variation of current in the thermistor against time t is shown in the figure.

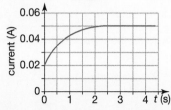

AO2 **i** Calculate the resistance in ohms (Ω) of the thermistor at time $t = 0$. [2]

AO3 **ii** Use your knowledge of thermistors and electrical circuits to explain the shape of the graph shown in the figure. [6]

[Total: 10]

Summary of Assessment Objectives

| AO1 recall the science | AO2 apply your knowledge | AO3 evaluate and analyse the evidence |

✳ Worked example

The graph below shows a velocity against time graph for a ball thrown vertically upwards.

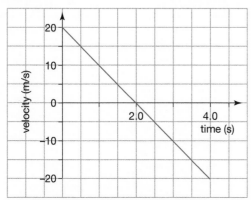

How to raise your grade

Take note of the comments from examiners – these will help you to improve your grade.

AO2 **a** Describe the motion of the ball from time t = 0 to 2.0 s. [1]

The ball has a constant deceleration. ✔

This is an excellent start from the candidate with a clear and succinct answer.

AO2 **b** Explain why the graph is negative after 2.0 s. [1]

Velocity is negative because the ball is returning back to the ground. ✔

This is once again a superb answer. The candidate is familiar with the vector nature of velocity.

AO2 **c** The ball reaches its maximum height at time t = 2.0 s. Calculate the maximum height of the ball. State the unit. [4]

height = area under the graph ✔

height = ½ × 20 × 2.0 ✔

height = 40 m ✘ ✔

This is a well structured response. Sadly, the candidate has made an arithmetic error; the correct answer is 20 m. The examiner has awarded a mark for the unit and workings even though the answer is incorrect. This shows how important it is to write down, and check, your workings.

AO2 **d** Another ball is thrown vertically at half the initial speed. Explain how the shape of the graph would change. [2]

The ball would take 2.0 s to reach its maximum height. ✘

The ball is still is free fall. ✘

[Total: 8]

This is a tough question and the candidate has failed to realise that the deceleration of the ball is the same. The first line of the answer is incorrect because the ball would take 1.0 s to reach the maximum height. The second line is not relevant at all to the question. The correct answer would have been 'A straight line starting at 10 m/s with the same slope as the original graph.'

This candidate scored 5 marks out of a possible 8. Doing the calculation correctly in **c** and gaining at least a mark in **d** would have helped this candidate to improve their grade. Grade A candidates always provide robust answers and make very few errors in calculations.

P2 Physics for your future (Topics 4–6)

What you should know

Momentum, energy, work and power

Energy transfers can occur when objects interact.

Energy can be transformed into heat.

Power = energy used/time (P1 – Topic 5).

Energy is always conserved (P1 – Topic 6).

 How would you increase an object's gravitational potential energy?

Nuclear fission and fusion

Nuclear fusion reactions produce energy (P1 – Topic 3).

Ionising radiations include alpha and beta particles and gamma rays (P1 – Topic 2).

 Why would nuclear fusion reactions be a useful form of energy?

Advantages and disadvantages of using radioactive materials

Ionising radiations transfer energy.

Gamma radiation is used for sterilising food and medical equipment, and for the detection and treatment of cancer (P1 – Topic 2).

 Of the three ionising radiations which has the strongest ionising effect?

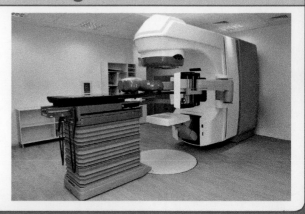

You will find out about

> thinking, braking and stopping distances

> momentum of an object and momentum = mass × velocity

> the role of momentum in understanding car safety features (e.g. crumple zones)

> the equation $F = \dfrac{mv - mu}{t}$

> work done by force and the equation $E = Fd$

> power (measured in watts) and the equation $P = E/t$

> the principle of conservation of energy

> gravitational potential energy and kinetic energy of objects

> the equations GPE = mgh and KE = $\frac{1}{2}mv^2$

> the meaning of the term isotope

> the properties of alpha, beta and gamma radiations emitted from radioactive sources

> nuclear fusion and fission as sources of energy

> nuclear fission of uranium-235

> controlled and uncontrolled chain reactions

> how energy is produced in nuclear reactors

> how stars produce energy through fusion reactions

> the conditions necessary for fusion

> 'cold fusion' and why scientific theories may be rejected by scientific communities

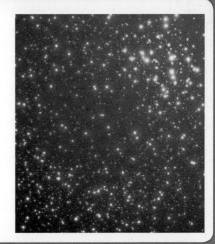

> background radiation and its origin

> the activity of radioactive sources (measured in becquerel)

> the uses of radioactivity, including smoke alarms and the diagnosis and treatment of cancer

> the dangers of ionising radiations

> half-life of isotopes

> advantages and disadvantages of nuclear power for generating electricity

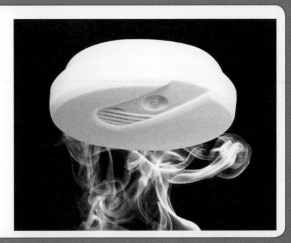

Stopping distance

You will find out:

> about thinking, braking and stopping distances

> about the factors affecting stopping distance

A little extra help

The space shuttle uses a parachute to stop safely on a short runway. If you are travelling very fast and need to stop quickly, then you need a big deceleration. A big deceleration requires a big force.

FIGURE 1: Why is this parachute helpful?

Thinking, braking, stopping

Cars use brakes to stop rather than parachutes. Cars rely on friction to stop. This is why it is important that brakes and tyres are properly maintained. The driver also has to be extra vigilant when the roads are wet or icy. Most accidents occur when the roads are slippery.

The **stopping distance** of a car is made up of two parts: **thinking distance** and **braking distance**:

> Stopping distance = thinking distance + braking distance.

> **Thinking distance** is the distance travelled by the car as the driver reacts to apply the brakes. It can be calculated using the equation:

$$\text{thinking distance} = \text{speed of car} \times \text{reaction time}$$
$$\text{(m)} \qquad\qquad \text{(m/s)} \qquad\qquad \text{(s)}$$

> **Braking distance** is the distance travelled by the car while the brakes are applied before the car comes to a stop.

When learning to drive, you will need to know the stopping distances for various speeds as given in the *Highway Code* (see Figure 2).

QUESTIONS

1 Use Figure 2 to state the relationship between thinking distance and speed.

2 The reaction time of a driver is 0.7 s. Calculate the thinking distance when a car is travelling at 40 m/s.

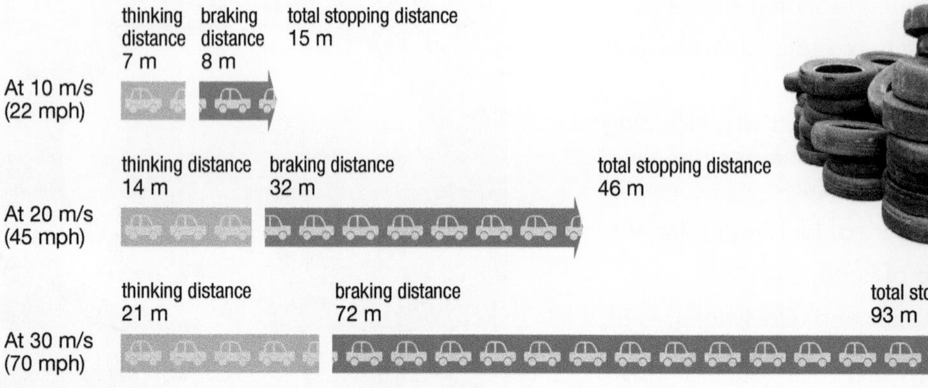

FIGURE 3: What effect would worn tyres have on braking distance?

thinking distance 7 m | braking distance 8 m | total stopping distance 15 m

At 10 m/s (22 mph)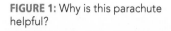

thinking distance 14 m | braking distance 32 m | total stopping distance 46 m

At 20 m/s (45 mph)

thinking distance 21 m | braking distance 72 m | total stopping distance 93 m

At 30 m/s (70 mph)

FIGURE 2: Minimum stopping distances for a car.

Thinking distances   Braking distances

Factors affecting stopping distance

Thinking distance

The thinking distance increases when:

> the speed of the car increases

> the driver's reaction time increases.

The driver's reaction time is increased when he or she:

> is tired

> is under the influence of drugs or alcohol

> is distracted (for example, by passengers or mobile phone calls).

Braking distance

The braking distance increases when:

> the mass of the car increases

> the speed of the car increases

> there is reduced friction:

   – between tyres and road because of worn tyres
   – between tyres and road because of wet or icy road surface
   – because of worn brakes.

QUESTIONS

3 The stopping distance of a car travelling at 30 m/s is 100 m. The reaction time of a driver is 0.5 s. Calculate the thinking distance and the braking distance.

4 Use $F = ma$ to explain why the braking distance increases when there is reduced friction.

5 Explain why it is dangerous to talk on a mobile phone when driving.

Friction

Friction is present whenever two surfaces rub against each other. Friction opposes motion. It can be a nuisance because it wastes energy. Friction can also be helpful. It helps us to walk and it also helps vehicles to slow down.

The amount of friction between two objects depends on their surfaces. Polished surfaces have less friction than rough surfaces. Lubricating two surfaces with oil will reduce the friction.

You can investigate the friction between two surfaces by pulling wooden blocks over different surfaces.

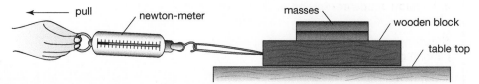

FIGURE 4: An experiment to investigate friction between two surfaces. The maximum friction is equal to the reading on the newton-meter when the wooden block slips.

Explaining stopping distance

The thinking distance and braking distance can be determined from a velocity–time graph for a car (see Figure 5).

The car has constant velocity before the brakes are applied and a constant deceleration when the brakes are applied. The area under a velocity–time graph is equal to distance travelled. Therefore:

> area A = thinking distance
> area B = braking distance
> area A + area B = stopping distance.

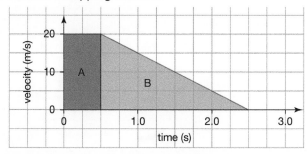

FIGURE 5: Thinking and braking distances can be found from a velocity–time graph.

QUESTIONS

6 Use Figure 5 to calculate the thinking distance, braking distance and stopping distance of the car.

7 The car with the velocity–time graph shown in Figure 5 has a mass of 1000 kg. Use $F = ma$ to calculate the braking force on the car.

8 Explain why the braking distance increases when:
   a the mass m of the car is greater and
   b the speed v of the car is greater.

Q Road conditions and stopping distance   Reaction time of drivers

Linear momentum

You will find out:
> about momentum
> about conservation of linear momentum
> about the vector nature of momentum

Amazing collisions

Have you ever hit a snooker ball straight at another stationary snooker ball? The results are quite unexpected. The colliding ball stops and the stationary ball moves off with a constant speed. The same thing would happen with bumper cars or atoms. In physics it is important to understand the behaviour of colliding bodies.

FIGURE 1: How can you sort out the physics of these bumper cars?

Linear momentum

The word **momentum** has a very precise meaning in physics. All moving objects have momentum. For an object moving in a straight line, its linear momentum depends on its mass m and its velocity v.

Linear momentum, or simply momentum, is defined as follows:

momentum		mass		velocity
(kilogram metre per second, kg m/s)	=	(kilogram, kg)	×	(metre per second, m/s)

or

momentum = $m \times v$

> Momentum is measured in kg m/s.

> The momentum of an object will be big if it is travelling quickly and it has a large mass.

> Momentum is a **vector** quantity.

Figure 2 shows two identical cars, each of mass 1000 kg, travelling in opposite directions at the same speed:

> momentum of the car moving to the *right* = 1000 kg × +30 m/s = 30 000 kg m/s

> momentum of the car moving to the *left* = 1000 kg × –30 m/s = –30 000 kg m/s

The minus sign implies that the object is moving to the left.

Remember!

Velocity is a vector quantity. Mass is a scalar quantity.

QUESTIONS

1 Calculate the momentum of each object:

a truck: mass = 12 000 kg; velocity = 20 m/s

b person: mass = 70 kg; velocity = 2 m/s

c apple: mass = 100 g: velocity = 5 m/s.

positive direction

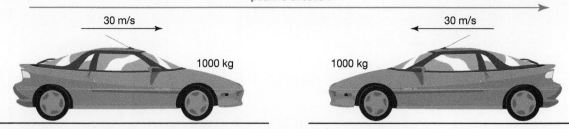

30 m/s   1000 kg   1000 kg   30 m/s

FIGURE 2: The velocity and the momentum of the car moving to the left are both negative.

Collisions

Figure 3 shows a ball X about to collide with a stationary ball Y. When they collide, each ball exerts an equal but opposite force on the other:

> the force from ball Y slows down ball X

> the force from ball X makes ball Y move.

The amazing fact is that the gain in momentum of ball Y is equal to the loss of momentum of ball X. This important idea is expressed as the **principle of conservation of momentum**:

> When two objects collide with each other, their total momentum remains constant, provided there are no external forces acting.

Therefore:

> total momentum before collision = total momentum after collision.

In Figure 3, the balls X and Y stick together after the collision and move with a common velocity v. This velocity can be calculated using the principle of conservation of momentum:

total momentum before the collision	=	total momentum after the collision
$(3.0 \times 2.0) + (1.5 \times 0)$	=	$(4.5 \times v)$
$4.5 \times v$	=	6.0

$$v = \frac{6.0}{4.5} = 1.33 \text{ m/s}$$

After the collision, the balls have a velocity of 1.33 m/s towards the right.

QUESTIONS

2 Two marbles are moving towards each other. Explain what happens when they collide in terms of conservation of momentum.

3 A 1200 kg car travelling at a speed of 10 m/s collides with a car of mass 800 kg travelling in the same direction at 5.0 m/s. The cars get tangled. Calculate the common velocity of the tangled cars.

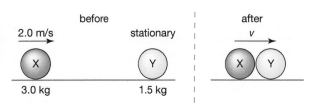

FIGURE 3: The balls before and after the collision.

The vector nature of momentum

When objects travelling in opposite directions collide, then we have to take the vector nature of momentum into account. Figure 4 shows two physics trolleys before and after a collision.

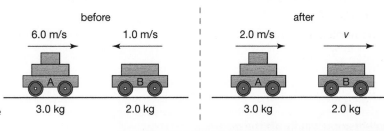

FIGURE 4: The trolleys before and after the collision.

total momentum before the collision	=	total momentum after the collision
$(3.0 \times 6.0) + (2.0 \times -1.0)$	=	$(3.0 \times 2.0) + (2.0 \times v)$
$18.0 - 2.0$	=	$6.0 + 2.0v$
$16.0 - 6.0$	=	$2.0v$

$$v = \frac{10.0}{2.0} = 5.0 \text{ m/s}$$

The 2.0 kg trolley changes direction and has a final velocity of 5.0 m/s to the right.

QUESTIONS

4 Calculate the change in momentum of each trolley in Figure 4. Explain why the size of the values is the same.

5 Calculate the common speed of the trolleys when, in Figure 4, the 3.0 kg trolley is travelling to the right at 2.0 m/s and the 2.0 kg trolley is travelling to the left at 4.0 m/s and the trolleys stick together after the collision.

Car safety and momentum

You will find out:

> about car safety features (seat belts, crumple zones and air bags)

> about rate of change of momentum

All smashed up

Cars are designed to crumple during an impact. This allows the driver to stop over a longer period of time and this prevents serious injuries. Knowledge of momentum is important in making cars safe.

FIGURE 1: A good feature of a car is that it buckles during a collision.

Modelling car crashes

Force and time

Imagine jumping off a wall and landing on solid ground. The impact force when you land can be reduced by buckling your legs. It would not be sensible to keep your legs rigid because you will stop in a shorter time and the impact force on your legs will be large.

> The impact force on an object can be reduced by increasing the time taken for the object to stop.

Investigating car crashes in the laboratory

You can simulate car crashes in the laboratory using trolleys. Figure 2 shows how you can investigate the impact forces on the trolley as it crashes into a brick.

A magnet is taped on the trolley. A ball-bearing is placed at the front of the magnet. The speed of the trolley can be changed by releasing it from different heights from the ramp. At a particular impact speed the ball-bearing will fly off the magnet.

By wrapping the front of the trolley with bubble wrap or with a crumple zone made from corrugated cardboard, the force on the ball bearing can be reduced.

FIGURE 3: Testing vehicle safety at a crash-test facility. What safety feature does this car have?

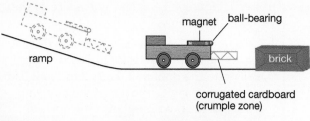

magnet ball-bearing

ramp

brick

corrugated cardboard (crumple zone)

FIGURE 2: An arrangement for investigating car crashes.

QUESTIONS

1 Explain why a having bubble wrap in front of the trolley reduces impact forces during a crash.

2 Suggest how you would assess the effectiveness of the bubble wrap or crumple zone in reducing the impact.

Q Car safety features   How do air bags work?   Car crumple zones

Car safety features

Seat belts

A seat belt is designed to stretch slightly during a crash. This increases the time taken for the driver, or passenger, to stop and the impact force is reduced to a safe level. A driver not wearing a seat belt will carry on moving within the car, until he or she hits the windscreen or steering wheel. Sadly, in this situation, the driver is going to stop in a very short time and this will increase the size of the impact force.

Crumple zones

As shown in Figure 1, cars are deliberately designed to crumple. The car, and hence the driver, takes a longer time to stop. This results in reducing the impact force on the driver.

Air bags

An air bag is inflated suddenly by a canister of gas during a collision. The air bag has holes to let the gas out as the driver's head hits it. As with seat belts, the stopping time is longer and the impact force on the driver is reduced.

> During a crash, seat belts, crumple zones and air bags help to reduce the *rate of change of momentum* of the driver or passenger. (As you will see later, this implies smaller impact force on the driver.)

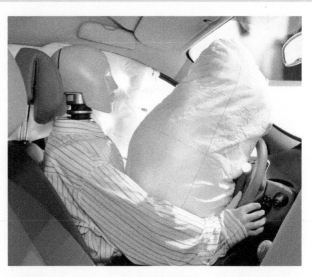

FIGURE 4: How does an air bag work?

Remember!

momentum =
mass × velocity
and
Rate of change means
'divide by time'.

QUESTIONS

3 Explain how an air bag reduces the impact force on a driver and prevents whiplash during a crash.

4 Write a report of 100 words on the importance of wearing a seat belt.

Force and momentum (Higher tier only)

A force F acts on an object of mass m for a time t. The velocity of the object changes from u to v. How is the force related to the momentum of the object?

$$\text{force} = \text{mass} \times \text{acceleration}$$

$$F = ma = m \times \left(\frac{v - u}{t}\right)$$

$$F = \frac{mv - mu}{t}$$

FIGURE 5: An accelerating object.

In words

$$\text{force (N)} = \frac{\text{change in momentum (kg m/s)}}{\text{time (s)}}$$

or

$$\text{force} = \text{rate of change of momentum}$$

In a collision, safety features such as seat belts reduce the rate of change of momentum of the driver by making the time to stop longer.

QUESTIONS

5 A car is travelling at 30 m/s. The car crashes into a barrier. The driver of mass 70 kg is brought to rest by the seat belt in a time of 5.0 s. Calculate the change in momentum of the driver and the impact force on the driver.

6 Explain how the change in momentum and the impact force in question 3 would change when the stopping time is 2.5 s.

Work, energy and power

You will find out:

> about work done by a force
> about the link between work and energy
> about power

A lot of work

The term *work* has a precise meaning in physics. As you will see here, it is linked to force and movement. The strongman shown in Figure 1 is doing lots of work because he is exerting a force on the truck and moving it.

FIGURE 1: Is this person doing work?

Work and energy

Work done

Imagine pushing a box along a floor. There is **work done** on the box because you apply a force and the box moves. You are able to supply energy to the box because of the chemical energy that you get from the food you eat.

Work done *E* is defined as follows:

work done = force (newton, N) × distance moved in the direction of the force (metre, m)

or

$E = F \times d$

> Work done is measured in newton metres or joules (J).

> 1 **joule** is the work done when a force of 1 newton moves through a distance of 1 metre in the direction of the force.

> Work done by a force = energy transferred.

Examples

> A force of 40 N is exerted on a box as it moves through a distance of 5.0 m along the floor:

work done by the force $= F \times d = 40 \times 5.0 = 200$ J

Note: the work done on the box is transferred to heat between the box and the floor.

> A person of weight 400 N on an escalator climbs a vertical height of 6.0 m.

work done *against* the weight $= F \times d = 400 \times 6.0 = 2400$ J

Note: the work done is transferred to gravitational potential energy.

QUESTIONS

1 Calculate the work done and state the energy transfer in the following questions:

a an apple of weight 1.2 N dropping through a vertical height of 4.0 m

b a strongman pulling a truck through 20 m when applying a force of 300 N.

FIGURE 2: Can you explain why there is work done on the person?

Power

Imagine two cars of the same weight racing up the same hill. Both cars will do the same amount of work against their weight. The car that climbs up the hill in the shorter time has greater **power**. The term power means the rate at which work is done or the rate at which energy is transferred:

> power $= \dfrac{\text{work done (joule, J)}}{\text{time taken (second, s)}}$

or

$P = \dfrac{E}{t}$

where E is the work done in time t.

> Power is measured in **watts** (W).

> 1 watt = 1 joule per second.

> Power is also measured in kW (1000 W) and MW (1 000 000 W).

Example

A crane lifts a weight of 1200 N through a vertical height of 40 m in 5 minutes (300 s):

work done E by the crane $= F \times d = 1200 \times 40 = 48\,000$ J

power $P = \dfrac{E}{t} = \dfrac{48\,000}{300} = 160$ W

FIGURE 4: How can you tell which car is the more powerful?

Did you know?

Car engine power is measured in horsepower (hp): 1 hp = 746 watts.

⊙ QUESTIONS

2 Write an equation for power in terms of energy and time.

3 Calculate the power generated by a person of weight 400 N climbing a vertical height of 10 m in 8.0 s.

Power at a constant speed

Figure 4 shows a car travelling at a constant speed v with the forward force provided by the car equal to the drag F. All the work done by the car engine is transferred into heat. You can calculate the output power of the car as follows:

output power $= \dfrac{\text{work done}}{\text{time}} = \dfrac{F \times d}{t} = F \times \left(\dfrac{d}{t}\right)$

The speed v of the car is equal to $\dfrac{d}{t}$. Therefore:

output power $P = Fv$

⊙ QUESTIONS

4 The output power of a crane is 1.0 kW. Calculate the time taken to lift a load of weight 1500 N through a vertical height of 20 m.

5 Calculate the output power of a car travelling at 20 m/s with a drag force of 400 N acting against the motion of the car.

6 Explain why '$P = Fv$' cannot be used when the car is accelerating.

This will not be assessed in your GCSE Additional Science exam but it will be useful for further study in Unit 3 and at A level.

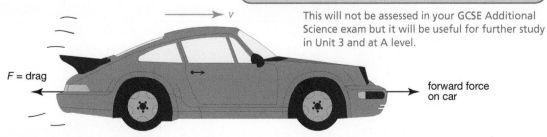

F = drag

forward force on car

FIGURE 4: A car travelling at a constant speed.

KE, GPE and conservation of energy

Falling

The speed of a diver entering the water depends on her height. The higher the jump, the greater is the speed at the bottom. The diver has stored energy before the jump and this is converted into movement energy. Surprisingly, the total energy of the diver remains constant throughout the fall.

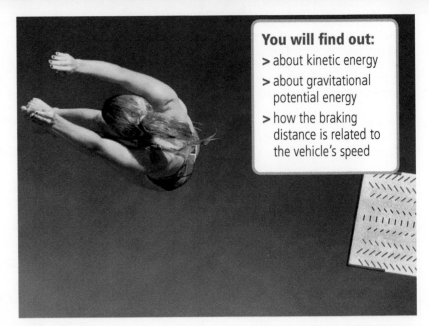

You will find out:

> about kinetic energy
> about gravitational potential energy
> how the braking distance is related to the vehicle's speed

FIGURE 1: What happens to the energy of this diver?

Kinetic energy

A moving object is said to have **kinetic energy**. Kinetic energy of an object depends on its mass and speed (or velocity).

An object has kinetic energy because of the work done on it. The force acting on an object accelerates it. The object travels faster when the force is applied for longer. A truck has greater kinetic energy than a car travelling at the same speed.

The kinetic energy (KE) of an object is given by the equation:

$$KE = \frac{1}{2} \times \text{mass} \times \text{velocity}^2 \text{ or } KE = \frac{1}{2} \times m \times v^2$$

> KE is measured in joule (J).

> Mass is measured in kilograms (kg).

> Velocity is measured in metres per second (m/s).

FIGURE 2: What makes this truck have a large amount of kinetic energy?

Remember!
Work done = energy transferred.

QUESTIONS

1 Explain what is wrong with this calculation:

$$KE = \frac{1}{2} \times m \times v^2 = (\frac{1}{2} \times 4 \times 3)^2 = 36 \text{ J.}$$

2 Calculate the kinetic energy of a 20 000 kg truck and a 1000 kg car travelling at 10 m/s.

 GPE and KE   GPE, KE and roller coasters

It is all about energy

Gravitational potential energy

Figure 3 shows an object of mass m moved from A to B through a vertical height h. The object gains **gravitational potential energy** (GPE). The term potential means stored.

The GPE of the object is equal to the work done against its weight. The object's weight is mg, where g is the gravitational field strength on the Earth's surface equal to 10 N/kg.

$$GPE = \text{work done}$$
$$GPE = \text{weight} \times \text{vertical height}$$

$$\underset{\text{(joule, J)}}{GPE} = \underset{\text{(kg)}}{\text{mass}} \times \underset{\substack{\text{strength (newton/} \\ \text{kilogram, N/kg)}}}{\text{gravitational field}} \times \underset{\substack{\text{height} \\ \text{(metre, m)}}}{\text{vertical}}$$

or $GPE = m \times g \times h$

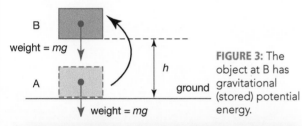

weight = mg

weight = mg

B

A

ground

h

FIGURE 3: The object at B has gravitational (stored) potential energy.

QUESTIONS

3 Calculate the GPE of a 70 kg climber on the top of a 6000 m high mountain.

4 A 70 kg skydiver jumps off a helicopter 1000 m above the ground. He lands on the ground with his parachute at a speed of 20 m/s. **a** Calculate the initial GPE and KE of the skydiver. **b** Explain why the GPE is not the same as the KE.

Conservation of energy

The principle of conservation of energy is very important in physics. It states that energy can neither be created nor destroyed; it can only be transformed into different forms. Here are some examples:

> *A braking cyclist*: the kinetic energy is transformed into heat in the brakes and sound.

> *A petrol car*: the chemical energy of the fuel is changed into KE of the car, heat and sound

> *A falling parachutist*: the GPE of the person is transformed into KE, heat and a bit of sound.

The diver in Figure 1 has GPE at the top of the diving board and this is converted into kinetic energy as she falls. We can use the principle of conservation of energy to determine the speed v of the diver just before entering the pool:

$$\text{mass of diver} = 70 \text{ kg; vertical drop} = 8.0 \text{ m}$$
$$\text{GPE at top} = \text{KE at the bottom}$$
$$m \times g \times h = \frac{1}{2} \times m \times v^2$$
$$70 \times 10 \times 8.0 = \frac{1}{2} \times 70 \times v^2$$
$$5600 = 35 \times v^2$$
$$v^2 = \frac{5600}{35} = 160$$
$$v = \sqrt{160} = 12.6 \text{ m/s}$$

Note: the final speed v is independent of the mass of the object; test this idea using a different mass.

Braking distance and velocity of a vehicle (Higher tier only)

A car of mass m is travelling at a velocity v. When the brakes are applied, the car decelerates and is brought to rest over a braking distance d. The kinetic energy of the car is transferred into heat by the brakes:

$$\text{work done by the brakes} = \text{initial KE of the car}$$
$$Fd = \frac{1}{2}mv^2$$

where F is the braking force. For a given car, the braking force and mass are constants. Therefore:

> braking distance is directly proportional to velocity^2: ($d \propto v^2$)

Doubling the velocity of the car will quadruple the braking distance. Table 1 shows how the braking distance of a particular car depends on its initial velocity v.

TABLE 1: Velocity and braking distance for a car.

v (m/s)	5	10	20	40
Braking distance (m)	2	8	32	128

QUESTIONS

5 a A 1200 kg car is travelling at 20 m/s. The brakes decelerate the car and bring it to rest over a distance of 30 m. Calculate the average braking force. **b** What does your answer to part **a** tell you about the relationship between KE and work done by the brakes?

6 Use Table 1 to predict the braking distance at 30 m/s.

Preparing for assessment: Analysis and conclusions

To achieve a good grade in science, you not only have to know and understand scientific ideas, but you also need to be able to apply them to other situations and investigations. This task will support you in developing these skills.

✴ Looking into friction

Friction is a force that resists the motion of an object. It is measured in newton (N).

Friction comes about when two surfaces rub against each other. The amount of friction depends on the surfaces and the size of the force pushing the surfaces together.

It is much more difficult for a car to stop when the roads are icy. This is because there is less friction between the tyres and the road.

✴ Task

Test the hypothesis that the amount of friction between a block of wood and a worktop is greater when the mass of the wooden block is greater.

✴ Method and results

In an experiment, a student pulled a block of wood on a table using a newton-meter (force-meter). The force pulling the wooden block was measured on the newton-meter. The student made sure that the force applied on the wooden block was horizontal. The mass of the wooden block was changed by placing known masses on the top of the block. He recorded the force F on the newton-meter when the block *just* started to slip and the total mass M of the 'loaded' block. He carried out each experiment three times.

M (kg)	F_1 (N)	F_2 (N)	F_3 (N)	Average force F (N)
0.220	1.6	1.5	1.7	1.6
0.320	2.1	2.2	2.3	2.2
0.420	2.7	2.9	2.9	
0.520	3.9	5.1	4.0	
0.620	4.3	4.1	4.2	
0.720	5.1	5.0	5.1	

Processing the evidence

1. Copy the table and complete the last column by calculating a value for the average force in newton (N).

2. Display the results on a suitable graph.

3. One of the recorded results is anomalous. What does this mean? Identify the value of mass *M* for which the result is anomalous.

4. Comment on the quality of the results.

> Make sure that your average values for *F* are given to an appropriate number of significant figures.

> Choose your scale with great care because your graph must be of appropriate size. Plot your points with a sharp pencil. Use a long ruler to draw a best-fit line. Joining the points 'dot-to-dot' will lose you marks.

> You can only identify the anomalous result when you have plotted the points. How will you deal with this anomalous result when drawing your best-fit line or when forming your conclusions? Does the anomalous result affect the hypothesis in any way?

Stating conclusions

1. Explain carefully what conclusions you can draw from the graph.

2. Explain whether or not the results support the hypothesis.

> Is the graph a straight line or a curve? Does it pass through the origin? Can you describe the relationship between the two variables qualitatively (without using mathematical terms) and quantitatively? Remember to take into account the anomalous result.

Evaluating the method

1. Describe the strengths and weaknesses of the investigation.

2. Suggest two possible reasons why the result was anomalous even though the experiment was performed with care.

3. Suggest how the method used to gather the results might be improved to produce better quality evidence.

> You must use scientific ideas and appropriate mathematical relationships to explain your observations in the light of the hypothesis and to gain Quality of Written Communication marks.

> Consider ways of minimising the risk of anomalies.

Evaluating the conclusion

1. How could you improve the evidence to better support your conclusion?

2. How might you reword your hypothesis in the light of your conclusions?

> Remember that reliable evidence is repeatable evidence. Scientists generally expect to have six or more points close to the best-fit line or curve before drawing conclusions from a graph.

> Carefully consider the hypothesis and scientific language used.

Connections

How Science Works

> Collecting and analysing scientific data.

> Evaluating the best methods of data collection and considering their reliability.

> Presenting information and drawing a conclusion and stating this in a scientific way.

> Interpreting data qualitatively and quantitatively.

> Analysing, interpreting, applying and questioning scientific information.

Maths in Science

> Carrying out calculations.

> Substituting numerical values into simple formulae using appropriate units.

> Providing answers to correct number of significant figures.

> Using proportion and ratios.

> Calculating means.

> Drawing graphs with appropriate scales.

> Interpreting data from tables and graphs.

Atomic nuclei

You will find out:
> about the structure of nuclei
> about isotopes
> how atoms can be ionised

Atoms do matter

An atom is tiny, but its nucleus is even smaller. The nucleus of an atom is about 100 000 times smaller in diameter than the atom. A single grain of sand can have as many 10^{18} atoms!

FIGURE 1: There are lots of atoms in this sand dune.

Atoms

Nuclear model of the atom

Figure 2 shows a diagram of an atom.

> The nucleus contains neutrons and protons. The protons and neutrons are collectively referred to as the **nucleons**.

> The nucleus is surrounded by electrons.

> A neutral atom has an equal number of electrons and protons.

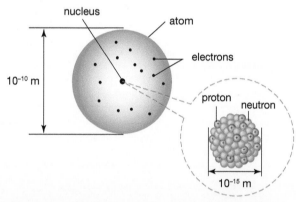

FIGURE 2: The nucleus is 100 000 times smaller than the atom. Can you explain why most of its matter is empty space? (Drawing is not to scale.)

Did you know?

Compact fluorescent lamps (energy-saving lamps) work by ionising the gas atoms.

Remember!
A proton has a positive charge, a neutron has no charge and an electron has a negative charge.

Ions

An ion is any atom that has lost or gained electrons. An ion will always have a charge. Adding electrons will make the atom a negative ion. Removing electrons from the atom will make it a positive ion.

Here are some methods of producing positive ions:

> Rubbing insulators together: the friction strips off electrons from the atoms of one insulator, making some of its atoms positive ions.

> Heating a gas: thermal energy ionises the gas atoms. In this process, electrons of the atoms gain energy and fly off, leaving behind positive ions.

FIGURE 3: These gold atoms are 0.000 0002 mm in diameter.

QUESTIONS

1 A particular atom of carbon has six protons and seven neutrons. State the number of electrons and nucleons in this carbon atom.

2 Atoms can be ionised by removing or adding a particle. Name this particle.

Proton and nucleon numbers

All objects around you have atoms. The carbon atoms in our bodies are different from the oxygen atoms we breathe. There are more than 100 different types of atoms. The simplest atom is that of hydrogen; it has a single electron and a single proton. On the other extreme, a particular atom of uranium has 238 nucleons and 92 electrons.

The nucleus of an atom is represented as:

$$^A_Z X$$

where

> X is the chemical symbol for the element

> A is the total number of neutrons and protons within the nucleus. It is called the **nucleon number** or **mass number**

> Z is the total number of protons inside the nucleus. It is called the **proton number** or **atomic number**.

The number of neutrons N inside the nucleus is equal to (A – Z).

Table 1 shows some examples of nuclei.

FIGURE 4: Sulfur: can you look up its atomic and mass numbers?

TABLE 1: Examples of some nuclei. How does the helium-4 atom differ from the hydrogen-2 atom?

		Representation	Z	A	N
Hydrogen-2		$^2_1 H$	1	2	1
Helium-4		$^4_2 He$	2	4	2
Carbon-14		$^{14}_6 C$	6	14	8

QUESTIONS

3 A particular uranium nucleus has 235 nucleons and 92 protons. Calculate the number of neutrons inside the nucleus.

4 Use the periodic table to represent a boron nucleus in the form $^A_Z X$ if there are six neutrons inside the nucleus.

Isotopes

The oxygen atoms we inhale are not all the same. There is a slight variation in the number of neutrons inside their nuclei although they all have eight protons.

The **isotopes** of an element are nuclei that have the same number of protons but different number of neutrons. The isotopes of a particular element have the same chemical properties because they all have the same number of electrons.

The six isotopes of oxygen are:

$$^{14}_8 O \quad ^{15}_8 O \quad ^{16}_8 O \quad ^{17}_8 O \quad ^{18}_8 O \quad ^{19}_8 O$$

Each isotope has eight protons inside the nucleus. The isotope $^{19}_8 O$ has five more neutrons than $^{14}_8 O$. The isotopes coloured purple are unstable and hence radioactive.

QUESTIONS

5 Using the periodic table and representing the final nucleus in the form $^A_Z X$, show what would be formed if:

a Two hydrogen $^2_1 H$ nuclei joined together to form a single nucleus.

b A nucleus of carbon $^{12}_6 C$ lost two of its protons and one of its neutrons.

Radioactivity

You will find out:

> about radioactivity
> about ionisation
> about alpha particles, beta particles and gamma rays

Alpha tracks

Figure 1 looks like a splash of paint on paper, but it is not. It shows tiny tracks left behind by alpha particles emitted from a radioactive source. These tracks are produced on a film as the alpha particles ionise the atoms in the film.

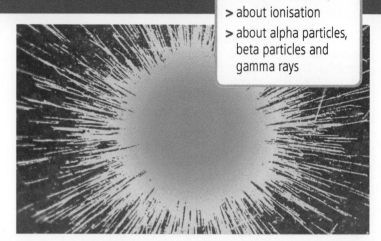

FIGURE 1: What has produced these tracks?

Radioactivity

Unstable nuclei

Hydrogen has three isotopes: ^1_1H, ^2_1H and ^3_1H. The first two isotopes are stable and their nuclei will remain intact forever. The third isotope, known as tritium, is unstable. In time, it will break up and emit a beta particle in an attempt to become more stable.

The breaking up (disintegration) of a nucleus is called *radioactive* decay. The particles and waves emitted from unstable nuclei are called nuclear *radiations*. The three types of nuclear radiations are:

> **alpha (α) particles**

> **beta (β) particles**

> **gamma (γ) rays**

An alpha particle is identical to a helium nucleus with two protons and two neutrons. A beta particle is an *electron* emitted from *inside* the nucleus. Gamma rays are electromagnetic waves of very short wavelength.

Remember!

Radioactivity is not affected by external conditions such as temperature or pressure.

Ionisation

The radiations from radioactive materials carry energy and can cause ionisation. **Ionisation** is the process of removing electrons from atoms. This leaves behind positive ions.

FIGURE 2: Cat litter is often made from clay, such as bentonite, which acts as an absorbent. As clay typically contains naturally occurring radionuclides, large amounts of cat litter can be measurably radioactive.

QUESTIONS

1 State why radioactive nuclei emit radiation.

2 Name the part of the atom that breaks up and emits radiation.

3 Name the two particles produced when an atom is ionised by nuclear radiation.

Alpha, beta and gamma

Random decay

Radioactive decay is described as a *random* process. For a large collection of nuclei, this means that we cannot predict when a particular nucleus will decay but we can predict roughly what percentage of the nuclei will decay in a given time. This behaviour of radioactive nuclei can be compared to rolling dice. You cannot predict which die when rolled will give a number 5, but you can safely say that for 600 dice rolled, there will be about 100 dice showing 5.

Ionisation and radioactivity   Nuclear radiation properties

FIGURE 3: What do dice and radioactivity have in common?

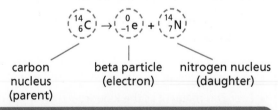

FIGURE 4: The penetration ability of nuclear radiations.

This random nature of radioactive decay can be observed with a Geiger–Müller (GM) tube and a radiation counter. The 'clicks' from a radioactive source are not regular but random.

Properties of nuclear radiations

Table 1 summarises the main properties of the different radiations.

TABLE 1: The main properties of the different radiations.

Radiation	What is it?	Charge*	Typical speed (m/s)	Mass*	Ionising effect	Penetration
α	Helium nucleus ($^4_2$He)	+2	10 million	4	Strong	Stopped by paper, skin or about 6 cm of air
β	Electron ($^0_{-1}$e)	−1	100 million	0.00055	Weak	Stopped by a few millimetres of aluminium
γ	Short-wavelength electromagnetic wave	0	3.0×10^8	0	Very weak	Never completely stopped, but reduced significantly by thick lead or concrete

*Charge and mass compared to a proton.

> ### QUESTIONS
>
> **4** Use Table 1 to explain why alpha particles have a short range in air and gamma rays are hardly affected by air.
>
> **5** Why would it be safe to work a few metres away from an alpha-emitting source?

Alpha or beta decay

A nucleus before it decays is known as the 'parent' and the nucleus left behind is known as the 'daughter'.

In an alpha decay, two protons and two neutrons are removed from the nucleus. The proton number decreases by two and the nucleon number decreases by four. The daughter nucleus is of a different element. When an americium nucleus decays, it leaves behind a neptunium nucleus.

$$^{241}_{95}\text{Am} \rightarrow {}^{4}_{2}\text{He} + {}^{237}_{93}\text{Np}$$

americium nucleus (parent)   alpha particle   neptunium nucleus (daughter)

This will not be assessed in your GCSE Additional Science exam but it will be useful for further study in Unit 3 and at A level.

A nucleus of carbon-14 emits a beta particle, as shown by the decay equation:

$$^{14}_{6}\text{C} \rightarrow {}^{0}_{-1}\text{e} + {}^{14}_{7}\text{N}$$

carbon nucleus (parent)   beta particle (electron)   nitrogen nucleus (daughter)

> ### QUESTIONS
>
> **6** A nucleus of uranium $^{235}_{92}$U emits an alpha particle. Determine the atomic and nucleon numbers of the daughter nucleus.
>
> **7** Use the nuclear decay equation for the carbon-14 nucleus above to explain the changes taking place within the nucleus during beta emission.

Nuclear fission

You will find out:
> about nuclear fission
> how nuclear reactions release energy
> about nuclear chain reactions

Nuclear powered

Space probes that are sent to explore distant planets have to be powered for a long time. Chemical cells are not viable because they run out quickly. Space probes like *Cassini* use radioisotope thermoelectric generators (RTGs). These generators use thermal energy produced by the radioactive decay of plutonium-238 to generate electricity. The RTG on *Cassini* produces 62 W and will last for hundreds of years.

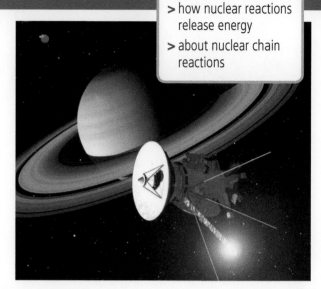

FIGURE 1: How is this space probe powered?

Understanding fission

Energy from nuclear reactions

Nuclear reactions produce energy:

> In radioactive decay, the kinetic energy of the alpha or beta particles emitted from the nuclei. This energy can be used, for example, to generate electricity on a small scale and is how a radioisotope thermoelectric generator (RTG) works.

> Nuclear reactions called **fusion** reactions are responsible for the energy generated by the Sun and the stars.

> A nuclear reactor uses **fission** reactions to generate electricity on a large scale.

Nuclear fission

Figure 2 shows a fission reaction of the uranium-235 ($^{235}_{92}$U) nucleus. Fission means 'splitting' the nucleus.

> A slow-moving neutron is absorbed by a $^{235}_{92}$U nucleus.

> The newly created $^{236}_{92}$U nucleus is highly unstable.

> The $^{236}_{92}$U nucleus almost immediately splits up into two smaller nuclei called **daughter nuclei** and two or more fast-moving neutrons.

> Energy is released as the kinetic energy of the daughter nuclei and the released neutrons.

Remember!
A neutron has no charge. It can travel easily towards the positive nucleus of an atom.

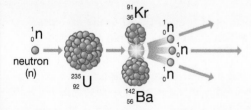

FIGURE 2: A fission reaction of the uranium-235 nucleus by a slow-moving neutron.

QUESTIONS

1 Explain how a nucleus of $^{235}_{92}$U differs from a nucleus of $^{236}_{92}$U.

2 Explain why a neutron is easily absorbed by a positive uranium nucleus.

3 Use Figure 2 to identify the two daughter nuclei.

Chain reaction

In natural radioactive decay, nuclei decay *spontaneously*. External factors, such as temperature and pressure, have no effect on the behaviour of the nuclei. Radioactive decay is a natural process, which we as humans have no control over. However, humans can trigger fission reactions by bombarding uranium-235 nuclei with neutrons.

In a large sample of uranium, the fast-moving neutrons from the fission reactions can go on to split other uranium-235 nuclei. This is a **chain reaction** (see Figure 3).

> A single neutron causes a fission reaction.

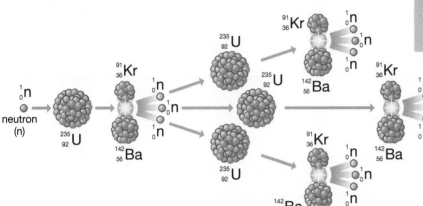

FIGURE 3: Chain reaction.

QUESTIONS

4 Draw a flowchart to describe the steps in the chain reaction shown in Figure 3.

Did you know?

A single neutron entering a sample of pure uranium-235 the size of a grapefruit will trigger uncontrolled fission.

Where does the energy come from?

The nuclear decay equation for the fission of a uranium-235 nucleus is as follows:

$$^{1}_{0}n + ^{235}_{92}U \rightarrow ^{91}_{36}Kr + ^{142}_{56}Ba + 3^{1}_{0}n + energy$$

> The **three** fast-moving neutrons, when slowed down, can go on to split three more U nuclei and produce **nine** neutrons. (The chance of a uranium nucleus capturing a slow neutron is much higher than capturing a fast neutron.)

> These **nine** neutrons can go on to split **nine** more $^{235}_{92}U$ nuclei.

and so on … .

An enormous amount of energy will be released in a short period of time if the chain reaction continues to grow. This is the basis of a nuclear bomb. In a nuclear power station, the chain reaction is controlled by preventing some neutrons triggering fission reactions. (See pages 236–7.)

In the fission reaction:

$$^{1}_{0}n + ^{235}_{92}U \rightarrow ^{91}_{36}Kr + ^{142}_{56}Ba + 3^{1}_{0}n$$

the total mass of the particles after the reaction is *less* than the total mass of the particles before the reaction. There is a very tiny decrease in mass. According to Albert Einstein's famous equation, $E = mc^2$, this tiny mass m is converted into energy E. The letter c is the speed of light in a vacuum (3.0×10^8 m/s). The energy in the fission reaction appears as the kinetic energy of the daughter nuclei and the fast-moving neutrons.

This will not be assessed in your GCSE Additional Science exam but it will be useful for further study in Unit 3 and at A level.

QUESTIONS

5 Describe the major difference between radioactivity and nuclear fission.

6 In a nuclear reaction, the total nucleon and total protons numbers remain the same. Use this to determine the number of neutrons in the fission reaction below:

$$^{1}_{0}n + ^{235}_{92}U \rightarrow ^{90}_{36}Kr + ^{144}_{56}Ba + ?^{1}_{0}n$$

7 A 1 kg sample of uranium has 2.6×10^{24} nuclei. Each fission reaction produces about 3.6×10^{-11} J of energy. Calculate the total energy that can be produced by 1 kg of uranium fuel.

Nuclear power stations

You will find out:
> about controlled nuclear chain reactions
> about nuclear power stations
> about radioactive waste products

The first fission reactor in the world

There are over 400 nuclear power stations around the world. The first nuclear reactor was secretly built in a squash court at the University of Chicago in 1942. It was safely tested and operated for 28 minutes in a densely populated area.

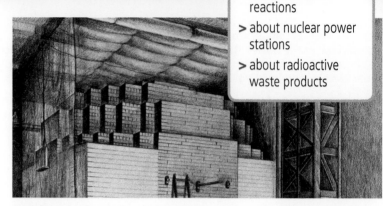

FIGURE 1: The first nuclear reactor in the world was tested in Chicago in 1942.

Nuclear power

Nuclear power stations get their energy from nuclear fission reactions.

> The fuel used in most nuclear power stations is uranium or plutonium.

> A large amount of energy, in the form of the kinetic energy of the neutrons and the daughter nuclei, is released in fission reactions.

> This kinetic energy is turned into heat and used to boil water to make steam.

> The steam is used to turn the turbines as in a conventional power station.

Controlled chain reactions

The chain reaction of the uranium nuclei in a nuclear power station has to be controlled. In a controlled chain reaction:

> a steady output power is produced

> on average a single neutron from the previous fission reaction is left to trigger the next fission reaction.

The daughter nuclei produced in fission reactions are radioactive. They can remain active for thousands of years. The disposal and storage of nuclear waste remains a major concern around the world.

QUESTIONS

1 A coal-powered station transfers chemical energy into electrical energy. State the energy transfer for a nuclear-powered station.

2 Explain in terms of neutrons the difference between controlled and uncontrolled nuclear chain reactions.

Nuclear power stations

Figure 2 shows a water-cooled nuclear fission reactor used in a nuclear power station.

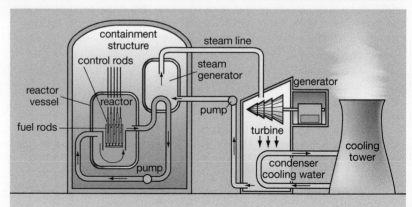

FIGURE 2: A nuclear power station. Suggest a suitable material for the containment structure.

The key components of the reactor are the fuel rods, the coolant, the moderator and the control rods.

> **Fuel rods**: these contain pellets of nuclear fuel in the form of uranium dioxide.

> **Coolant**: the coolant can either be gas (for example, carbon dioxide) or liquid (for example, water). The coolant removes the thermal energy produced in the fission reactions in the reactor core. In a water-cooled reactor, the thermal energy is used to heat water and create high-pressurised steam to drive the turbines of the generators.

> **Moderator**: the nuclear fuel rods are surrounded by the moderator. A commonly used material for the moderator is graphite. The purpose of the moderator is to slow down the fast-moving neutrons produced in the fission reactions. Slow-moving neutrons have a greater chance of reacting with uranium nuclei than fast-moving neutrons, enhancing the chain reaction.

> **Control rods**: the purpose of these rods is to absorb the neutrons and so control the chain reaction. The two commonly used materials used for control rods are boron and cadmium. The control rods can be lowered into the reactor to slow down the fission reactions.

The entire reactor is enclosed in shielding made from concrete and steel. This prevents the ionising radiations escaping into the environment.

QUESTIONS

3 According to a student, the moderator and the control rods serve the same function in a nuclear reactor. Discuss whether or not she is correct.

4 Suggest why the moderator gets very hot in a nuclear reactor.

5 Explain the purpose of graphite in a nuclear reactor.

Did you know?

A kilogram of uranium produces three million times more energy than a kilogram of coal.

FIGURE 3: The inside of a nuclear reactor during construction. The holes are for the control rods.

Critical mass

A tiny sample of uranium-235 cannot sustain a chain reaction because too many neutrons will escape through and not take part in fission reactions. Increasing the mass of the sample will reduce the number of neutrons escaping and increase the chance of fission reactions. A 50 kg sample of pure uranium-235 can just about sustain a chain reaction and produce a stable power output. The minimum mass of a fissile material required to sustain a chain reaction is known as its **critical mass**.

QUESTIONS

6 Explain why a denser fissile material will have a lower critical mass.

7 Research the types and locations of nuclear reactors around the world, and document your findings in a 100 word report.

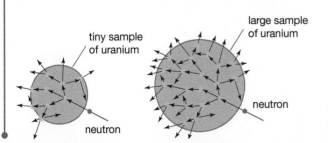

large sample of uranium

tiny sample of uranium

neutron

neutron

FIGURE 4: Can you explain why there is a greater chance of a chain reaction for the larger uranium sample on the right?

Fusion on the Earth

You will find out:
> about nuclear fusion
> the conditions required for nuclear fusion
> about the scientific theory of 'cold fusion'

Energy from water

The stars in the sky produce their energy by fusing together lighter nuclei such as hydrogen. The Sun produces about 10^{26} watts of energy from such reactions. Hydrogen is found in water. Scientists predict that by the 2030s, hydrogen in water could be used to produce safe and cheap electricity.

FIGURE 1: How do these stars produce their energy?

Fission and fusion

In a nuclear fission reaction, a neutron causes the splitting of a uranium-235 nucleus to produce two radioactive daughter nuclei and two or more neutrons. The energy released in fission reactions is used by nuclear reactors to produce electricity.

In a **nuclear fusion** reaction, two smaller and lighter nuclei join or fuse together to produce one larger nucleus. Figure 2 shows the fusion of two isotopes of hydrogen – deuterium $^2_1$H and tritium $^3_1$H – which produces a stable nucleus of helium $^4_2$He and a neutron.

> Fusion reactions also produce a vast amount of energy.

> Fusion of hydrogen and other lighter nuclei (such as lithium) is the energy source that keeps stars burning bright in the night sky.

> Fusion requires extremely high temperatures.

QUESTIONS

1 State a common feature in both fission and fusion reactions.

2 Describe the difference between nuclear fission and nuclear fusion reactions.

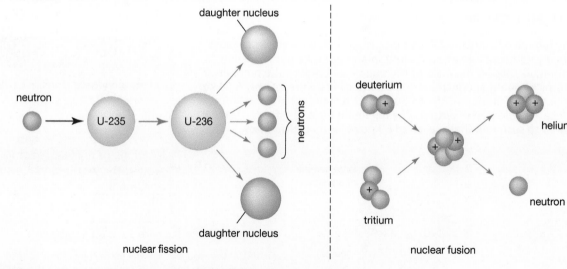

FIGURE 2: Can you spot any differences between fission and fusion reactions?

Cold fusion

On the 23 March 1989, Stanley Pons and Martin Fleischmann announced to the world that they had produced nuclear fusion at room temperature. This theory became known as **cold fusion**.

Their experiment, which involved 'the electrolysis of heavy water in a cell with platinum anode and palladium cathode', was alleged to have produced lots of thermal energy and fusion by-products in the form of neutrons and tritium, $^3_1$H.

Their astonishing news was worthy of front-page coverage in all leading newspapers of the world. Pons and Fleischmann were criticised by many scientists because they failed to publish sufficient technical details of their experiment. Scientists around the world were unable to reproduce their experiment.

New scientific theories are only accepted after rigorous and independent testing by the scientific community. The majority of scientists now reject Pons and Fleischmann's theory of cold fusion because their theory could not be validated by reproducing their experiment.

 QUESTIONS

3 Explain why scientists have rejected the theory of cold fusion.

Remember!

Particles move faster at higher temperatures.

Bringing fusion to the Earth (Higher tier only)

Fission reactions are triggered by uncharged neutrons. Neutrons are not affected by the positive charge on the uranium-235 nuclei. Fusion reactions are more difficult to start because the positively charged hydrogen nuclei (protons) repel each other. However, the chances are increased by moving the nuclei move quickly. At temperatures around 10 million °C, the hydrogen nuclei move rapidly enough to overcome the electrostatic repulsive forces and join together in fusion reactions. For this reason, nuclear fusion cannot happen at low temperatures and pressures.

Fusion reactions in the interior of stars are possible because of the high temperatures. The high pressure and high particle density inside stars also helps because the hydrogen nuclei do not have to travel too far before interacting with each other.

In order to create fusion on Earth, hydrogen nuclei have to be heated to high temperatures of about 100 million °C and contained by very strong magnetic fields produced by super-cooled electromagnets. This has proved to be challenging for the production of energy as such conditions are not economic and are difficult to manage when considering large-scale commercial power stations.

The International Thermonuclear Experimental Reactor (ITER) is currently under construction in France and will be the first ever fusion reactor producing energy. It is planned to begin its operations early in the 2030s and will be producing 500 million watts of power for the grid.

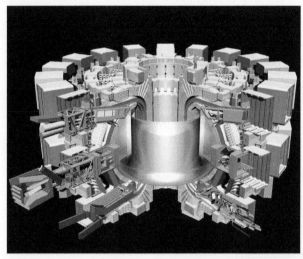

FIGURE 3: Design of the ITER. The hydrogen nuclei (pink) have to be squeezed by strong magnetic fields in order to keep them away from the container walls.

Did you know?

The world's first controlled fusion took place at the University of Princeton in 1978. A temperature of 60 million °C was created for about a tenth of a second.

QUESTIONS

4 Explain why fusion reactions are much more difficult to create than fission reactions.

5 By examining Figure 2, explain why the operation of a fusion reactor could be more environmentally friendly than a fission reactor.

Background radiation

You will find out:

> about background radiation

> about the dangers of radon gas

> about the origin of background radiation

Nuts

Brazil nuts naturally have small traces of radium-226 and radium-228 which make them slightly more radioactive than other food found in our cupboards. Do not panic, they are safe to eat because the activity from the nuts is very low. In fact, everything we eat and all the objects around us are slightly radioactive.

FIGURE 1: What makes these Brazil nuts radioactive?

Radioactive rocks

What happens when you switch on a Geiger counter in the laboratory? You will hear random clicking even though there are no obvious sources of radioactivity close to the counter. The radiation comes from a variety of sources (see page 241) and is referred to as the **background radiation**. Human beings have been exposed to this radiation ever since they walked the Earth.

> All rocks around us are naturally radioactive because they contain small traces of radioactive isotopes of elements such as uranium, thorium and potassium.

> Granite is slightly more radioactive because it contains about 20 parts per million of uranium atoms.

> The uranium nuclei decay naturally eventually to produce radon nuclei. **Radon** is a colourless and odourless radioactive gas.

> Houses built over granite can trap radon gas.

> Exposure to radioactive radon can lead to lung cancer.

Figure 2 shows a map of England. The darker shades of brown show higher levels of activity from radioactive radon emitted from granite. This shows that the amount of background radiation that people are exposed to will vary from region to region.

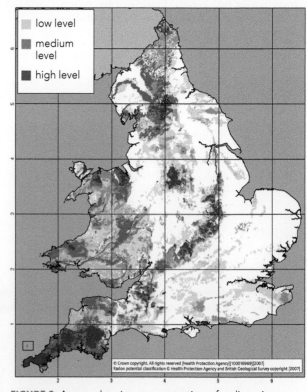

low level

medium level

high level

FIGURE 2: A map showing concentration of radioactive radon. Where are the highest and lowest levels of radiation?

QUESTIONS

1 State two reasons why radon cannot be detected easily.

2 Explain what makes granite radioactive.

3 Is it true that all atoms within a rock are radioactive?

Origin of background radiation   Dangers of radon

Origins of background radiation

Most background radiation comes from natural sources but humans have also had a small effect.

Here is a list of natural sources that contribute towards the background radiation:

> *Cosmic rays.* Cosmic rays are energetic particles such as electrons, protons and neutrinos that come from the Sun and outer space. They penetrate the Earth's atmosphere to reach the Earth's surface. The danger from cosmic rays increases with altitude because there is less atmosphere to stop the radiation. Mountaineers and people flying in planes have a greater exposure to cosmic rays than people at sea level.

> *Rocks.* As mentioned earlier, some rocks such as granite contain uranium, which decays to produce radioactive radon gas.

> *Food.* All foods will have minute traces of radioactive nuclei. Shellfish, tea, coffee and Brazil nuts have higher than average levels of radioactivity.

Here is a list of artificial sources that contribute towards the background radiation:

> Nuclear power stations.

> Fallout from previous nuclear weapons tests, explosions and accidents.

> Radiation from equipment or waste from hospitals and industry.

Figure 3 shows a pie chart of the main contributors to the background radiation in the UK for an individual.

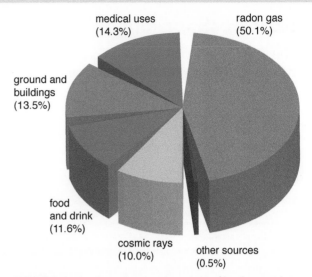

medical uses (14.3%)
radon gas (50.1%)
ground and buildings (13.5%)
food and drink (11.6%)
cosmic rays (10.0%)
other sources (0.5%)

FIGURE 3: A pie chart showing the origin of background radiation for an average individual in the UK. Which is the second highest contribution to background radiation?

QUESTIONS

3 Explain why cosmic rays can potentially cause more damage at high altitudes.

4 A Geiger counter records 20 counts per minute from background radiation. Use Figure 3 to estimate the counts from 'food and drink'.

The dangers of radon gas

Radon gas rises from ground that contains granite. Radon gas is particularly dangerous if it remains trapped in the walls of buildings or under floorboards. As Figure 2 shows, not every town in England is exposed to the dangers of radon gas. The dangers from radon gas can be minimised by ventilating rooms or using an extractor fan that removes radon gas through a pipe on the external wall of the building (see Figure 4).

Radon-222 is one of the isotopes of radon gas. Radon-222:

> nuclei are produced by the decay of radium-226 nuclei

> is a non-reactive noble gas and itself is not a health hazard

> nuclei decay by alpha emission with a short half-life of 3.8 days

> has daughter nuclei that also emit alpha particles

> can potentially cause cellular damage in the lungs.

FIGURE 4: An extractor fan in the loft. What does it remove from the house?

QUESTIONS

5 Show how the decay of a radium-226 into radon-222 is consistent with alpha decay.

6 Explain why radon, an inert gas, has the potential to cause lung cancer.

Uses of radioactivity

You will find out:
> about irradiating food
> about tracing and gauging thickness
> how smoke alarms work

Stay fresh for longer

The strawberries shown in Figure 1 were harvested at the same time. The ones on the left were exposed to intense gamma radiation. Contrary to what most people think, irradiating food with gamma rays does not make it radioactive.

FIGURE 1: What has been done to the strawberries on the left to keep them fresh looking?

 Some applications of radioactivity

Radioactive materials emit:

> alpha particles

> beta particles

> gamma rays.

These three types of ionising radiation have several uses, some of which are outlined below.

Food industry

Irradiating food (for example, strawberries and prawns) with gamma rays is used to prolong its life, which gives more time for transportation and a longer shelf-life. The gamma rays kill off micro-organisms on the food even after it has been packaged. Some people believe that this process changes the taste of the food.

Metal working

In industry, gamma rays are used to check the quality of welding or detecting cracks in metals. Checks can also be carried out using X-rays. Equipment using gamma rays has the benefit of being portable.

Water industry

The water industry uses radioactivity to detect leaks in underground pipes. A beta-particle emitting radioactive material, known as a **tracer**, is fed into the pipe. A radiation detector is used above the ground to detect increased levels of radiation.

FIGURE 2: Engineers setting up an X-ray machine to X-ray an aeroplane wing. Aeroplanes undergo regular inspections to check for any defects that could cause parts, or the entire aircraft, to fail. X-rays are used to detect faults within the structure. What else can be used to detect faults?

Remember!
Alpha, beta and gamma radiation are all ionising radiations.

QUESTIONS

1 State one advantage and one disadvantage of irradiating food.

2 Explain why the tracer used for detecting leaks in pipes cannot be an alpha emitter.

Monitoring thickness

In a paper mill, the thickness of paper can be monitored and controlled using a beta source. Figure 3 shows the details of the production process.

The thickness of the paper is continuously controlled by the amount of pressure applied by the rollers. A beta source of strontium-90 is placed above the paper. (Strontium-90 has a long half-life of 29 years.)

A radiation detector is placed directly below the source and the paper. If the paper thickness is more than the required thickness, the number of beta particles recorded per unit time by the detector decreases. A signal is sent to the rollers to increase the pressure so as to reduce the thickness of the paper.

QUESTIONS

3 Suggest why a beta source is used in a paper mill rather than an alpha source.

4 In a paper mill, the desired count-rate for the paper thickness is 200 counts per second. Explain whether the pressure exerted by the rollers would be the same, increase or decrease when the count-rate detected is 250 counts per second.

5 Use the internet to find out about another industry where radiation is used to gauge thickness. Write 100 words on what you find.

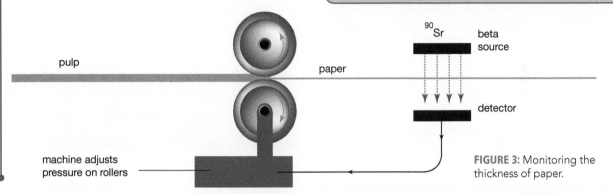

pulp

paper

^{90}Sr beta source

detector

machine adjusts pressure on rollers

FIGURE 3: Monitoring the thickness of paper.

Smoke alarms

Many homes are now fitted with smoke alarms. These have undoubtedly saved many lives. How does a smoke alarm work?

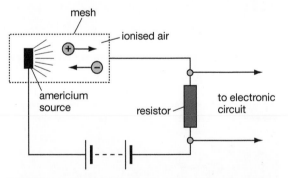

mesh

ionised air

americium source

resistor

to electronic circuit

FIGURE 4: A diagram of a smoke alarm. What does the americium source do to the air?

Did you know?

Americium-241 is a waste product from nuclear reactors. One kilogram of pure americium-241 produces 114 watts of power.

Most smoke alarms use a weak source of americium-241, which emits alpha particles. Alpha particles are the most ionising radiation. The alpha particles from the americium source ionise the air. This produces positive ions and electrons. The positive ions are attracted towards the negative terminal of the battery. The electrons travel in the opposite direction towards the positive terminal. The ionisation of the air produces a tiny current in the constant circuit.

When smoke enters the casing of the smoke alarm, it absorbs the alpha particles. There is less ionisation of the air and hence the current and p.d. across the resistor drops. The electronic circuit detects the decrease in the potential difference and triggers the alarm.

Americium-241 has a half-life of 430 years. The smoke alarm will continue to work as long as you regularly check the battery!

QUESTIONS

6 Discuss the suitability of an alpha source instead of a beta source in a smoke alarm.

Medical uses of radioactivity

Sterilising

How can you sterilise the medical equipment shown in Figure 1? One option would be to heat it at a very high temperature and another would be to expose it to an intense beam of gamma rays.

FIGURE 1: How are surgical instruments sterilised?

Sterilising instruments

Gamma rays are used to sterilise hospital equipment. Gamma rays have sufficient energy to kill off bacteria. In hospitals, metal instruments are heated to destroy the germs but the same cannot be done to plastic syringes and bandages. Syringes sealed in plastic bags can be sterilised using gamma rays. This makes the package and the content sterile. The **sterilisation** process minimises the risks of infection.

Gamma rays kill bacteria such as *Staphylococcus*, including MRSA (methicillin-resistant *Staphylococcus aureus*) and *E. coli* (*Escherichia coli*).

FIGURE 2: These sealed syringes have been sterilised using gamma rays.

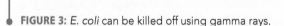

QUESTIONS

1 State what is destroyed when equipment is sterilised.

2 Explain why it is sensible to sterilise a syringe and its packaging.

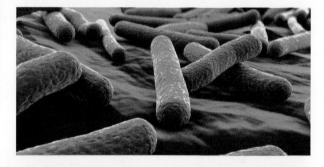

 FIGURE 3: *E. coli* can be killed off using gamma rays.

Cancer therapy

Radioactivity can also be used with patients to detect and treat cancer.

Detecting cancer

The patient is injected with a small amount of radioactive tracer. Technetium-99m is a versatile tracer used in hospitals. It emits gamma rays and has a half-life of about 6 hours. The tracer is carried around the body by the blood. It builds up in the cancerous regions of the patient's body. A special camera, known as a gamma camera, is used to detect and display the gamma rays that pass through the patient. Figure 4 shows a gamma camera scan of a patient suffering from bone cancer. Images like this help hospital doctors to decide what to do next.

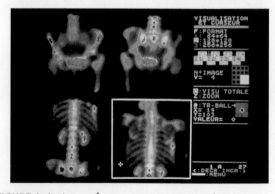

FIGURE 4: An image from a gamma camera showing a patient with severe cancer of the bones.

Treating cancer

In a technique known as **radiotherapy**, the gamma source of cobalt-60 is used in the treatment of cancer. Gamma rays destroy all cells. However, by targeting the cancerous cells and rotating the intense beam of gamma rays, most of the cancerous cells can be killed off with as little damage as possible being done to healthy cells (see Figure 5).

Figure 6 shows a patient about to receive radiotherapy treatment. The green laser crosshair over the patient's face indicates the exact location of the treatment.

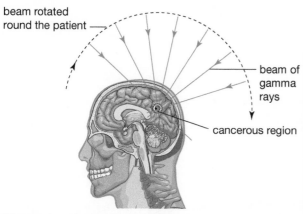

FIGURE 5: In radiotherapy the source of gamma rays is rotated round the patient. Does this technique only destroy the cancerous cells?

beam rotated round the patient

beam of gamma rays

cancerous region

QUESTIONS

3 Explain why medical tracers have a short half-life.

4 Explain why the gamma ray beam in radiotherapy is rotated.

5 Is Technetium-99m the only tracer used in hospitals? Use the internet to research your answer.

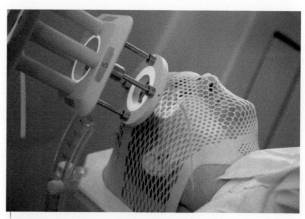

FIGURE 6: A patient having radiotherapy. What radioactive source is used in this treatment?

Other diagnostic techniques for detecting cancer

Cancer can be detected and diagnosed using other techniques that do not involve radioactivity.

Magnetic resonance imaging (MRI)

The technique uses radio waves, a large superconducting electromagnet and a computer. It does not use any form of ionising radiation. Pulses of radio waves are sent into the patient. The radio waves are absorbed by protons spinning about the strong magnetic field. After some time, the protons return the energy by re-emitting radio waves. These radio waves are analysed and used to produce a comprehensive three-dimensional image of the patient. Even small cancerous regions can be pinpointed. The images from an MRI scan are extremely detailed (see Figure 7).

Computed tomography (CT) scanners

This technique uses X-rays. A CT scanner takes multiple images of the patient. It displays bone and soft tissue. A three-dimensional image of the body is viewed on a monitor. A radiographer can easily identify cancerous regions from the images.

This will not be assessed in your GCSE Additional Science exam but it will be useful for further study in Unit 3 and at A level.

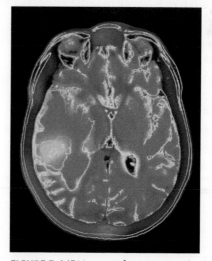

FIGURE 7: MRI image of a patient with a brain tumour (shown by the red colour).

Did you know?

In a CT scanner, 1000 images are collected in less than 1 second.

QUESTIONS

6 Discuss the advantages of MRI and CT scans, compared with radioactive tracer.

Activity and half-life

You will find out:

> about the random nature of radioactive decay
> about activity
> about half-life

Adding neutrons

All living things have carbon-14 and carbon-12 in a known ratio. When an organism dies, the amount of ^{12}C remains constant, but ^{14}C decays. Measuring the ratio in a sample indicates how long ago the organism died.

FIGURE 1: Carbon-14 helps us to date archeological finds.

Radioactivity and half-life

Radioactive decay is a *random* and *spontaneous* event:

> Random means that it is impossible to predict when a particular nucleus will decay.

> Spontaneous means that radioactivity is unaffected by external conditions such as pressure and temperature.

You can simulate the random nature of radioactive decay by flipping coins, picking M&M's from a jar or rolling a large number of dice. With the die, it is impossible to predict which one will show a 4 but you can safely predict that one-sixth of the rolled dice will show a 4.

Amazingly, you can also simulate radioactive decay by cooking popcorn in a microwave oven. The popcorns represent nuclei and the popping represents decay. At the start, there are many popcorns and the popping rate is high. The number of unpopped corn decreases in time and hence the popping rate decreases.

Some nuclei are very unstable and hence decay very quickly. Others take a long time to decay. It is helpful to describe the behaviour of isotopes in terms of their half-lives.

> The **half-life** of an isotope is the average time taken for half of the undecayed nuclei in a sample to decay.

FIGURE 2: What do these coins have in common with radioactive nuclei?

TABLE 1: The half-lives of some isotopes.

Isotope	Half-life
Beryllium-8 ($^{8}_{4}Be$)	3×10^{-16} seconds
Radon-219 ($^{219}_{86}Rn$)	3.9 seconds
Hydrogen-3 ($^{3}_{1}H$)	12.3 years
Carbon-14 ($^{14}_{6}C$)	5700 years
Thorium-232 (^{232}Th)	1.4×10^{10} years

Did you know?

Lead-204 has a half-life 10 million times longer than the age of our Universe.

QUESTIONS

1 Define the term 'half-life'.

2 A sample of wood originally has 5000 nuclei of carbon-14. State the number of undecayed nuclei of carbon-14 after 5700 years.

3 The count-rate from a radioactive source decreases from 4000 counts per second to 2000 counts per second in a time of 24 days. What is the half-life of the isotope?

Q Half-life of isotopes   Factors affecting radioactivity

Activity

The **activity** of a source is the rate of decay of nuclei. Activity is measured in **becquerel** (Bq). An activity of 2000 Bq means that 2000 nuclei decay per second. It also means that 2000 alpha or beta particles are emitted per second.

> The activity of a source is directly proportional to the number of undecayed nuclei. The activity doubles when the mass of the material is doubled.

> The activity is inversely proportional to the half-life of the isotope. A source with a short-lived isotope will have a large activity.

As radioactive nuclei decay, there are fewer undecayed nuclei and hence the activity of a source will decrease in time. Table 2 shows what happens to the number of undecayed nuclei and the activity after time equal to multiples of the half-life T.

QUESTIONS

4 A alpha emitting source has an activity of 500 Bq. Calculate the number of alpha particles emitted in 60 s. State any assumptions made.

5 The number of undecayed nuclei in a source decreases from eight million to two million in 24 hours. Determine the half-life of the isotope.

TABLE 2: Undecayed nuclei and activity after multiples of the half-life T.

Time	0	T	$2T$	$3T$	$4T$
Number of undecayed nuclei	N_0 (Number of undecayed nuclei at the start)	$\dfrac{N_0}{2}$	$\dfrac{N_0}{4}$	$\dfrac{N_0}{8}$	$\dfrac{N_0}{16}$
Activity	A_0 (Activity at the start)	$\dfrac{A_0}{2}$	$\dfrac{A_0}{4}$	$\dfrac{A_0}{8}$	$\dfrac{A_0}{16}$

Exponential decay

Figure 3 shows the variation of the activity with time for a sample of an isotope with a half-life of 15 hours. Notice how the activity is halved every 15 hours. The type of graph shown is known as **exponential decay**.

The activity A at any time can be determined using the equation:

$$A = A_0 \times 0.5^n$$

where A_0 is the initial activity and n is the number of half-lives.

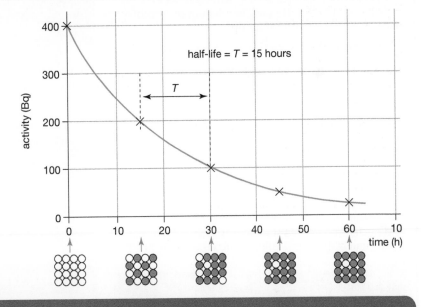

half-life = T = 15 hours

FIGURE 3: The activity of a source decreases with time. What happens to the activity after one half-life?

QUESTIONS

6 Describe and explain how the shape of the graph shown in Figure 3 would change when the same source with half the number of nuclei is used.

7 Estimate the number of half-lives it would take to reduce the activity of a source to less 1%.

🔍 Exponential decay of nuclei   Stability of nuclei

Dangers of radioactivity

You will find out:
> about the dangers of ionising radiation
> about the storage and disposal of nuclear waste
> about the advantages and disadvantages of nuclear power

What a waste

There are more than 400 nuclear power stations around the world. On average, each produces 30 tonnes of high-level waste every year. Disposal of this waste is a big issue for countries reliant on nuclear power.

FIGURE 1: Sellafield nuclear power station. How many nuclear reactors are there in the UK?

Dangers of radioactivity

Alpha, beta and gamma radiations are all ionising radiations:

> Ionising radiations carry sufficient energy to cause tissue damage in our bodies. The cells cannot repair themselves if the damage is too severe.

> Ionising radiations also damage DNA causing mutation of cells, which may lead to cancer.

Working safely with radioactivity

The radioactive sources used in schools have low activities and pose little danger when used sensibly. Here are some helpful safety tips:

> Never point the source towards other people.

> Use special holders to handle the source

> Only remove the source from its lead-lined container when doing experiments

> Wash your hands after using the source.

Scientists now have a better understanding of the dangers posed by radioactivity. This has developed over time through controlled experiments in the laboratories. Sadly, lessons were also learnt from observing the effects on humans after atomic bombs were dropped on Hiroshima and Nagasaki in 1945 and nuclear power plant accidents such as in Chernobyl in 1986 and Fukushima, Japan in 2011.

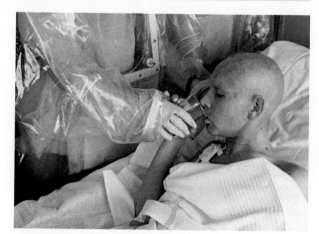

FIGURE 3: A patient suffering from the effects of excess radiation following the disaster at a nuclear power station in Chernobyl. Why is the nurse wearing a plastic suit?

Did you know?

Early pioneering scientists like Marie Curie were unaware of the dangers of radioactivity. Curie handled radioactive substances with her bare hands. She developed leukaemia in later life. Even after more than 100 years, her notebooks remain radioactive.

QUESTIONS

1 State what is damaged in humans by the three ionising radiations.

2 Explain why it is sensible to use a holder when handling an alpha source.

FIGURE 2: Radioactive sources are kept in lead-lined boxes.

🔍 Marie Curie and radioactivity   Advantages of nuclear power   Chernobyl disaster

Using nuclear power

Fossil fuel or nuclear power?

The world will face a severe energy crisis with both coal and uranium running out. Many countries are turning to renewable resources such as solar energy and wind energy. Perhaps the ultimate solution may be fusion reactors.

Table 1 compares coal-burning and nuclear power stations.

TABLE 1: Comparison of power station fuels.

Power station	Positives	Negatives
Coal	Cheap fuel Over 100 years' worth of coal reserves Relatively cheap to build	Expensive air pollution controls CO_2 and SO_2 emissions Extensive transport system Public perception is poor as it is seen to be a limited resource with a negative effect on the environment.
Nuclear	No CO_2 and SO_2 emissions Waste is more compact Little background radiation Located far away from populated areas Low risk of 1 in 5 million of a nuclear accident	Costly to build and decommission Nuclear waste is radioactive for thousands of years and affects future generations Can cause leukaemia/cancer Severe storage and disposal problems of nuclear waste Public perception is poor because of the long-term dangers posed by accidents

QUESTIONS

3 Explain why the public perception of nuclear power stations in the UK remains poor.

4 Evaluate the advantages and disadvantages of nuclear power for generating electricity.

Disposal and storage of nuclear waste

The waste from nuclear power stations is radioactive and therefore has to be disposed of with care. It is important that nuclear waste does not get into our water and food.

> *Low-level* nuclear waste consists of paper, rags, tools, clothing, etc. which contain small amounts of short-lived radioactivity. This type of waste is buried in shallow trenches in steel drums (see Figure 4).

> *Intermediate-level* waste contains higher levels of radioactivity and requires shielding. This type of waste is buried about 8 m under the ground and shielded by water, concrete or lead.

> *High-level* waste contains fission products generated in the reactor core and is highly radioactive. This type of waste can only be stored in deep disused mines or special tunnels made under mountains (see Figure 5).

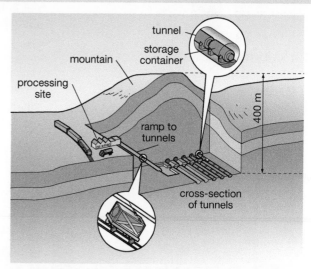

FIGURE 5: A typical burial site for high-level waste.

FIGURE 4: Low-level waste is buried in shallow trenches. What do you notice about the landscape?

QUESTIONS

5 Explain why it would not be sensible to shield low-level waste products.

6 Explain why nuclear wastes are buried in dry climate regions.

Preparing for assessment: Applying your knowledge

To achieve a good grade in science, you not only have to know and understand scientific ideas, but you also need to be able to apply them to other situations. This task will support you in developing these skills.

✺ The risks from radon

Ellie lives in a house in Cornwall, in the south-west of England, with her parents and brother. The house is quite a new one, but it is built in an area where there is a lot of granite. In Science lessons at Ellie's school her teacher had explained about a gas called radon.

Radon is a gas that forms naturally due to the decay of uranium in the ground. It forms in larger amounts in areas such as Devon and Cornwall where there is a large amount of granite in the ground. Radon decays to form radioactive particles, which remain suspended in the air. Normally this is not a problem, but if the particles are in air that is inside a building, the levels can rise further.

People inhaling air that contains these radioactive particles are exposed to alpha radiation and are at a greater risk of developing lung cancer. This is a particular problem in houses with well-fitting doors and windows, as the air does not circulate as easily.

Ellie told her parents about what she had learnt and her mother said, 'I've been meaning to get something done about this. Diane, over the road, got some detector device to put in the house to see if the radon was a problem. We should do that as well.'

Her dad said that he would find out where they could get the detectors from. 'I don't know if we have to pay for them,' he said, but we should get them anyway. I just don't like the idea of there being any of that radiation here in our house.'

Ellie laughed. 'Don't be daft,' she said, 'There's radiation around wherever you are. It's the amount that matters.'

Task 1

Think about Ellie's reaction to her dad, when he said that he did not want any radiation in their house. What might she have said to him to explain her ideas?

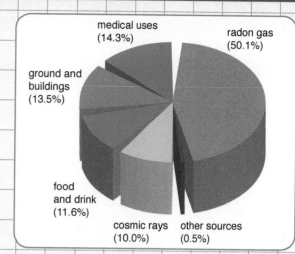

medical uses (14.3%)

radon gas (50.1%)

ground and buildings (13.5%)

food and drink (11.6%)

cosmic rays (10.0%)

other sources (0.5%)

Task 2

If they lived somewhere far away from granite rocks and radon, where might the radiation around them have come from?

Task 3

In fact, Ellie's Science teacher had been explaining to them about the uses and dangers of ionising radiation. Explain, using diagrams if it helps, what the word 'ionising' means.

Task 4

Ellie has to do Science homework. She has to explain how the ionisation effects of radiation involve electrons being transferred. Using words or diagrams, suggest what she might write.

Maximise your grade

These sentences show what you need to be including in your work. Use these to improve your work and to be successful.

E
For grade E, your answers should show that you can:
> suggest a source of background radiation
> state and recognise that there is background radiation in the environment that is always present.

C
For grade D, C, in addition show that you can:
> describe background radiation and state what it is caused by
> explain the meaning of ionisation.

A
For grades B, A, in addition show that you can:
> explain ionisation in terms of electron transfer.

P2 checklist (Topics 4–6)

To achieve your forecast grade in the exam you'll need to revise

Use this checklist to see what you can do now. Refer back to pages 218–51 if you're not sure.

Look across the rows to see how you could progress – **bold italic** means Higher tier only.

Remember you'll need to be able to use these ideas in various ways, such as:
> interpreting pictures, diagrams and graphs
> applying ideas to new situations
> explaining ethical implications
> suggesting some benefits and risks to society
> drawing conclusions from evidence you've been given.

Look at pages 264–86 for more information about exams and how you'll be assessed.

This checklist accompanies the exam-style questions and the worked examples. The content suggestions for specific grades are suggestions only and may not be replicated in your real examination. Remember, the checklists do not represent the complete content for any topic. Refer to the Specification for complete content details on any topic and any further information.

To aim for a grade E	To aim for a grade C	To aim for a grade A
recall that stopping distance = thinking distance + braking distance describe the factors that affect stopping distance	demonstrate an understanding of how thinking and braking distance affect stopping distance	
recall that momentum is a vector quantity	use the equation: momentum = mass × velocity	describe conservation of linear momentum
describe the rate of change of momentum when applied to seat belts, crumple zones and air bags		*use and apply the equation: force = rate of change of momentum or* $F = \dfrac{mv - mu}{t}$
use the equation: work done = force × distance moved in the direction of force or $E = F \times d$	describe power as the rate of doing work and is measured in watts recall 1 watt = 1 joule per second	use the equation: power = work done/time
use the equation: $KE = \frac{1}{2}mv^2$	use the equation: $GPE = mgh$ describe the idea of conservation of energy in energy transfers	*use calculations to show that braking distance is directly proportional to the square of speed*
describe the structure of nuclei state how atoms may gain or lose electrons to form ions	describe the terms proton and mass numbers and use notation in the format $^{14}_{6}C$	describe the nuclei of isotopes explain how atoms form ions

To aim for a grade E   To aim for a grade C   To aim for a grade A

recall that alpha and beta particles and gamma rays are ionising radiations

describe an alpha particle as a helium nucleus, beta particle as an electron and gamma ray as electromagnetic radiation

compare alpha, beta and gamma radiations in terms of ionisation and abilities to penetrate

---

recall that the products of nuclear fission are radioactive

describe nuclear fusion and fission reactions as a source of energy

explain fission of uranium-235 and the principles of a controlled chain reaction

---

describe how nuclear power stations get their energy from fission reactions and convert this into electricity

explain how chain reaction is controlled in a nuclear reactor

describe how heat energy in a reactor is turned into electrical energy

---

describe the process of nuclear fusion and recognise it as the energy source for stars

explain the difference between nuclear fission and nuclear fusion

explain why nuclear fusion cannot occur at low pressures and temperatures and the difficulties of using it for power generation

---

describe background radiation and the regional variation of radon gas

explain the origins of background radiation on the Earth

---

describe uses of radioactivity including irradiating food and sterilising equipment

describe uses of radioactivity including smoke alarms, tracing and gauging thicknesses and diagnosis and treatment of cancer

---

recall how activity of a source decreases over a period of time

state that half-life is the time taken for half the undecayed nuclei to decay

name the unit of activity as the becquerel (Bq)

use the concept of half-life to carry out calculations of the decay of nuclei

---

demonstrate an understanding that ionising radiations damage tissues and can cause mutations

describe how scientists have changed their awareness of the hazards of radioactivity over time

discuss the long-term disposal and storage of nuclear waste

evaluate the advantages and disadvantages of nuclear power for generating electricity

AO1 **1 a** The nucleus of carbon-14 may be written as $^{14}_{6}C$. Carbon-14 emits beta radiation.

i Carbon-14 nucleus has …

A ☐ 19 protons   C ☐ 7 protons

B ☐ 13 protons   D ☐ 6 protons.   [1]

AO1 **ii** A nucleus emitting beta radiation emits …

A ☐ helium nuclei

B ☐ electrons

C ☐ gamma radiation

D ☐ carbon nuclei.   [1]

AO1 **b i** Describe gamma radiation.   [2]

ii State one of the applications of gamma radiation.   [1]

AO2 **c** A radioactive sample emits beta radiation. The radioactive nuclei have a half-life of 10 minutes. The sample has 1000 radioactive nuclei. Calculate the number of radioactive nuclei left after 20 minutes. Show your working.   [3]

[Total: 8]

2 a The figure below shows the gravitational potential energy (GPE) and kinetic energy (KE) of a rollercoaster at the top and bottom of a slope.

top: GPE = 150 kJ
KE = 0 kJ

bottom: GPE = 0 kJ
KE = 50 kJ

AO1 **i** Describe the main energy transformation of the rollercoaster as it travels down the slope.   [1]

AO2 **ii** Explain why the KE of the rollercoaster at the bottom is not equal to its GPE at the top of the slope.   [2]

b The escalator lifts each person through a vertical height of 15 m in a time of 30 s. Calculate:

AO2 **i** The gravitational potential energy of a person of weight 700 N at the top of the escalator. State the unit.   [3]

AO2 **ii** The minimum power in watts used to lift the person.   [2]

[Total: 8]

3 Uranium-235 is used as fuel in nuclear reactors. The energy in a nuclear power station is produced by fission of uranium-235 nuclei. The figure shows a typical fission reaction.

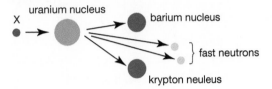

uranium nucleus

X

barium nucleus

} fast neutrons

krypton neuleus

AO1 **a** The particle labelled X is a …

A ☐ proton

B ☐ neutron

C ☐ electron

D ☐ alpha particle.   [1]

AO3 **b** Use the diagram to describe what is meant by fission.   [3]

AO1 **c** Explain the purpose of the moderators in a nuclear reactor.   [2]

AO1 **d** A nuclear power station does not emit greenhouse gases. State two drawbacks of nuclear power stations.   [2]

[Total: 8]

4 a The figure shows a 1000 kg car travelling at 5.0 m/s.

AO2 **i** Calculate the momentum of the car in kg m/s.   [2]

AO2 **ii** Calculate the kinetic energy in joules of the car.   [2]

AO1 **b** The photograph
AO2   shows a car involved in an accident during winter time.

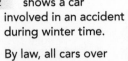

By law, all cars over 3 years old must be tested once a year at a test centre. The test involves a number of checks, including checking the condition of the brakes and tyres.

Discuss how the stopping distance of a car is affected by the condition of the brakes and tyres on an icy road and on the reaction time of the driver.   [6]

[Total: 10]

Summary of Assessment Objectives

AO1 **recall the science**   AO2 **apply your knowledge**   AO3 **evaluate and analyse the evidence**

✳ Worked example

a Americium-241 is used in a smoke alarm made of plastic. Americium is an alpha emitter.

AO2 **i** Explain why a radiation counter placed close to the smoke detector does not detect any radiation. [1]

The plastic stops (absorbs) all the alpha particles. Therefore, none of the radiation gets out of the detector. ✔

AO1 **ii** A nucleus of americium-241 can be represented as $^{241}_{95}$Am. This nucleus has …

A ☐ 309 neutrons

B ☐ 241 neutrons

C ☒ ✔ 146 neutrons

D ☐ 95 neutrons. [1]

b The figure shows the number of active (undecayed nuclei) of two radioactive sources.

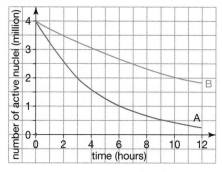

AO2 **i** Determine the half-life of the nuclei of source A. Show your working. [2]

The time taken for the number of nuclei to halve from 4 million to 2 million is equal to 3 hours. ✔ ✔

AO3 **ii** Both sources are gamma emitters. Use the figure to describe the storage problems of sources A and B in thin lead-lined containers. [2]

Source A disappears much more than source B. ✘

[Total: 6]

This candidate scored 4 marks out of a possible 6. The candidate's answer to **bii** shows poor powers of analysis. Extra practice on AO3 questions would familiarise the candidate with how to answer longer questions involving data, and should raise their exam performance.

How to raise your grade

Take note of the comments from examiners – these will help you to improve your grade.

> The candidate's answer is correct. Plastic, like paper, is a good absorber of alpha particles.

> The top number is the nucleon number and the bottom number is the number of protons. The number of neutrons is equal to 241 – 95, this gives the correct answer of 146 neutrons. 241 (B) and 95 (D) both appear in the question – avoid the common mistake of thinking one of these numbers must be the correct answer.

> The candidate's answer is perfect. They have read the graph correctly and explained their answer very clearly.

> There are 2 marks for this question but the candidate has written just one line with no discussion of the storage issues. In order to get 2 marks, the candidate would have to mention: source B has a longer half-life and hence stays radioactive much longer than source A, thin lead-lined containers will not absorb all the gamma radiation. It is important to keep an eye on the number of marks because it gives a clue to the number of separate statements required for the answer.

AO1 **1 a** The two isotopes of lithium are $^{7}_{3}$Li and $^{8}_{3}$Li.

i The nuclei of both isotopes of lithium have the same numbers of

A ☐ protons

B ☐ neutrons

C ☐ nucleons

D ☐ electrons. [1]

AO2 **ii** Explain which of the two isotopes has greater mass. [2]

AO1 **iii** $^{8}_{3}$Li is radioactive and emits a beta particle. What is a beta particle? [1]

b The activity of a radioactive source is 20 000 Bq. After 60 hours the activity decreases to 5000 Bq.

AO1 **i** Explain what is meant by activity. [1]

AO2 **ii** Determine the half-life of the nuclei of the radioactive source. Show your working. [3]

[Total: 8]

2 The figure shows a crane lifting a car of mass 900 kg.

In a time of 15 s, the car is lifted through a vertical height of 18 m at a constant speed. The electric motor of the crane has an input power of 16 kW.

AO2 **a** What is the net force acting on the car as it is vertically lifted at a constant speed? [2]

AO2 **b** Calculate the gain in gravitational potential energy in joules of the car. [2]

AO2 **c** Calculate the input energy to the motor of the crane in joules. [2]

AO2 **d** Explain why the answers to **a** and **b** are not equal. [2]

[Total: 8]

3 The Sun produces its energy by fusion of nuclei including protons.

AO1 **a** Explain what is meant by fusion. [2]

AO2 **b** Describe the conditions in the core of the Sun that makes fusion of protons possible. [4]

AO1 **c** On 23 March 1989, Martin Fleischmann and Stanley Pons announced that they had discovered 'cold fusion'. Explain why their discovery was not accepted by the scientific community. [2]

[Total: 8]

AO2 **4 a** A car of mass 800 kg has kinetic energy of 240 kJ. Calculate the speed of the car in m/s. [3]

AO2 **b** A space rocket of mass 20 000 kg blasts off from the surface of the Earth. It reaches a velocity of 80 m/s in 10 s. Calculate the net force acting on the rocket. State the unit. [3]

AO3 **c** The table below shows the variation of thinking distance and braking distance with the speed of the car.

Speed (m/s)	5	10	15	20
Thinking distance (m)	2.5	5.0	7.5	10
Braking distance (m)	4	16	36	64

Use the two graphs shown below to discuss the relationship between thinking distance, braking distance and speed. [6]

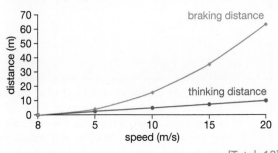

[Total: 12]

AO1 recall the science | AO2 apply your knowledge | AO3 evaluate and analyse the evidence

✳ Worked example

AO2 **a** A car of mass 900 kg is travelling at a constant velocity. The momentum of the car is 18 000 kg m/s. Calculate the velocity of the car in m/s. [2]

momentum = mass × velocity

18 000 = 900 × v ✔

V = 18 000/900 = 20 m/s ✔

| The candidate's answer shows good structure. The momentum equation has been correctly rearranged. This is a good start from the candidate. |

AO2 **b** The diagram shows the state of a car before and after a collision.

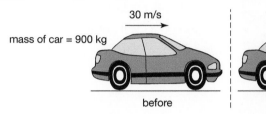

30 m/s   5.0 m/s

mass of car = 900 kg

before   after

The collision lasts for a time of 1.5 s. Use the information given in the diagram to determine the net force acting on the car during the collision. State the unit. [3]

net force = change in momentum/time

$$net\ force = \frac{(900 \times 5) - (900 \times 30)}{1.5}$$ ✔

net force = 3000 kg m/s² ✘ ✔

The candidate started well by setting up the correct equation and substitution. Sadly, the candidate has made an error with the calculation. The correct answer is –15 000 N; the minus sign indicating a decelerating force. Always check that your answer makes sense – in this instance, you would expect deceleration and a minus sign. The examiner has awarded a mark for the correct unit. However, the standard notation for the unit is newton (N).

AO1 **c** Explain how seat belts reduce the impact forces on the driver during an accident. [3]

The seat belt increases the time taken for the driver to stop. ✔

It also absorbs the momentum of the car. ✘

The driver stays in the seat and does not hit something hard in the car. ✘

[Total: 8]

This candidate scored 5 marks out of a possible 8. Grade A candidates rarely make mistakes in calculations and usually show good use of physics in extended writing questions.

How to raise your grade

Take note of the comments from examiners – these will help you to improve your grade.

This is a poor answer from the candidate. The second line makes no sense at all and is an example of how candidates often use scientific terms to cover lack of knowledge. The candidate could have scored 2 further marks by mentioning the following:

> The rate of change of momentum of the driver is reduced and hence the driver experiences a smaller force.

> The seat belt prevents the driver from hitting the steering wheel or the windscreen.

Bad Science for Schools

When the evidence doesn't add up

Sometimes people use what sound like scientific words and ideas to sell you things or persuade you to think in a certain way. Some of these claims are valid, and some are not. The activities on these pages are based on the work of Dr Ben Goldacre and will help you to question some of the scientific claims you meet. Read more about the work of Ben at www.badscience.net.

Brown goo

You may have seen adverts for a foot spa that can remove toxins from your body. They are sometimes used in beauty salons or you might even buy one to use at home. The basin is filled with water, a sachet of special salts is added and then it is plugged in. You put your feet in to soak and the water turns brown!

It looks impressive, but is that because toxins have left your body through your feet?

Now, the advertisers of these products would tell us that we are being 'detoxed' and that horrible chemicals, toxins, which have accumulated in our bodies are at long last being released. It's perhaps not surprising that people are keen to be cleansed. However the talk doesn't match the facts. The chemicals in the water didn't come from your body which (as you know) is quite capable of getting rid of substances it doesn't need without using special equipment.

We are learning to:

> use primary and secondary evidence to investigate scientific claims

> apply scientific concepts to evaluate 'health products'

> explore the implications of these evaluations

✲ CAN YOU DETOX VIA YOUR FEET?

Read the leaflet – it sounds scientific but is it? Think about what you have learnt in science.

> Human metabolism is complex with the 'building blocks' of molecules being reshaped into new arrangements. The same molecule can be a waste product or a valued ingredient, depending on when and where it is in the body. There is no such thing as a 'detox system' in any medical textbook. Sometimes the body does need to dispose of waste but it does so by well-known ways.

> Electrolysis occurs when a direct electric current is passed through a liquid containing mobile ions, resulting in a chemical reaction at the electrodes.

Can you come up with a hypothesis about what's going on? How would you prove it? Ben came up with a good idea and gave his Barbie™ a foot bath – you might get a chance to replicate his experiment. Can you predict what might happen?

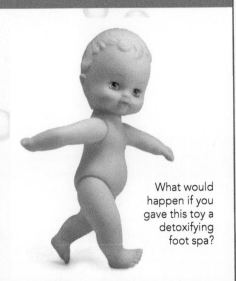

What would happen if you gave this toy a detoxifying foot spa?

Collins
Detox Foot Bath

Before

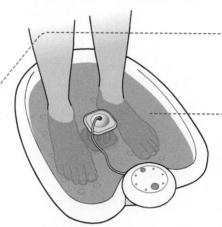

After 30 minutes

This looks like a serious piece of equipment.

This brown water looks horrible but is it brown because of toxins from the body?

This explanation sounds scientific, but is it?

The patented Collins Detox Foot Bath stimulates the active release of tingling ions that surge back and forth around your feet generating a flow of both negative and positive energy. This refreshes and renews the tissues, cleansing your body of accumulated toxins, readjusting the balance of energy at a bio-cellular level and removing excretory residues.

The centrally located micro-voltaic electrodes cause the flow of bi-polar ions producing an energy field that carries essential nutrients and life-giving oxygen. The release of toxins takes places through the myriad of microscopic pores in the soles of your feet. Graduated colour changes in the water present conclusive evidence of the beneficial effects.

The many enthusiastic users report a range of exhilarating effects including a heightened sense of awareness, improved circulation and relief of arthritic pain. The results are personal to each user as their toxin levels and combinations vary, but all report positive outcomes. One recent example of enthusiastic feedback said "The colour of the water shocked me in the realisation of what had accumulated in my body but the lightness I felt lasted for days!"

The people who tested it were impressed but did they enjoy the effects of detox or a relaxing foot bath?

✱ DETOX SELLS!

Words like 'toxins' and 'detoxification' (the removal of toxins) are sometimes used to promote products and techniques. Nobody likes to think of toxins accumulating in their body but we must consider whether there's any scientific basis for these ideas.

> Can you think of other products that claim to 'detox'?

> Why do you think that 'detoxing' can be used to sell these products?

> These treatments could all be said to be a little theatrical. How does this help to convince people that they're effective?

Bad Science for Schools

When the evidence doesn't add up

Sometimes people use what sound like scientific words and ideas to sell you things or persuade you to think in a certain way. Some of these claims are valid, and some are not. The activities on these pages are based on the work of Dr Ben Goldacre and will help you to question some of the scientific claims you meet. Read more about the work of Ben at www.badscience.net.

Bad news

In science you learn about ideas that scientists have developed by collecting evidence from experiments; you are also learning to collect and evaluate evidence yourself. You can use this outside of the laboratory to weigh up information you come across every day. Let's look at this example about how data can be used to support a story for a newspaper.

When data is produced you might think that there's only one way it can be used, and only one meaning that can be supported. This isn't always true.

We are learning to:

> understand how data can be used to make a good news story

> understand how science reports may be distorted to make headlines

> consider why science reports may be represented in various different ways

✱ GOOD ADVICE?

If a woman wants to be sexually active but doesn't want to get pregnant, one of the contraceptive methods available to her is to use a contraceptive implant. There are a number of factors to take into account; one of the most important ones is, of course, 'how well does it work?' Think about the headline on the right. What kind of questions might you ask that would reveal whether this method is, in fact, a failure?

600 pregnancies despite contraceptive implant

✱ STICKING TO THE NUMBERS

One of the questions we might want to consider is 'over what timescale?' Is this 600 over the last month, last year or since records began? In fact, the contraceptive implant had been available for 10 years when this data was released, so it's 60 unintended pregnancies per year, on average. Still not ideal, but maybe not as disastrous as at first thought.

We might also want to know how widespread the use of the implant was. If the 60 pregnancies a year was out of say, 1000 people, then that's not very good: it would mean that six out of every 100 women with an implant had got pregnant over a year.

If it was out of 100 000 then that means six out of every 10 000 women got pregnant over a year, so this method of contraception would compare well with other methods.

In fact, around 1.3 million implants have been used over the last 10 years, and each lasts for 3 years. This works out as 1.4 unwanted pregnancies for every 10 000 women using the method per year if we assume that each implant lasts for the full 3 years.

Making the headlines

Four students are talking about this story.

Jo says

I think the journalists were doing a good job here to tell people about the fact that 600 women who thought that they couldn't get pregnant, then did. They got hold of the facts and then reported them.

Adam says

The journalists didn't write this up very well. Most of the people reading this story would be women who would be wondering if this method of contraception was one that they should use. The headline suggests that it's not safe and it is. Well, most of the time.

Will says

Journalists have to be responsible. If this story frightens women off one of the safest methods of contraception they've let people down.

Emma says

The main job of journalists is to be entertaining. Boring stories don't get read. '600 women using contraceptive get pregnant' makes you read the story. '0.014% of women using contraceptive get pregnant' looks boring.

■ Look at these comments. Who do you think is right?

■ Do you think the main purpose of a journalist is:
- To be informative, even if it's sometimes boring?
- To be engaging, even if it may sometimes give a false impression?

■ If you had been the journalist assigned to this story, what headline would you have used?

✳ NUMBERS IN THE REAL WORLD

A useful way of presenting data like this is to use what's called the natural frequency. Out of a set number, this indicates how many will have a changed outcome as a result of this. In this case it's 1.4 out of 10 000. The figure of 60 per year isn't wrong, neither is the 0.014%, but 1.4 in 10 000 puts it in a simple form that people can make sense of and use to assess the likely impact on them.

When the evidence doesn't add up

Sometimes people use what sound like scientific words and ideas to sell you things or persuade you to think in a certain way. Some of these claims are valid, and some are not. The activities on these pages are based on the work of Dr Ben Goldacre and will help you to question some of the scientific claims you meet. Read more about the work of Ben at www.badscience.net.

MMR – don't die of ignorance

Autism is a condition which affects between one and two people in every thousand, affecting neural development and causing restricted and repetitive behaviour. It affects social behaviour and language. It is usually diagnosed from the age of three onwards.

In Britain, as in many countries, the majority children are vaccinated against measles, mumps and rubella using a combined vaccine (MMR) between the ages of one and two. In 1998 a British doctor wrote a report on 12 children who had been vaccinated with the MMR vaccine and were subsequently diagnosed as autistic. The result of this report was that media interest was raised, many anti-MMR stories appeared and there was a significant fall in the number of children who were given the MMR vaccine.

Consider these questions:

> Does the fact that the children in the report were diagnosed with autism after being given the MMR vaccine prove that the vaccine caused the autism?

> At the time of the report being written well over 90% of children had the MMR vaccine. Why should it not be a surprise if some of those children are diagnosed with autism?

> What kind of survey would have helped to identify whether the MMR vaccine caused autism?

✳ THE RISE OF MEASLES

As the number of MMR vaccinations fell, the number of measles cases rose. Measles is a very dangerous disease that even in developed countries kills one in every 3000 people and causes pneumonia in one in 20.

It was subsequently established beyond reasonable doubt that there is no causal link between MMR vaccination and autism. The doctor had a commercial interest in the alleged link and was subsequently struck off. The scare affected no other countries. MMR vaccination rates in Britain are rising again. Doctors are still not sure why some children develop autism; its causes are unknown.

Consider these points of view:

"The doctor who wrote the report was right to alert people to his concerns and suggest that more research should be carried out."

"The media got hold of the story and turned it into a huge scare. It's their fault."

"There was never any evidence to prove a link. Thousands of children have caught diseases that could otherwise have been avoided."

We are learning to:

> understand the difference between correlation and cause and effect

> to apply this understanding to a variety of contexts

> to explore the professional dilemma facing scientists who have concerns and whose actions have serious consequences

✳ THE RISE OF MEASLES

One of the things this story illustrates is what can happen when you look at only a very small sample and the importance of working with large-scale surveys wherever possible. Such a study was carried out in Denmark: the Madsen study. Because Denmark tracks patients and the care they receive on a central system they have been able to study the correlation between vaccination and illness. The data clearly shows that there is no correlation between MMR vaccination and the incidence of autism.

The study was based on data from over half a million children: over 440 000 had been vaccinated and there was no greater incidence of autism in children vaccinated than in those not vaccinated.

> Identify the features of this study that make its findings reliable.

> What might you say to someone who still wasn't convinced by this study and decided to 'play it safe' by not having their child vaccinated for MMR?

Cause and effect?

Sometimes it looks like something causes something else, perhaps because they both happen at the same time. But scientists need to be very careful before saying that one thing causes another.

• Often you need to use common sense and extra information to help decide if there is true causation. For example, cocks crow in the morning, but nobody thinks that cocks crowing causes the sun to come up, because there's no conceivable mechanism for that, and it conflicts with everything we know about the Sun and the Earth. On the other hand, we can observe that when it gets warmer, people wear fewer clothes, and it seems reasonable to say that the warm weather causes people to wear less.

• Sometimes two things are correlated, but it's harder to say what causes what, and there might be a third factor causing both of the things that we are observing. Let's say, for example, that a study finds that there is a strong correlation between a child's IQ and their height: perhaps both height and IQ are themselves related, through a complex causal pathway, to something else, like general health, or diet, or social deprivation

• Often, although things happen at the same time, there is no link at all. For example, Halley's Comet appears once every 76 years. Previous appearances have coincided with King Harold's defeat at the Battle of Hastings, Genghis Khan's invasion of Europe and both the birth and death of great American novelist Mark Twain, author of *The Adventures of Tom Sawyer.*

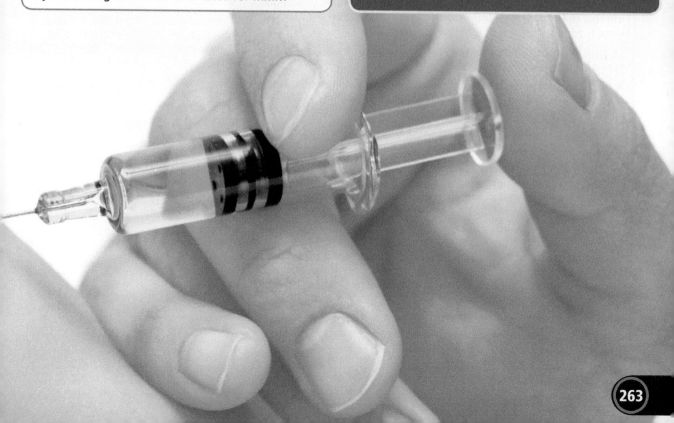

Carrying out practical investigations in GCSE science

Introduction

As part of your GCSE science course, you will develop practical skills and carry out investigative work as part of the scientific process.

Your investigative work will be divided into several parts:

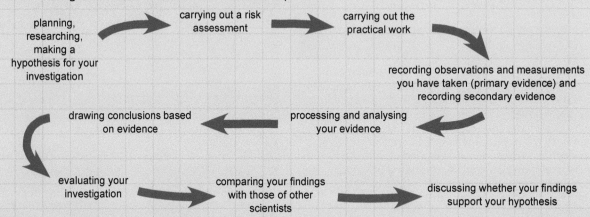

planning, researching, making a hypothesis for your investigation → carrying out a risk assessment → carrying out the practical work → recording observations and measurements you have taken (primary evidence) and recording secondary evidence → processing and analysing your evidence → drawing conclusions based on evidence → evaluating your investigation → comparing your findings with those of other scientists → discussing whether your findings support your hypothesis

✳ Planning and researching your investigation

A scientific investigation usually begins with you considering an idea, answering a question or trying to solve a problem.

Researching what other people know about the idea or problem should suggest some variables that have an effect on the problem.

From this you should develop a hypothesis. For example, you might observe during a fermentation with yeast investigation that beer or wine is produced faster at a higher temperature.

So your hypothesis might be that 'as the temperature increases, the rate of fermentation increases'.

A good starting point for your research is to use your lesson notes and textbook. The topic you've been given to investigate will relate to the science you've learned in class.

Also make use of the internet, but make sure that your internet search is closely focused on the topic you're investigating.

✔ The search terms you use on the internet are very important. 'Investigating fermentation' is a better search term than just 'fermentation', as it's more likely to provide links to websites that are more relevant to your investigation.

✔ The information on websites also varies in its reliability. Free encyclopaedias often contain information that hasn't been written by experts. Some question and answer websites might appear to give you the exact answer to your question, but be aware that they may sometimes be incorrect.

✔ Most GCSE science websites are more reliable, but, if in doubt, use other information sources to verify the information.

As a result of your research, you may be able to extend your hypothesis and justify it using scientific ideas.

Definition

A **hypothesis** is a possible explanation that someone suggests to explain some scientific observations.

Assessment tip

When making your hypothesis, it's important that it's testable. In other words, you must be able to test the hypothesis in the school lab.

Assessment tip

Your need to use your research to explain why you made your hypothesis.

You would then plan how you will carry out an investigation to test this hypothesis.

> *Example 1*
>
> Investigation: Plan and research an investigation into the effect of temperature on the change in height of a plant over 2 weeks.
>
> Your hypothesis might be 'when I increase the temperature, the percentage increase in the height of the plant will be greater'.
>
> You should be able to justify the hypothesis by some facts you have found. For example, 'growing lettuces in greenhouses halves the time it takes for them to be ready to sell'.

Choosing a method and suitable equipment

As part of your planning, you must choose a suitable way of carrying out the investigation.

You will have to choose suitable techniques, equipment and technology, if this is appropriate. How do you make this choice?

You will have already carried out the techniques you need to use during the course of practical work in class (although you may need to modify these to fit in with the context of your investigation). For most of the experimental work you do, there will be a choice of techniques available. You must select the technique:

✔ that is most appropriate to the context of your investigation, and

✔ that will enable you to collect valid data; for example, if you are measuring the effects of light intensity on photosynthesis, you may decide to use an LED (light-emitting diode) at different distances from the plant, rather than a light bulb. The light bulb produces more heat, and temperature is another independent variable in photosynthesis.

Your choice of equipment, too, will be influenced by measurements you need to make. For example:

✔ you might use a one-mark or graduated pipette to measure out the volume of liquid for a titration, but

✔ you may use a measuring cylinder or beaker when adding a volume of acid to a reaction mixture, so that the volume of acid is in excess to that required to dissolve, for example, the calcium carbonate.

> **Assessment tip**
>
> Carrying out a preliminary investigation, along with the necessary research, may help you to select the appropriate technique to use.

> **Assessment tip**
>
> You should always be ready to explain your choice of equipment.

> **Assessment tip**
>
> Technology, such as data-logging and other measuring and monitoring techniques – for example, heart sensors – may help you to carry out your experiment.

Variables

In your investigation, you will work with independent and dependent variables.

The factors you choose, or are given, to investigate the effect of are called **independent variables**.

What you choose to measure, as affected by the independent variable, is called the **dependent variable**.

Independent variables

In your practical work, you will be provided with an independent variable to test, or will have to choose one – or more – of these to test. Some examples are given in the table.

Investigation	Possible independent variables to test
activity of yeast	> temperature > sugar concentration
rate of a chemical reaction	> temperature > concentration of reactants
stopping distance of a moving object	> speed of the object > the surface on which it's moving

Independent variables can be **discrete** or **continuous**.

> When you are testing the effect of different disinfectants on bacteria you are looking at discrete variables.

> When you are testing the effect of a range of concentrations of the same disinfectant on the growth of bacteria you are looking at continuous variables.

Range

When working with an independent variable, you need to choose an appropriate **range** over which to investigate the variable.

You need to decide:

✔ what you will test, and/or

✔ the upper and lower limits of the independent variable to investigate, if the variable is continuous.

Once you have defined the range to be tested, you also need to decide the appropriate intervals at which you will make measurements.

The range you would test depends on:

✔ the nature of the test

✔ the context in which it is given

✔ practical considerations, and

✔ common sense.

Example 2

1 Investigation: Investigating the factors that affect how quickly household limescale removers work in removing limescale from an appliance.

You may have to decide on which acids to use from a range you're provided with. You would choose a weak acid, or acids, to test rather than a strong acid, such as concentrated sulfuric acid. This is because of safety reasons, but also because the acid might damage the appliance you were trying to clean. You would then have to select a range of concentrations of your chosen weak acid to test.

> **Definition**
>
> Variables that fall into a range of separate types are called **discrete** (also known as **categorical**) **variables**.

> **Definition**
>
> Variables that have a continuous range are called **continuous variables**.

> **Definition**
>
> The **range** defines the extent of the independent variables being tested, e.g. from 15 cm to 35 cm.

> **Assessment tip**
>
> Again, it's often best to carry out a trial run or preliminary investigation, or carry out research, to determine the range to be investigated.

Concentration

You might be trying to find out the best, or optimum, concentration of a disinfectant to prevent the growth of bacteria.

The 'best' concentration would be the lowest in a range that prevented the growth of the bacteria. Concentrations higher than this would be just wasting disinfectant.

If, in a preliminary test, no bacteria were killed by the concentration you used, you would have to increase it (or test another disinfectant). However, if there was no growth of bacteria in your preliminary test, you would have to lower the concentration range. A starting point might be to look at concentrations around those recommended by the manufacturer.

✳ Dependent variables

The dependent variable may be clear from the problem you're investigating; for example, the stopping distance of moving objects. But you may have to make a choice.

Example 3

1 Investigation: Measuring the rate of photosynthesis in a plant.

There are several ways in which you could measure the rate of photosynthesis in a plant. These include:

> counting the number of bubbles of oxygen produced in a minute by a water plant such as *Elodea* or *Cabomba*

> measuring the volume of oxygen produced over several days by a water plant such as *Elodea* or *Cabomba*

> monitoring the concentration of oxygen in a polythene bag enclosing a potted plant using an oxygen sensor

> measuring the colour change of hydrogen carbonate indicator containing algae embedded in gel.

2 Investigation: Measuring the rate of a chemical reaction.

You could measure the rate of a chemical reaction in the following ways:

> the rate of formation of a product

> the rate at which the reactant disappears

> a colour change

> a pH change.

✳ Control variables

The validity of your measurements depends on you measuring what you're supposed to be measuring.

Some of these variables may be difficult to control. For example, in an ecology investigation in the field, factors such as varying weather conditions are impossible to control.

Assessment tip

The value of the *depend*ent variable is likely to *depend* on the value of the independent variable. This is a good way of remembering the definition of a dependent variable.

Definition

Other variables that you're not investigating may also have an influence on your measurements. In most investigations, it's important that you investigate just one variable at a time. So other variables, apart from the one you're testing at the time, must be controlled, and kept constant, and not allowed to vary. These are called **control variables**.

Assessment tip

Always identify all the variables to be controlled and how you will control them.

Experimental controls

Experimental controls are often very important, particularly in biological investigations where you're testing the effect of a treatment.

Example 4

Investigation: The effect of temperature on the growth of tomato plants.

The tomato plants grow most at 35 °C, but some plants at lower temperatures grow just as well. You need to be certain that the effect is caused by the temperature. There are lots of things that affect plant growth, so you should make sure these variables are controlled. These include the volume of water they receive, the soil that the plants are grown in, the nutrients present in the soil, and that the plants are as genetically similar as possible. Farmers often use F1 hybrid seeds as the plants are virtually genetically identical and will be ready to harvest at the same time.

Definition

An **experimental control** is used to find out whether the effect you obtain is from the treatment, or whether you get the same result in the absence of the treatment.

✳ Assessing and managing risk

Before you begin any practical work, you must assess and minimise the possible risks involved.

Before you carry out an investigation, you must identify the possible hazards. These can be grouped into biological hazards, chemical hazards and physical hazards.

Biological hazards include:	Chemical hazards can be grouped into:	Physical hazards include:
> microorganisms > body fluids > animals and plants.	> irritant and harmful substances > toxic > oxidising agents > corrosive > harmful to the environment.	> equipment > objects > radiation.

Scientists use an international series of symbols so that investigators can identify hazards.

Hazards pose risks to the person carrying out the investigation.

Many acids, for instance, while being corrosive in higher concentrations, are harmful or an irritant at low concentrations.

A risk posed by concentrated sulfuric acid, for example, will be lower if you're adding one drop of it to a reaction mixture to make an ester, than if you're mixing a large volume of it with water.

When you use hazardous materials, chemicals or equipment in the laboratory, you must use them in such a way as to keep the risks to an absolute minimum. For example, one way is to wear eye protection when using hydrochloric acid.

Definition

A **hazard** is something that has the potential to cause harm. Even substances, organisms and equipment that we think of being harmless, used in the wrong way, may be hazardous.

Hazard symbols are used on chemical bottles so that hazards can be identified

Definition

The **risk** is the likelihood of a hazard causing harm in the circumstances it's being used in.

Assessment tip

Your method should show how you will manage risks and make your experiment safe.

Risk assessment

Before you begin an investigation, you must carry out a risk assessment. Your risk assessment must include:

✔ all relevant hazards (use the correct terms to describe each hazard, and make sure you include them all, even if you think they will pose minimal risk)

✔ risks associated with these hazards

✔ ways in which the risks can be minimised

✔ results of research into emergency procedures that you may have to follow if something goes wrong.

You should also consider what to do at the end of the practical. For example, used agar plates should be left for a technician to sterilise; solutions of heavy metals should be collected in a bottle and disposed of safely.

Assessment tip

When assessing risk and suggesting control measures, these should be specific to the hazard and risk, and not general. Hydrochloric acid is dangerous as it is 'corrosive, and skin and eye contact should be avoided' will be given credit but 'wear eye protection' is too vague.

Overall plan

You should write up your overall plan – including method, equipment, variables to test and control, and risk assessment – before beginning your experiment. Arrange your plan logically. Remember, another student should be able to use it to carry out the same experiment.

Collecting primary evidence

✔ You should be sure to collect evidence that is appropriate for the topic.

✔ You should make sure that observations, if appropriate, are recorded in detail. For example, it is worth recording the colour of your precipitate when making an insoluble salt, in addition to any other measurements you make.

✔ Measurements should be recorded in tables. Have one ready so that you can record your readings as you carry out the practical work.

✔ Think about the dependent variable and define this carefully in your column headings.

✔ You should make sure that the table headings describe properly the type of measurements you've made, for example 'time taken for magnesium ribbon to dissolve'.

✔ It's also essential that you include units – your results are meaningless without these.

✔ The units should appear in the column head, and not be repeated in each row of the table.

Definition

When you carry out an investigation, the data you collect are called **primary evidence.** The term 'data' is normally used to include your observations as well as any measurements you might make.

Repeatability and reproducibility of results

When making measurements, in most instances, it's essential that you carry out repeats.

These repeats are one way of checking your results.

Results will not be repeatable, of course, if you allow the conditions the investigation is carried out in to change.

You need to make sure that you carry out sufficient repeats, but not too many. In a titration, for example, if you obtain two values that are within $0.1\,cm^3$ of each other, carrying out any more will not improve the reliability of your results.

This is particularly important when scientists are carrying out scientific research and make new discoveries.

Collecting secondary evidence

As part of Controlled Assessment, you will be expected to collect **secondary evidence**. The secondary data you collect must be appropriate for the topic.

One of the simplest ways of doing this is to collect evidence from other groups in your class who have carried out an identical practical investigation.

You should also, if possible, search through the scientific literature – in textbooks, the internet and databases – to find evidence from similar or identical practical investigations.

Ideally, you should use secondary evidence from a number of sources and record it appropriately.

You should review secondary data and evaluate it. Scientific studies are sometimes influenced by the **bias** of the experimenter.

✔ One kind of bias is having a strong opinion related to the investigation, and perhaps selecting only the results that fit with a hypothesis or prediction.

✔ Or the bias could be unintentional. In fields of science that are not yet fully understood, experimenters may try to fit their findings to current knowledge and thinking.

There have been other instances where the 'findings' of experimenters have been influenced by organisations that supplied the funding for the research.

You must fully reference any secondary data you have used, using one of the accepted referencing methods.

Referencing methods

The two main conventions for writing a reference are the:

✔ Harvard system
✔ Vancouver system.

In your text, the Harvard system refers to the authors of the reference, for example 'Smith and Jones (1978)'.

The Vancouver system refers to the number of the numbered reference in your text, for example '... the reason for this hypothesis is unknown.[5]'

Assessment tip

One set of results from your investigation may not reflect what truly happens. Carrying out repeats enables you to identify any results that don't fit.

Definition

If you carry out the same experiment several times and get the same, or very similar, results, we say the results are **repeatable**.

Definition

Taking more than one set of results will improve the **reliability** of your data.

Definition

Secondary evidence is measurements/observations made by anyone other than you.

Assessment tip

Always comment on the quality of your secondary evidence – including bias.

Though the Harvard system is usually preferred by scientists, it is more straightforward for you to use the Vancouver system.

Harvard system

In your references list a book reference should be written:

> Author(s) (year of publication). *Title of Book*, publisher, publisher location.

The references are listed in alphabetical order according to the authors.

Vancouver system

In your references list a book reference should be written:

> 1 Author(s). *Title of Book*. Publisher, publisher location: year of publication.

The references are numbered in the order in which they are cited in the text.

✳ Processing evidence

You may be required to use formulae when processing data. Sometimes, these will need rearranging to be able to make the calculation you need. Practise using and rearranging formulae as part of your preparation for assessment.

Calculating the mean

Using your repeat measurements you can calculate the arithmetical mean (or just 'mean') of these data. Often, the mean is called the 'average'.

Here are the results of an investigation into the energy requirements of three different mp3 players. The students measured the energy using a joulemeter for 10 seconds.

mp3 player	Energy used in joules (J)			
	Trial 1	Trial 2	Trial 3	Mean
Viking	5.5	5.3	5.7	5.5
Anglo	4.5	4.6	4.9	4.7
Saxon	3.2	4.5	4.7	4.6

Significant figures

When calculating the mean, you should be aware of significant figures.

For example, for the set of data below:

18	13	17	15	14	16	15	14	13	18

The total for the data set is 153, and 10 measurements have been made. The mean is 15, and not 15.3.

This is because each of the recorded values has two significant figures. The answer must therefore have two significant figures. An answer cannot have more significant figures than the number being multiplied or divided.

Assessment tip

Remember to write out the URL of a website in full. You should also quote the date when you looked at the website.

Assessment tip

Remember to process all your collected evidence – primary and secondary.

Definition

The **reproducibility** of data is the ability of the results of an investigation to be reproduced by someone else, who may be in a different lab, carrying out the same work.

Definition

The **mean** is calculated by adding together all the measurements, and dividing by the number of measurements.

Definition

Significant figures are the number of digits in a number based on the precision of your measurements.

Using your data

When calculating means (and displaying data), you should be careful to look out for any data that do not fit in with the general pattern. In the table above one result has been excluded from the mean calculation because it was more than 10% lower than the other values. This suggests it may be anomalous.

It might be the consequence of an error made in measurement. But sometimes anomalous results are genuine results. If you think an anomalous result has been introduced by careless practical work, you should ignore it when calculating the mean. But you should examine possible reasons carefully before just leaving it out.

Presenting your evidence

Presenting your evidence – usually the means – makes it easy to pick out and show any patterns. It also helps you to pick out any anomalous results.

It is likely that you will have recorded your results in tables, and you could also use additional tables to summarise your results. The most usual way of displaying data is to use graphs. The table will help you to decide which type to use.

Type of graph	When you would use the graph	Example
Bar charts or bar graph	Where one of the variables is discrete	'The energy requirements of different mp3 players'
Line graph	Where independent and dependent variables are both continuous	'The volume of carbon dioxide produced by a range of different concentrations of hydrochloric acid'
Scatter graph	To show an association between two (or more) variables	'The association between length and breadth of a number of privet leaves' In scatter graphs, the points are plotted, but not usually joined

If it's possible from the data, join the points of a line graph using a straight line, or in some instances, a curve. In this way graphs can also help us to process data.

Spread of data

Plotting a graph of just the means doesn't tell you anything about the spread of data that has been used to calculate the mean.

You can show the spread of the data on your graphs using error bars or range bars.

Range bars are very useful, but they don't show how the data are spread between the extreme values. It is important to have information about this range. It may affect your analysis of the data, and the conclusions you draw.

Definition

An **anomaly** (or **outlier**) is a reading that is very different from the rest.

Assessment tip

Remember when drawing graphs, plot the independent variable on the *x*-axis, and the dependent variable on the *y*-axis.

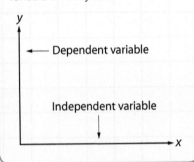

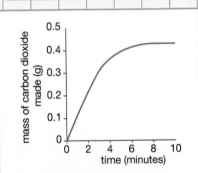

We can calculate the rate of production of carbon dioxide from the gradient of the graph

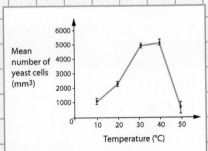

Range bars

✳ Differences in data sets and probability

When comparing two (or more) sets of data, we often compare the values of two sets of means.

Example 5

Investigation: Comparing the braking distance of two tyres.

Two groups of students compared the braking distance of two tyres, labelled A and B. Their results are shown in the table.

Tyre	Baking distance in metres (m)										Mean
	1	2	3	4	5	6	7	8	9	10	
A	15	13	17	15	14	16	15	14	13	18	15
B	25	23	24	23	26	27	25	24	23	22	24

When the means are compared, it appears that tyre A will bring a vehicle to a stop in a shorter distance than tyre B. The difference might have resulted from some other factor, or could be purely by chance.

Scientists use statistics to find the probability of any differences having occurred by chance. The lower this probability is, which is found out by statistical calculations, the more likely it is that tyre A is better at stopping a vehicle than tyre B.

Statistical analysis can help to increase the confidence you have in your conclusions.

Assessment tip

You have learned about probability in your Maths lessons.

Definition

If there is a relationship between dependent and independent variables that can be defined, we say there is a **correlation** between the variables.

✳ Drawing conclusions

Observing trends in data or graphs will help you to draw conclusions. You may obtain a linear relationship between two sets of variables, or the relationship might be more complex.

Example 6

The higher the concentration of acid, the shorter the time taken for the magnesium ribbon to dissolve.

When drawing conclusions, you should try to relate your findings – including mathematical relationships, primary evidence and secondary evidence – to the science involved. You should also relate your conclusion to your hypothesis.

In this example, your discussion should focus on the greater possibility/increased frequency of collisions between reacting particles as the concentration of the acid is increased.

But we sometimes see correlations between data in science which are coincidental, where the independent variable is not the cause of the trend in the data.

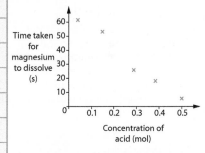

This graph shows **negative correlation**

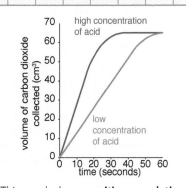

This graph shows **positive correlation**

Example 7

Studies have shown that levels of vitamin D are very low in people with long-term inflammatory diseases. But there's no scientific evidence to suggest that these low levels are the cause of the diseases.

✳ Accounting for errors

Your conclusion will be based on your evidence, but must take into consideration any uncertainty in your results introduced by any possible sources of error. You should discuss where these have come from in your evaluation.

The two types of errors are:

✔ random error
✔ systematic error.

This can occur when the instrument you're using to measure lacks sufficient sensitivity to indicate differences in readings. It can also occur when it's difficult to make a measurement. If two investigators measure the height of a plant, for example, they might choose different points on the compost and the tip of the growing point to make their measurements.

The volume of liquid in a burette must be read to the bottom of the meniscus

Your results may be either consistently too high or too low. One reason could be down to the way you are making a reading; for example, taking a burette reading at the wrong point on the meniscus. Another could be the result of an instrument being incorrectly calibrated, or not being calibrated.

✳ Accuracy and precision

When evaluating your investigation, you should mention accuracy and precision. But if you use these terms, it's important that you understand what they mean, and that you use them correctly.

Precise but not accurate

Precise and accurate

Neither precise nor accurate

The terms accuracy and precision can be illustrated using shots at a dartboard.

In science, the measurements you make as part of your investigation should be as precise as you can, or need to, make them. To achieve this, you should use:

✔ the most appropriate measuring instrument

✔ the measuring instrument with the most appropriate size of divisions.

The smaller the divisions you work with, the more precise your measurements. For example:

✔ In an investigation on how your heart rate is affected by exercise, you might decide to investigate this after a 100 m run. You might measure out the 100 m distance using a trundle wheel, which is sufficiently precise for your investigation.

✔ In an investigation on how light intensity is affected by distance, you would make your measurements of distance using a metre rule with millimetre divisions; clearly a trundle wheel would be too imprecise.

✔ In an investigation on plant growth, in which you measure the thickness of a plant stem, you would use a micrometer or Vernier callipers. In this instance, a metre rule would be too imprecise.

✹ Evaluating your method and conclusion

When evaluating your method, you should identify the strengths of your method and discuss how your investigation could be improved. You should consider improving:

✔ the reliability of your data. For example, you could make more repeats, or more frequent readings, or 'fine-tune' the range you choose to investigate, or refine your technique in some other way

✔ the accuracy and precision of your data, by using more precise measuring equipment.

Taking this into account, you can evaluate your conclusion – how could you improve or extend your evidence to give further support to your conclusion? An important way to extend your evidence is by carrying out repeats.

Assessment tip

Your evaluation of method should be related to your hypothesis and reasons should be given for anomalies.

✹ Does the evidence support your hypothesis?

You need to discuss, in detail, whether all, or which of your primary evidence and the secondary evidence you have collected supports your original hypothesis. It may, or may not.

You should communicate your points clearly, using the appropriate scientific terms, and checking carefully your use of spelling, punctuation and grammar. You will be assessed on this written communication as well as your science.

If your evidence does not completely match your hypothesis, it may be possible to modify the hypothesis or suggest an alternative one. You should suggest any further investigations that can be carried out to support your original hypothesis or the modified version.

It is important to remember, however, that if your investigation does support your hypothesis, it can improve the confidence you have in your conclusions and scientific explanations, but it can't prove your explanations are correct.

✳ Your controlled assessment

The assessment of your investigation will form part of what's called Controlled Assessment. Edexcel will provide the task for you to investigate.

You may be able to work in small groups to carry out the practical work, but you will have to work on your own to write up your investigation.

Controlled assessment is worth 25% of the marks for your GCSE. It's worth doing it well!

Your Additional Science Controlled Assessment Task (CAT) will consist of three parts:

✔ Part A – Planning
✔ Part B – Observations
✔ Part C – Conclusions

To achieve a final grade in your Controlled Assessment Unit, you must complete all three parts of at least one CAT.

Part A – Planning

In Part A you must write a plan to test a specific hypothesis.

You will be briefed with an outline of a scientific concept and task.

In your **Science** CAT you were given a hypothesis to test. In your **Additional** and **Separate Sciences** CATs you must write a hypothesis in line with the brief you have been given.

To produce a complete plan you must:

✔ Select and justify the equipment for your investigation
✔ Choose and explain the variables you will change, measure and control
✔ Identify risks and explain how you will manage them
✔ Write a plan that includes your method, equipment and variables, and reflects how risks will be managed.

Your plan must be clear and produce results that will test your hypothesis.

You will complete Part A under 'limited' controlled conditions. This means that you will be allowed to collaborate with other students and use research to complete the task.

Part B – Observations

In Part B you will carry out an experiment to test your hypothesis from Part A, using the plan you produced also in Part A.

You will use your plan to collect and record primary evidence.

You must also collect and record secondary evidence that is relevant to your hypothesis.

You may collect secondary evidence in class or at home from:

✔ the internet
✔ other students, or
✔ textbooks.

You will be expected to reference all secondary sources fully and comment on the quality of the source of evidence.

You will also complete Part B under 'limited' controlled conditions.

Part C – Conclusions

In Part C you will process and draw conclusions from the evidence you collected in Part B.

✔ Process all your evidence (primary and secondary) suitably using digital technology and maths as appropriate.

✔ Decide whether to include or exclude anomalies when processing evidence, explaining your reasons why.

✔ Produce a conclusion based on all processed evidence and appropriate scientific ideas. Does your evidence prove or disprove your hypothesis?

✔ Evaluate your method, describing strengths, weaknesses and improvements, and explaining reasons for anomalies.

✔ Suggest how you could improve or extend your evidence to support your conclusion further.

✔ Review your hypothesis in light of the evidence.

You will complete Part C under 'high' controlled conditions. This means that you must complete your write-up individually and completely under teacher supervision.

Quality of Written Communication

Be aware of the quality of your written communication in all parts of the CAT. You must ensure that the marker understands your ideas and evidence.

At all times you must communicate clearly using:

✔ an appropriate form and style
✔ clear and logical presentation, and
✔ scientific language where appropriate.

Assessment tip

If your plan from Part A was unusable – for example, because it was potentially dangerous – your teacher will give you a plan to work from for Part B. Remember, you will receive no marks for a Part A plan that is given to you.

Assessment tip

You will achieve top marks in Part B by:

> Collecting a suitable range of data.

> Carrying out repeat experiments as appropriate

> Recording all evidence – primary and secondary – appropriately.

Assessment tip

You will achieve top marks in Part C by:

> Presenting evidence so that you can draw conclusions from it

> Explaining your conclusions using maths, scientific ideas and data

> Relating your conclusion and evaluation back to your hypothesis.

Assessment tip

Your teacher will give you a copy of the Assessment Criteria so that you can see what you need to do to access all marks.

How to be successful in your GCSE science written assessment

Introduction

Edexcel uses assessments to test how good your understanding of scientific ideas is, how well you can apply your understanding to new situations, and how well you can analyse and interpret information you've been given. The assessments are opportunities to show how well you can do these.

To be successful in exams you need to:

✔ have a good knowledge and understanding of science

✔ be able to apply this knowledge and understanding to familiar and new situations, and

✔ be able to interpret and evaluate evidence that you've just been given.

You need to be able to do these things under exam conditions.

✹ The language of the external assessment

When working through an assessment paper, make sure that you:

✔ re-read a question enough times until you understand exactly what the examiner is looking for

✔ highlight key words in a question

✔ look at how many marks are allocated to each part of a question. In general, you need to write at least as many separate points in your answer as there are marks.

✹ What verbs are used in the question?

A good technique is to see which verbs are used in the wording of the question and to use these to gauge the type of response you need to give. The table lists some of the common verbs found in questions, the types of responses expected and examples.

Verb used in question	Response expected in answer	Example question
write down; state; give; identify	These are usually more straightforward types of question in which you're asked to give a definition, make a list of examples, or choose the best answer from a series of options	'Write down three types of microorganism that cause disease' 'State one difference and one similarity between radio waves and gamma rays'
calculate	Use maths to solve a numerical problem	'Calculate the percentage of carbon in copper carbonate ($CuCO_3$)'

estimate	Use maths to solve a numerical problem, but you do not have to work out the exact answer	'Estimate from the graph the speed of the vehicle after 3 minutes'
describe	Use words (or diagrams) to show the characteristics, properties or features of, or build an image of, something	'Describe how meiosis halves the number of chromosomes in a cell to make egg or sperm cells'
suggest	Come up with an idea to explain information you're given, usually in a new or unfamiliar context	'Suggest why tyres with different tread patterns will have different braking distances'
demonstrate; show how	Use words to make something evident using reasoning	'Show how temperature can affect the rate of a chemical reaction'
compare	Look for similarities and differences	'Compare aerobic and anaerobic respiration'
explain	To offer a reason for, or make understandable, information you're given	'Explain why alpha and beta radiations can be deflected by a magnetic field, but gamma rays are not'
evaluate	To examine and make a judgement about an investigation or information you're given	'Evaluate the benefits of using a circuit breaker instead of a fuse in an electrical circuit'

What is the style of the question?

Try to get used to answering questions that have been written in lots of different styles before you sit the exam. Work through past papers, or specimen papers, to get a feel for these. The types of questions in your assessment fit the three assessment objectives shown in the table.

Assessment objective	Your answer should show that you can...
AO1 Recall the science	Recall, select and communicate your knowledge and understanding of science
AO2 Apply your knowledge	Apply skills, knowledge and understanding of science in practical and other contexts
AO3 Evaluate and analyse the evidence	Analyse and evaluate evidence, make reasoned judgements and draw conclusions based on evidence

How to answer questions on: AO1 Recall the science

These questions, or parts of questions, test your ability to recall your knowledge of a topic. There are several types of this style of question:

✔ Fill in the spaces (you may be given words to choose from)
✔ Multiple choice
✔ Use lines to link a term with its definition or correct statement
✔ Add labels to a diagram
✔ Complete a table
✔ Describe a process

Example 8

a What is meant by the term *exothermic reaction*?

  A ☒ a reaction that gives out heat energy
  B ☒ a reaction that takes in energy from the surroundings
  C ☒ a reaction that can go in either direction.

AO1 questions on practical techniques

You may be asked to recall how to carry out certain practical techniques; either ones that you have carried out before, or techniques that scientists use.

To revise for these types of questions, make sure that you have learned definitions and scientific terms. Produce a glossary of these, or key facts cards, to make them easier to remember. Make sure your key facts cards also cover important practical techniques, including equipment, where appropriate.

Example 9

1 Describe how to find the work done when an object of 15 N is moved 1 metre.
2 Describe how DNA fragments can be separated by electrophoresis.

Assessment tip

Don't forget that mind maps – either drawn by you or made using a computer program – are very helpful when revising key points.

 How to answer questions on: AO2 Apply skills, knowledge and understanding

Some questions require you to apply basic knowledge and understanding in your answers.

You may be presented with a topic that's familiar to you, but you should also expect questions in your science exam to be set in an unfamiliar context.

Questions may be presented as:

✔ short questions referring to an unfamiliar object, process or organism
✔ experimental investigations
✔ data or diagrams for you to interpret
✔ a short paragraph or article.

The information required for you to answer the question might be in the question itself, but, for later stages of the question, you may be asked to draw on your knowledge and understanding of the subject material in the question.

Practice will help you to become familiar with contexts that examiners use and question styles. But you will not be able to predict many of the contexts used. This is deliberate; being able to apply your knowledge and understanding to different and unfamiliar situations is a skill the examiner tests.

Practise doing questions where you are tested on being able to apply your scientific knowledge and your ability to understand new situations that may not be familiar. In this way, when this type of question comes up in your exam, you will be able to tackle it successfully.

Assessment tip

Work through the Preparing for Assessment: Applying your knowledge tasks in this book as practice.

Example 10

The force of gravity acts on all objects falling towards the Earth. Two identical packages are dropped out of an aircraft at the same time. Both have parachutes. One package's parachute opens, the other doesn't.

Suggest which package will hit the ground first. Explain your answer.

AO2 questions on practical investigations

Some opportunities to demonstrate your application of skills, knowledge and understanding will be based on practical investigations. You may have carried out some of these investigations, but others will be new to you, and based on data obtained by scientists. You will be expected to describe patterns in data from graphs you are given or that you will have to draw from given data.

Again, you will have to apply your scientific knowledge and understanding to answer the question.

Example 11

1 Look at the graph showing the volume of gas collected when 10 g of calcium carbonate is reacted with three different concentrations of hydrochloric acid.

   a What is the maximum volume of gas that can be produced using 1 mole per dm^3 of hydrochloric acid?

   b Explain why this volume of gas is produced more quickly when using 2 moles per dm^3 of hydrochloric acid

   c Suggest why 0.5 mole per dm^3 of hydrochloric acid does not produce this volume of gas.

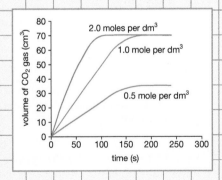

How to answer questions on: AO3 Analysing and evaluating evidence

For these types of questions, you will analyse and evaluate scientific evidence or data given to you in the question. It's likely that you won't be familiar with the material.

Analysing data may involve drawing graphs and interpreting them, and carrying out calculations. Practise drawing and interpreting graphs from data.

When drawing a graph, make sure you:

✔ choose and label the axes fully and correctly

✔ include units, if this hasn't been done for you already

✔ plot points on the graph carefully – the examiner will check individual points to make sure that they are accurate

✔ join the points correctly; usually this will be by a line of best fit.

When reading values off a graph you have drawn or one given in the question, make sure you:

✔ do it carefully, reading the values as accurately as you can

✔ double-check the values.

When describing patterns and trends in the data, make sure you:

✔ write about a pattern or trend in as much detail as you can

✔ mention anomalies where appropriate

✔ recognise there may be one general trend in the graph, where the variables show positive or negative correlation

✔ recognise the data may show a more complex relationship. The graph may demonstrate different trends in several sections. You should describe what's happening in each

✔ describe fully what the data shows.

You must also be able to evaluate the information you're given. This is one of the hardest skills. Think about the validity of the scientific data: did the technique(s) used in any practical investigation allow the collection of accurate and precise data?

Your critical evaluation of scientific data in class, along with the practical work and Controlled Assessment work, will help you to develop the evaluation skills required for these types of questions.

> *Example 12*
> 1 Explain why it is cheaper to produce chlorine gas by the electrolysis of a sodium chloride solution, rather than the electrolysis of molten sodium chloride.

Your AO3 questions may also require you to demonstrate an understanding of how evidence is used and validated in the scientific community.

What type of line is drawn on this graph?

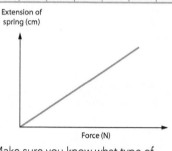
Make sure you know what type of relationship is shown in this graph

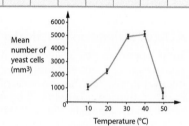
What type of relationship does this graph show?

✳ How to answer questions needing calculations

✔ The calculations you're asked to do may be straightforward; for example, the calculation of the mean from a set of practical data.

✔ Or they may be more complex; for example, calculating the yield of a chemical reaction.

✔ Other questions will require the use of formulae.

Remember, this is the same maths that you learned in your Maths lessons.

Example 13

1 A parachutist with a mass of 75 kg is taken up 3000 metres in an aircraft. Calculate the parachutist's gravitational potential energy on leaving the plane. Assume gravitational field strength is 9.8 N/kg.

Assessment tip

Remember, you calculate the mean by adding up all the numbers in the data set, and dividing by how many numbers there are.

Assessment tip

Formulae are often given to you on the question paper, but sometimes you will be expected to recall and use these. When completing your calculation, make sure you include the correct units.

Check the specification, or check with your teacher, to make sure that you know the formulae that you have to learn and remember.

✳ The quality of your written communication

Scientists need good communication skills to present and discuss their findings. You will be expected to demonstrate these skills in the exam. Questions where quality of written communication is likely to be particularly important are marked with an *. However, this doesn't mean quality of written communication isn't important in other questions – it is!

✔ You must also try to make sure that your spelling, punctuation and grammar are accurate, so that it's clear what you mean in your answer. Examiners can't award marks for answers where the meaning isn't clear.

✔ Present your information in a form that suits the purpose. For example, think about the form, style of writing and level of complexity.

✔ Organise information clearly, coherently and logically.

✔ When describing and explaining science, use correct scientific vocabulary.

Practise answering some questions where quality of written communication is important. Look at how marks are awarded in mark schemes provided by Edexcel. You'll find these in the specimen question papers, and past papers.

You will also need to remember the writing and communication skills you've developed in English lessons. For example, make sure that you understand how to construct a good sentence using connectives.

Assessment tip

Remember, when carrying out any calculations, you should include your working at each stage. You may get credit for getting the process correct, even if your final answer is wrong.

Assessment tip

Organising information clearly, coherently and logically is the most important skill in QWC.

Assessment tip

When answering questions, you must make sure that your writing is legible. An examiner can't award marks for answers that he or she can't read.

Revising for your science exam

You should revise in the way that suits you best. But it's important that you plan your revision carefully, and it's best to start well before the date of the exams. Take the time to prepare a revision timetable and try to stick to it. Use this during the lead up to the exams and between each exam.

When revising:

✔ find a quiet and comfortable space in the house where you won't be disturbed. It's best if it's well ventilated and has plenty of light

✔ take regular breaks. Some evidence suggests that revision is most effective when you revise in 30 to 40 minute slots. If you get bogged down at any point, take a break and go back to it later when you're feeling fresh. Try not to revise when you are feeling tired. If you do feel tired, take a break

✔ use your school notes, textbook and, possibly, a revision guide. But also make sure that you spend some time using past papers to familiarise yourself with the exam format

✔ produce summaries of each topic or unit

✔ draw mind maps covering the key information on a topic or unit

✔ set up revision cards containing condensed versions of your notes

✔ ask yourself questions, and try to predict questions, as you're revising topics or units

✔ test yourself as you're going along. Try to draw key labelled diagrams, and try some questions under timed conditions

✔ prioritise your revision of topics. You might want to allocate more time to revising the topics you find most difficult.

Assessment tip

Try to make your revision timetable as specific as possible – don't just say 'science on Monday, and Thursday', but list the units that you'll cover on those days.

Assessment tip

Start your revision well before the date of the exams, produce a revision timetable, and use the revision strategies that suit your style of learning. Above all, revision should be an active process.

How do I use my time effectively in the exam?

Timing is important when you sit an exam. Don't spend so long on some questions that you leave insufficient time to answer others. For example, in a 60-mark question paper, lasting one hour, you will have, on average, one minute per question.

If you're unsure about certain questions, complete the ones you're able to do first, then go back to the ones you're less sure of.

If you have time, go back and check your answers at the end of the exam.

On exam day...

A little bit of nervousness before your exam can be a good thing, but try not to let it affect your performance in the exam. When you turn over the exam paper keep calm. Look at the paper and get it clear in your head exactly what is required from each question. Read each question carefully. Don't rush.

If you read a question and think that you have not covered the topic, keep calm – it could be that the information needed to answer the question is in the question itself or the examiner may be asking you to apply your knowledge to a new situation.

Finally, good luck!

Periodic table

Group

1	2												3	4	5	6	7	0
																		$^{4}_{2}$He helium
$^{7}_{3}$Li lithium	$^{9}_{4}$Be beryllium												$^{11}_{5}$B boron	$^{12}_{6}$C carbon	$^{14}_{7}$N nitrogen	$^{16}_{8}$O oxygen	$^{19}_{9}$F fluorine	$^{20}_{10}$Ne neon
$^{23}_{11}$Na sodium	$^{24}_{12}$Mg magnesium												$^{27}_{13}$Al aluminium	$^{28}_{14}$Si silicon	$^{31}_{15}$P phosphorus	$^{32}_{16}$S sulfur	$^{35}_{17}$Cl chlorine	$^{40}_{18}$Ar argon
$^{39}_{19}$K potassium	$^{40}_{20}$Ca calcium	$^{45}_{21}$Sc scandium	$^{48}_{22}$Ti titanium	$^{51}_{23}$V vanadium	$^{52}_{24}$Cr chromium	$^{55}_{25}$Mn manganese	$^{56}_{26}$Fe iron	$^{59}_{27}$Co cobalt	$^{59}_{28}$Ni nickel	$^{64}_{29}$Cu copper	$^{65}_{30}$Zn zinc		$^{70}_{31}$Ga gallium	$^{73}_{32}$Ge germanium	$^{75}_{33}$As arsenic	$^{79}_{34}$Se selenium	$^{80}_{35}$Br bromine	$^{84}_{36}$Kr krypton
$^{85}_{37}$Rb rubidium	$^{88}_{38}$Sr strontium	$^{89}_{39}$Y yttrium	$^{91}_{40}$Zr zirconium	$^{93}_{41}$Nb niobium	$^{96}_{42}$Mo molybdenum	$^{99}_{43}$Tc technetium	$^{101}_{44}$Ru ruthenium	$^{103}_{45}$Rh rhodium	$^{106}_{46}$Pd palladium	$^{108}_{47}$Ag silver	$^{112}_{48}$Cd cadmium		$^{115}_{49}$In indium	$^{119}_{50}$Sn tin	$^{122}_{51}$Sb antimony	$^{128}_{52}$Te tellurium	$^{127}_{53}$I iodine	$^{131}_{54}$Xe xenon
$^{133}_{55}$Cs caesium	$^{137}_{56}$Ba barium	$^{139}_{57}$La lanthanum	$^{178}_{72}$Hf hafnium	$^{181}_{73}$Ta tantalum	$^{184}_{74}$W tungsten	$^{186}_{75}$Re rhenium	$^{190}_{76}$Os osmium	$^{192}_{77}$Ir iridium	$^{195}_{78}$Pt platinum	$^{197}_{79}$Au gold	$^{201}_{80}$Hg mercury		$^{204}_{81}$Tl thallium	$^{207}_{82}$Pb lead	$^{209}_{83}$Bi bismuth	$^{210}_{84}$Po polonium	$^{210}_{85}$At astatine	$^{222}_{86}$Rn radon
$^{223}_{87}$Fr francium	$^{226}_{88}$Ra radium	$^{227}_{89}$Ac actinium																

$^{1}_{1}$H
hydrogen

You need to remember the symbols for the highlighted elements.

✳ Physics formulae

The relationship between electric charge, current and time:

charge (coulomb, C) = current (ampere, A) × time (second, s)

$Q = I \times t$

The relationship between voltage, current and resistance:

potential difference (volt, V) = current (ampere, A) × resistance (ohm, Ω)

$V = I \times R$

The relationship between power, current and voltage:

electrical power (watt, W) = current (ampere, A) × potential difference (volt, V)

$P = I \times V$

Calculate electrical energy:

energy transferred (joule, J) = current (ampere, A) × potential difference (volt, V) × time (second, s)

$E = I \times V \times t$

Calculate speed:

speed (m/s) = distance (m)/time (s)

Calculate acceleration:

acceleration (metre per second squared, m/s^2) = change in velocity (metre per second, m/s) ÷ time taken (second, s)

$a = \dfrac{(v - u)}{t}$

The relationship between force, mass and acceleration:

force (newton, N) = mass (kilogram, kg) × acceleration (metre per second squared, m/s^2)

$F = m \times a$

The relationship between mass, weight and gravitational field strength:

weight (newton, N) = mass (kilogram, kg) × gravitational field strength (newton per kilogram, N/kg)

$W = m \times g$

The relationship between momentum, mass and velocity:

momentum (kilogram metre per second, kg m/s) = mass (kilogram, kg) × velocity (metre per second, m/s)

Calculate the momentum conservation for a two-body collision (in one dimension only):

force (newton, N) = change in momentum (kilogram metre per second, kg m/s) ÷ time (second, s)

$F = \dfrac{(mv - mu)}{t}$

The relationship between work done, force and distance:

work done (joule, J) = force (newton, N) × distance moved in the direction of the force (metre, m)

$E = F \times d$

The relationship between power, work done and time taken:

power (watt, W) = work done (joule, J)/time taken (second, s)

$P = \dfrac{E}{t}$

Calculate potential energy:

gravitational potential energy (joule, J) = mass (kilogram, kg) × gravitational field strength (newton per kilogram, N/kg) × vertical height (metre, m)

$GPE = m \times g \times h$

Calculate kinetic energy:

kinetic energy (joule, J) = $\frac{1}{2}$ × mass (kilogram, kg) × velocity^2 ((metre/second)^2 (m/s)^2)

$KE = \frac{1}{2} \times m \times v^2$

Glossary

abiotic environment the non-living parts of the environment

acceleration rate of change of velocity of an object

active site part of an enzyme to which a substrate bonds

active transport movement of molecules through a cell membrane against the concentration gradient; this process requires energy

activity the activity of a source is the rate of decay of nuclei

aerobic respiration respiration that involves oxygen

alkali metals very reactive metals in group 1 of the periodic table, e.g. sodium

alpha particle a helium nucleus emitted from an unstable nucleus

ammeter meter used in an electric circuit for measuring current

amperes (amps) units used to measure electrical current

amylase enzyme that catalyses reactions that break down starch to the sugar maltose

anaerobic respiration respiration without using oxygen

anatomy the form and structure of animals and plants

anion a negatively charged ion

arteries blood vessels that carry blood away from the heart

atom the basic 'building block' of an element which cannot be chemically broken down

atomic lattice a fixed arrangement of atoms in a solid

atomic mass unit a unit of mass for expressing the mass of atoms or molecules

atomic number number of protons inside the nucleus of an atom (same as the proton number)

atomic radius the distance from the nucleus to the outer electrons

atria chambers of the heart that receive blood from the veins

background radiation radiation from natural radioactive sources around us and from outer space

barium meal barium sulfate swallowed just before an X-ray

base (1) part of a nucleotide unit of DNA which is adenine (A), thymine (T), guanine (G) or cytosine (C) (2) any substance that neutralises an acid

becquerel the unit for activity: one becquerel is equal to one nucleus decaying per second

beta particle an electron emitted from the inside of an unstable nucleus

beta-carotene an orange–yellow pigment that human cells convert into vitamin A

bile chemical produced by the liver which digests fats

bioinformatics analysis of biological information (e.g. DNA base sequences/protein amino acid sequences) using computers and statistical techniques

biosphere the sum of all ecosystems

biotic community the living parts of the environment

boiling point the temperature at which a substance changes its state from a liquid to a gas

bonding, covalent bonding between atoms when electrons are shared between atoms

bonding, ionic bonding between ions resulting from the attraction between positive and negative ions

braking distance distance travelled by a car while the brakes are applied and the car comes to a stop

Cancer Genome Project uses the human genome sequence and mutation detection techniques to identify genes important in the development of human cancers (began in 2000)

capillaries small blood vessels that join arteries to veins

capillary beds dense networks of capillaries

capillary vessels small blood vessels that join arteries to veins

cardiac muscle muscle found in the heart which squeezes and relaxes continuously

catalyst substance added to a chemical reaction to alter the speed of the reaction; it is effective in small amounts and unchanged at the end of the reaction

cation a positively charged ion

cell membrane a membrane surrounding the cell and through which substances pass in solution into and out of the cell

cell wall surrounds plant cells and some bacterial cells – the cell wall of plants consists of 40% cellulose; the bacterial cell wall does not contain cellulose

chain reaction a process in which an enormous amount of energy is produced when neutrons from previous fission reactions go on to produce further uncontrolled fission reactions

chemical formula the name of a compound written down as chemical symbols

chemical properties properties that cannot be observed just by looking at a substance – a chemical property depends on how that substance reacts chemically with other substances, e.g. flammability, reactions with acids and bases

chlorides a group of chemicals all containing the anion chloride

chlorophyll pigment found in plants which is used in photosynthesis (gives green plants their colour)

chloroplast a structure in plant cells and algae that absorbs light energy – where photosynthesis takes place

cholesterol fatty substance which can block blood vessels

chromatids produced as a result of replication of a chromosome (DNA replication); appear as a pair joined by a centromere under the high power of a light microscope

chromatogram the final result of the chromatography: the chromatography paper with the result on

chromatography a method of separating substances using solvent passing through paper or similar medium

chromosome contained in the nucleus of a cell, consisting of a double-stranded DNA molecule wrapped around a core of proteins

clone an organism whose genetic information is identical to that of the organism from which it was created

codon triplets of base pairs in DNA that contain the instructions for making protein

cold fusion an invalidated theory that proposed nuclear fusion occurring at room temperature

collision theory idea that relates collisions among particles to their reaction rate

common ancestor an individual from which organisms are directly descended

companion cells cells in the phloem tissue of plants that support the function of sieve cells

complementary base pairing bonding between the bases of each strand of a double-stranded DNA molecule – each base on one strand of DNA bonds with its complementary partner on the other strand: adenine always bonds with thymine; guanine always bonds with cytosine

concentration gradient the difference in concentration of a substance between regions where it is in high concentration and regions where it is in lower concentration

control rods material used to absorb the neutrons in a nuclear reactor in order to produce a controlled chain reaction

conventional current the flow of positive charges

coolant gas or liquid used to remove thermal energy from a nuclear reactor

coulomb the unit for charge

covalent bond a chemical bond that involves sharing a pair of electrons between atoms in a molecule

critical mass the minimum mass of fissile material that can sustain a chain reaction

crystal lattice a regular and repeating structure of many millions of ions strongly held together

culture a combination of microorganisms and all the substances they need to live and multiply; the substances may be in solution or part of a jelly-like material (e.g. agar) on which microorganisms grow

culturing method of making microorganisms multiply rapidly

cytoplasm a jelly -like material that fills the cell, giving it shape

daughter cells the new cells produced when parent cells divide

daughter nuclei the nuclei produced in a fission reaction

deactivated inhibited, blocked or disrupted

deceleration negative acceleration

denatured refers to irreversible changes in the structure of proteins (including enzymes); the changes stop the proteins from working properly

deoxygenated blood blood where the oxyhaemoglobin has reverted to haemoglobin

deoxyribonucleic acid a large molecule consisting of two joined strands of building block units called nucleotides

diatomic elements elements that exist as pairs of covalently bonded atoms

differentiation the process during which a stem cell (unspecialised) develops into a particular type of cell (specialised)

diffusion the spread of particles through random motion from regions of higher concentration to regions of lower concentration

diode a device made from semiconductor material that conducts in one direction only

diploid refers to cells with two sets of chromosomes (one set from each parent) –most cells are diploid (except gametes) and the symbol 2n represents the diploid state

direct current an electric current that flows in one direction only

discrete individually separate and distinct

displacement distance in a specified direction

displacement reaction a reaction in which one substance displaces another substance from a compound

DNA polymerase enzyme that catalyses reactions that join up nucleotides forming DNA

donor eggs   eggs taken from a female animal and fertilised in the laboratory

dot and cross diagram   a way of drawing the formation of covalent bonds using dots and crosses to represent electrons in the outer shells of the atoms involved

double bond   a bond formed by two shared pairs of electrons

double covalent bond   two pairs of electrons shared in a covalent bond

earthing   a method used for ensuring the safe discharge of charges to the Earth

ecology   the study of the relationship of living organisms with each other and their surroundings

ecosystem   a habitat and all the living things in it

effervescence   fizzing due to gas bubbles escaping from a liquid

electric current   when electricity flows through a material we say that an electric current flows

electric force field   a region where electric charges experience a force

electrical conductivity   how well a substance conducts an electrical current

electrical conductor   a material that lets electricity pass through it

electrical power   defined as the rate of energy transfer

electron configuration   notation indicating the distribution of electrons in electron shells

electron shell   location of electrons around the nucleus

electrons   tiny negatively charged particles within an atom that orbit the nucleus – responsible for current in electrical circuits

electrostatic forces   the very strong forces between positive and negative ions in an ionic substance

electrostatic induction   the redistribution of electrical charge in an object

elements   substances made out of only one type of atom

embryo   the early stages in the development of an organism, from the time of first cell division

embryonic stem cells   undifferentiated cells that are able to develop (differentiate) into any type of body cell

emission spectrum   the specific frequencies of light an element emits or gives out

empirical formula   a formula that shows the correct ratio of all of the elements in a compound

emulsification   breaking down of fat into more manageable molecules

endothermic reaction   chemical reaction that takes in heat

energy profile diagram   diagram showing energy taken in or given out during a chemical reaction

enzyme–substrate complex   the combination of an enzyme and its substrate

enzymes   biological catalysts (usually proteins) produced by cells which control the rate of chemical reactions in cells

ethnic cleansing   policy of one ethnic group of removing by force the civilian population of another ethnic or religious group from particular geographical areas

excess post-exercise oxygen consumption (EPOC)   additional oxygen required after a period of anaerobic respiration

exothermic reaction   chemical reaction in which heat is given out

exponential decay   a graph in which the quantity halves after a given interval of time

fermenter   a large vessel containing a liquid culture of microorganisms and all the substances (nutrients) they need to live and multiply

fibre   the indigestible portion of plant foods

fibrin   an insoluble protein involved in the clotting of blood

filament lamp   a lamp that emits light when its thin metal filament gets very hot

filtrate   the soluble material that passes through a filter paper

fission   the splitting of a nucleus when it absorbs a neutron

flaccid   soft, droopy, lacking turgor

flagellum   whip-like extension of a cell that lashes from side to side, driving the cell through liquid

flame test   the heating of metal ions in a flame to produce a colour as an aid to identifying the metal ion

foetus   a stage in the development of an organism when tissues and organs are forming; after the embryo stage

fossils   the preserved remains of organisms that lived long ago

fractional distillation   a method of separating liquid mixtures by evaporation

free-body force diagram   a diagram showing all the forces acting on an object

friction   energy losses caused by two or more objects rubbing against each other

fuel rods   rods containing nuclear fuel for a fission reactor

functional foods any healthy foods claimed to have health-promoting or disease-preventing properties

fusion a reaction in which lighter nuclei join together (fuse) and produce energy

gall bladder a small sac-like structure connected to the small intestine by the bile duct; it stores bile, which breaks down fats in partly digested food

gametes sex cells: sperm and eggs

gamma rays electromagnetic waves of short wavelength emitted from unstable nuclei

genetic code all of the base sequences of the genes that enable cells to make proteins

genetic engineering techniques used to identify, isolate and insert useful genes from the genetic material of one species into the genetic material of the cells of another species

genetically modified (GM) species into which genes are transferred, using techniques of genetic engineering

genome all of the DNA in each cell of an organism

genomics the study of an organism's genome and the systematic use of genomic information (genes)

giant molecular covalent compounds very large molecules consisting of non-metals covalently bonded together

gradient a quantity determined by dividing the change in *y* by the change in *x*; it is the slope of a line

gravitational field strength gravitational force acting on an object per unit mass

gravitational potential energy the energy associated with the position of an object in the Earth's gravitational field

group a vertical column in the periodic table

group number the number of electrons in the outer shell of an atom

haemoglobin chemical found in red blood cells which carries oxygen

half-life the half-life of an isotope is the average time taken for half of the undecayed nuclei in a sample to decay

halogens reactive non-metals in group 7 of the periodic table, e.g. chlorine

haploid refers to cells with only one set of chromosomes – gametes are haploid; the symbol n represents the haploid state

heart rate the number of heartbeats every minute

heartbeat the two-tone sound of one complete contraction and relaxation of the heart

herbicides chemicals that kill plants – used to remove weeds (unwanted plants) from crops, gardens and public places

host mother an animal that receives cells that are not its own

Human Genome Project (HGP) an international group of scientists aiming to map the human genome

hypothesis a possible explanation for an observation

immiscible two liquids that are completely insoluble in each other

inert an inert substance is one that is not chemically reactive

insecticides chemicals used to kill insects

insulators materials that are poor electrical conductors, such as glass

intensity the radiant power per unit area

invertebrates animals that do not have a backbone

ion an electrically charged particle

ionic bond a chemical bond in which one atom loses an electron to form a positive ion and the other atom gains an electron to form a negative ion

ionic bonding chemical bonding between two ions of opposite charge

ionic compounds compounds that contain positively charged metal ions and negatively charged non-metal ions

ionisation a process where an atom loses (or gains) electrons

ionisation energy the energy required to remove an electron from an atom

ions charged atoms (positive or negative)

isotopes (1) nuclei of atoms with the same number of protons but a different number of neutrons
(2) atoms with the same number of protons but different numbers of neutrons

joule the unit of work done and energy: one joule is the work done when a force of 1 N moves a distance of 1 m in the direction of the force

kinetic energy the energy associated with a moving object

leukaemia cancer of the blood cells

ligases enzymes that catalyse reactions that insert (paste in) pieces of DNA into lengths or loops of other DNA

light-dependent resistor (LDR) device in an electric circuit whose resistance falls as the light falling on it increases

limiting factor a factor that limits a process

malleable can be hammered into thin sheets

mass   the amount of matter inside an object, measured in kilograms

mass number   total number of neutrons and protons within the nucleus of an atom (same as the nucleon number)

matter   a general term to describe anything that has mass and volume

meiosis   a type of division of the cell nucleus that results in four daughter cells, each with half the number of chromosomes (haploid) of the parent cell (diploid)

melting point   the temperature at which a solid becomes a liquid

meristem   the tissue in most plants where growth occurs

messenger RNA (mRNA)   a molecule of RNA with the code for a protein

metallic compounds   compounds composed of individual metal ions floating in a sea of electrons

microorganisms   single-celled organisms that are only just visible in the light microscope

mitochondria   structures in cells just visible in the light microscope where the breakdown of sugars begun in the cytoplasm continues, releasing energy

mitosis   a type of division of the cell nucleus that results in two daughter cells, each with the same number of chromosomes as the parent cell (usually 2n)

mobile phase   the solvent in the chromatography process

moderator   material used to slow down the fast-moving neutrons in a nuclear reactor

momentum   a quantity calculated by multiplying the mass of an object by its velocity

multicellular   an organism made of many cells

neutrons   small particles that do not have a charge found in the nucleus of an atom

Newton's first law   a body will remain at rest or continue to travel at a constant velocity unless acted on by an external force

Newton's second law   a law expressed by the equation: force = mass × acceleration

Newton's third law   when two bodies interact, each exerts an equal but opposite force on the other

noble gases   elements of group 0 in the periodic table, also called the inert gases

nuclear fusion   a nuclear reaction in which two smaller nuclei (hydrogen) fuse together to produce a larger nucleus (helium) and energy

nucleon number   total number of neutrons and protons within the nucleus of an atom (same as the mass number)

nucleons   a term used to refer to either protons or neutrons

nucleotides   the building block units that combine to form a strand of DNA; each nucleotide unit consists of the sugar deoxyribose, a base and phosphate

nucleus   (1) the central core of an atom, which contains protons and neutrons and has a positive charge
(2) structure containing the chromosomes, which carry genes that control the activities of the cell

organ   a collection of tissues joined in a structural unit to serve a common function

osmosis   movement of water from a less concentrated solution to a more concentrated solution through a partially permeable membrane

oxidation   combining another substance with oxygen

oxygenated blood   blood containing oxyhaemoglobin

oxyhaemoglobin   the result of oxygen binding to haemoglobin in red blood cells

pacemaker   the mechanism that creates rhythmical impulses in the heart

parallel   when components are connected across each other in a circuit

pentadactyl limb   the basic arrangement of five digits present in most vertebrates

pepsin   enzyme that catalyses reactions that break down protein to peptides (short-chain amino acids)

peptides   short polymers of amino acids, generally 2–20 amino acid units in length

percentage composition   the proportion of a compound's relative formula mass composed of a specific element

percentage yield   the ratio of actual yield to theoretical yield

percentile   the value of a variable below which a certain percentage of observations fall

period   a horizontal row in the periodic table

periodic table   a table of all the chemical elements based on their atomic number

periodicity   the characteristics of repeating patterns of properties in the periodic table

peristalsis   contraction and relaxation of muscles, which propagates in a wave down the muscular tube

pharmacogenomics   the study of how variations in the human genome affect an individual's response to drugs; may lead to the development of drugs tailored to be the most effective according to an individual's genetic make-up

phloem   columns of living cells in plant cells

photomicrograph   photomicrograph of the image of a specimen seen with the help of a microscope

photosynthesis   process carried out by green plants where sunlight, carbon dioxide and water are used to produce glucose and oxygen

physical properties   properties that can be observed without changing the chemical composition of a substance, e.g. colour, density, melting point and boiling point

plant stanol esters   substances found in food such as wheat and maize that reduce the absorption of harmful cholesterol

plasmid DNA   loops of DNA found in the cytoplasm of bacterial and yeast cells

plasmolysis   shrinkage of the cell membrane from the cell wall

polyatomic ions   ions containing more than one type of atom

polypeptides   polymers of amino acids, generally 21–50 amino acid units in length

population   organisms of the same species that live in the same geographical area

positrons   particles that have the same mass as electrons but with a positive charge

potential difference   the energy transferred per unit charge; also known as voltage

power   the rate of work done or the rate of energy transfer

prebiotics   non-digestible food ingredients to stimulate growth of bacteria in the digestive system

precipitate   insoluble solid formed in a solution during a chemical reaction

precipitation reaction   a reaction that results in an insoluble product

principle of conservation of momentum   for a system of colliding objects, where there are no external forces, the total momentum before and after the collision remains the same

probiotics   live microorganisms thought to be beneficial to health

product   the substance formed in a reaction

proteins   molecules made up of amino acids, more than 50 amino acids in length

proton number   number of protons inside the nucleus of an atom (same as the atomic number)

protons   small positive particles found in the nucleus of an atom

pulse   a ripple of blood as it is forced along the arteries by the beating heart

radiotherapy   a technique that uses gamma rays to kill cancerous cells in a patient

radon   a colourless, odourless and radioactive gas originating from rocks such as granite

recombinant DNA   a combination of DNA from one species with the DNA of another species

recovery period   period during which lactic acid is removed and breathing and heart rates return to normal after exercise

relative atomic mass   the average atomic mass of an element taking into account the relative abundance of the isotopes of that element

relative formula mass   the sum of all of the relative atomic masses for all of the atoms in a molecule

replication   when organisms or cells make copies of themselves

residue   the solid material collected in a filter paper after filtration

resistance   an electrical quantity determined by dividing potential difference by current

resolving power   the ability to see objects close together as separate from one another

resultant force   the combined effect of forces acting on an object

restriction enzymes   enzymes that catalyse reactions that cut strands of DNA into shorter pieces

R_f value   the ratio of how far the substance has moved up the chromatography paper relative to the solvent front

rheostat   a variable resistor

ribonucleic acid (RNA)   a type of nucleic acid found in cells but not used to build chromosomes; some types of RNA are involved in protein synthesis

ribosome   a component of a cell that creates proteins from all amino acids and RNA representing the protein

salt   an ionic compound composed of positive ions (cations) and negative ions (anions)

scalar   a quantity that only has size or magnitude

sedimentary rock   rock formed by the sedimentation of material on riverbeds and ocean floors

semiconductor   a group of materials with electrical conductive properties between metals and insulators

sequence   arrangement in which things follow a pattern

sequencers   machines that automatically determine (work out) the base sequences of DNA (or amino acid sequence of proteins)

series   when components are connected end-to-end in a circuit

shell electrons are arranged in shells (or orbits) around the nucleus of an atom

sieve cells tube-like cells in the phloem tissue of plants

silent mutation a mutation that alters the base sequence of a codon but does not result in alteration of the sequence of amino acid units of the protein in question

simple molecular covalent compounds small molecules consisting of non-metals covalently bonded together

solubility the amount of a substance that will dissolve

solubility rules the rules that let us know which common substances are soluble and which are insoluble

solvent front the distance the solvent travels up the chromatography paper

species a group of individuals able to mate and reproduce offspring, which themselves are able to mate and reproduce

specific each enzyme catalyses a particular reaction or type of reaction

spectroscope a machine that detects and analyses specific substances

spectroscopy a sophisticated type of flame test: substances are heated until they produce their own unique emission spectrum

speed how fast an object travels, calculated using the equation: speed (metres per second) = distance/time

state symbols the symbols that describe the state of a substance: solid, liquid, gas or aqueous (dissolved in water)

stationary phase the paper used in the chromatography process

stem cells undifferentiated (unspecialised) cells able to develop (differentiate) into differentiated (specialised) cells

sterilisation a technique used to kill bacteria using intense gamma rays

stoichiometry a branch of chemistry dealing with calculations based on chemical equations

stoma (plural stomata) a pore found in plants used for gas exchange

stopping distance thinking distance + braking distance

substrate molecules at the start of a chemical reaction; the substance that an enzyme helps to react

sulfates a group of chemicals all containing the anion sulfate

symbol one- or two-letter designation for the elements in the periodic table

symbol equation a shorthand way of representing a chemical reaction using the symbols of the compounds

tangent a line drawn to a curve to determine the gradient of a curve at a point

terminal velocity the constant velocity of a falling object when the net force acting on it is zero

tetrahedral having four faces, like a four-sided pyramid

theoretical yield predicted yield of a chemical reaction based on calculations

thermistor sensor in an electric circuit that detects temperature

thinking distance distance travelled by a car as the driver reacts to apply the brakes

tissue culture growth of fragments of tissue in a liquid or on gel which provides all the substances needed for their development; conditions are sterile and controlled

tissue fluid a solution that bathes and surrounds the cells of multicellular animals

tissues groups of cells that work together and carry out a similar task, e.g. lung tissue

tracer a radioactive material used to monitor the flow of a liquid

transfer RNA (tRNA) a molecule of RNA that transports amino acids to ribosomes

transition metals elements between group 2 and group 3 in the periodic table

translocation the process of transporting dissolved glucose through the phloem tissue

transpiration the movement of water and mineral salts from roots to leaves in plants

triple covalent bond three pairs of electrons shared in a covalent bond

turgid rigid owing to high fluid content

turgor pressure pressure inside a cell due to the entry of water

urea nitrogen-containing substance cleared from the blood by kidneys and excreted in urine

vacuole a fluid-filled space in the cytoplasm of cells – most plant cells have a permanent vacuole; if vacuoles are present in animal cells they are temporary

vector a quantity that has both magnitude and direction

vegetative reproduction asexual reproduction from the vegetative parts of a plant: the roots, leaves and stem

veins blood vessels that carry blood back to the heart

velocity how fast an object is travelling in a certain direction: velocity = displacement/time

ventricles chambers of the heart that pump blood into the arteries

villi finger-like structures on the surface of the small intestine which give it a greater surface area for absorption

vitamin A a vitamin that is essential for growth and vision

voltmeter   a device used to measure the voltage across a component

waste   unwanted products of a chemical reaction, usually not commercially valuable

water potential   the tendency of water to move from one area to another due to osmosis

watt   the unit of power: one watt is equal to one joule per second

waxy cuticle   a tough outer covering to the upper surface of a plant leaf

weight   the gravitational force acting on an object, measured in newtons

word equations   a shorthand way of representing a chemical reaction

work done   the product of force and distance moved in the direction of the force

xylem   columns of hollow, dead reinforced cells in plant stems

yield   useful product made from a chemical reaction

zygote   a fertilised egg

Index

William Collins' dream of knowledge for all began with the publication of his first book in 1819. A self-educated mill worker, he not only enriched millions of lives, but also founded a flourishing publishing house. Today, staying true to this spirit, Collins books are packed with inspiration, innovation and practical expertise. They place you at the centre of a world of possibility and give you exactly what you need to explore it.

Collins. Freedom to teach

Published by Collins
An imprint of HarperCollins*Publishers*
77–85 Fulham Palace Road
Hammersmith
London
W6 8JB

Browse the complete Collins catalogue at
www.collinseducation.com

© HarperCollins*Publishers* Limited 2011

10 9 8 7 6 5 4 3 2

ISBN-13 978 0 00 741508 3

John Adkins, David Applin and Gurinder Chadha assert their moral rights to be identified as the authors of this work

British Library Cataloguing in Publication Data
A Catalogue record for this publication is available from the British Library

Commissioned by Letitia Luff
Project managed by Alexandra Riley and Gray Publishing
Production by Kerry Howie

Designed, edited, proofread and indexed by Gray Publishing
New illustrations by Gray Publishing
Picture research by Caroline Green
Concept design by Anna Plucinska
Cover design by Julie Martin
Development editor Lesley Gray
Technical review by Dr Christopher R.J. Woolston
Contributing authors John Beeby, Ed Walsh, Kiran Webber and Gemma Young
'Bad Science' pages based on the work of Ben Goldacre

Printed and bound by CPI Group (UK) Ltd, Croydon, CR0 4YY

Edexcel disclaimer
This material has been endorsed by Edexcel and offers high quality support for the delivery of Edexcel qualifications.

Edexcel endorsement does not mean that this material is essential to achieve any Edexcel qualification, nor does it mean that this is the only suitable material available to support any Edexcel qualification. No endorsed material will be used verbatim in setting any Edexcel examination and any resource lists produced by Edexcel shall include this and other appropriate texts. While this material has been through an Edexcel quality assurance process, all responsibility for the content remains with the publisher.

Copies of official specifications for all Edexcel qualifications may be found on the Edexcel website – www.edexcel.com

Acknowledgements
The publishers wish to thank the following for permission to reproduce photographs. Every effort has been made to trace copyright holders and to obtain their permission for the use of copyright materials. The publishers will gladly receive any information enabling them to rectify any error or omission at the first opportunity.

cover & p.1 Edward Kinsman/Science Photo Library, p.8t Henrik Jonsson/iStockphoto, p.8u wong sze yuen/Shutterstock, p.8l sonya etchison/Shutterstock, p.8b tatniz/Shutterstock, p.9t Teun van den Dries/iStockphoto, p.9u Olena Timashova/iStockphoto, p.9l Eric Gevaert/Shutterstock, p.9b amlet/Shutterstock, p.10t Biodisc, Visuals Unlimited/Science Photo Library, p.10l Astrid & Hanns-Frieder Michler/Science Photo Library, p.10tr Photographer, Visuals Unlimited/Science Photo Library, p.10br Dr Gopal Murti/Science Photo Library, p.11 Astrid & Hanns-Frieder Michler/Science Photo Library, p.12 Francis Leroy, Biocosmos/Science Photo Library, p.13a CNRI/Science Photo Library, p.13b Dr Kari Lounatmaa/Science Photo Library, p.14 A. Barrington Brown/Science Photo Library, p.16 James King-Holmes/Science Photo Library, p.17 Science Photo Library, p.18 Eric Carr/Alamy, p.20t Barry Batchelor/PA Archive/Press Association Images, p.20b Corbis Bridge/Alamy, p.21 International Rice Research Institute (IRRI)/Wikimedia Commons, p.22t Power and Syred/Science Photo Library, p.22b Gerd Guenther/Science Photo Library, p.23 Science Photo Library, p.24t Science Pictures Limited/Science Photo Library, p.24b Barry Lewis/Alamy, p.25 Claude Nuridsany & Marie Perennou/Science Photo Library, p.26t Nigel Cattlin/Alamy, p.26b aletermi/Shutterstock, p.27 GardenPhotos.com/Alamy, p.28 Rex Features, p.29 Young-Ho/Sipa Press/Rex Features, p.30 PHOTOTAKE Inc./Alamy, p.32t Mopic/Shutterstock, p.32c Fdardel/Wikimedia Commons, p.32b Lawrence Berkeley National Laboratory/Science Photo Library, p.33 Department of Clinical Radiology, Salisbury District Hospital/Science Photo Library, p.34 Aleksandar Todorovic/Shutterstock, p.36 Martin Shields/Alamy, p.38t Oliver Hoffmann/Shutterstock, p.38b fotografaw/Shutterstock, p.40 sciencephotos/Alamy, p.42t Dr. William Weber/Science Photo Library, p.42b Sebalos/Shutterstock, p.52t Maridav/Shutterstock, p.52u Marek Mnich/iStockphoto, p.52l katatonia82/Shutterstock, p.52b Andreas Odersky/Shutterstock, p.53t Sebastian Kaulitzki/Shutterstock, p.53u Ken Graff/iStockphoto, p.53l Paul Maguire/Shutterstock, p.53b auremar/Shutterstock, p.54 2happy/Shutterstock, p.55 Roger De Marfa/Shutterstock , p.56 studio_chki/Shutterstock, p.58 Paul Cooper/Rex Features, p.60 Eye of Science/Science Photo Library, p.62 Patrick Poendl/Shutterstock, p.64 Power and Syred/Science Photo Library, p.66 DNY59/iStockphoto, p.67 David Nunuk/Science Photo Library, p.68t Krasowit/Shutterstock, p.68c J.C. Revy, ISM/Science Photo Library, p.68b J.C. Revy, ISM/Science Photo Library, p.70 HartmutMorgenthal/Shutterstock, p.72 Ttphoto/Shutterstock, p.74t Christian Darkin/Science Photo Library, p.74b Scott Latham/Shutterstock, p.76t vblinov/Shutterstock, p.76b M.I. Walker/Science Photo Library, p.77 Brandon Cole Marine Photography/Alamy, p.78 Dr G. Moscoso/Science Photo Library, p.79 Steve Gschmeissner/Science Photo Library, p.80t withGod/Shutterstock, p.80b National Cancer Institute/Science Photo Library, p.81t Eye of Science/Science Photo Library, p.81b CNRI/Science Photo Library, p.82 marema/Shutterstock, p.84 Professors P.M. Motta & S. Correr/Science Photo Library, p.85 Amandine Wanert/Science Photo Library, p.86 smikhailov/Shutterstock, p.87 Gastrolab/Science Photo Library, p.88 Gelpi/Shutterstock, p.90t stocksnapp/Shutterstock, p.90b Cordelia Molloy/Science Photo Library, p.91 SCIMAT/Science Photo Library, p.92t Gina Sanders/Shutterstock, p.92c phanlop88/Shutterstock, p.92b vladm/Shutterstock, p.99 Sinclair Stammers/Science Photo Library, p.100t Sashkin/Shutterstock, p.100c Jiri Hera/Shutterstock, p.100b africanstuff/Shutterstock, p.101t concept w/Shutterstock, p.101c Denis Larkin/Shutterstock, p.101b Thum Chia Chieh/Shutterstock, p.102 David Parker/Science Photo Library, p.104 Heidas/Wikimedia Commons, p.106 INTERFOTO/Alamy, p.108t Charles D. Winters/Science Photo Library, p.108b Chris Fertnig/iStockphoto, p.110l Martyn F. Chillmaid/Science Photo Library, p.110r Martyn F. Chillmaid/Science Photo Library, p.111 Vaughan Fleming/Science Photo Library, p.112 Science Photo Library, p.113 Diego Cervo/iStockphoto, p.114t fokusgood/Shutterstock, p.114b Eye of Science/Science Photo Library, p.115 Andrew Lambert Photography/Science Photo Library, p.116t Kevin Schafer/Alamy, p.116b Andrew Lambert Photography/Science Photo Library, p.117 Lawrence Migdale/Science Photo Library, p.118 Power and Syred/Science Photo Library, p.119 Scott Camazine/Science Photo Library, p.120 Juhana Lampinen/Shutterstock, p.121 European Space Agency/Science Photo Library, p.122t Andrew Lambert Photography/Science Photo Library, p.122b Andrew Lambert Photography/Science Photo Library, p.124 Tischenko Irina/Shutterstock, p.126 Geoff Tompkinson/Science Photo Library, p.128 MaxFX/Shutterstock, p.130 david pearson/Alamy, p.131 Chris H. Galbraith/Shutterstock, p.132 Leslie Garland Picture Library/Alamy, p.134l Sandra Caldwell/Shutterstock, p.134r michaeljung/Shutterstock, p.142t Christian Lagerek/Shutterstock, p.142c Laurence Gough/Shutterstock, p.142b mikeledray/Shutterstock, p.143t Karin Hildebrand Lau/Shutterstock, p.143c James Thew/Shutterstock, p.143b Alexander Raths/Shutterstock, p.144 Ames Research Center/NASA, p.146 charles taylor/Shutterstock, p.148t Charles D. Winters/Science Photo Library, p.148b Charles D. Winters/Science Photo Library, p.150 Trinity Mirror/Mirrorpix/Alamy, p.152t Pslawinski/Wikimedia Commons, p.152b Brilliant photography/Alamy, p.153 Alexander Tsiaras/Science Photo Library, p.154t Mary Evans Picture Library/Alamy, p.154b Charles D. Winters/Science Photo Library, p.156 john t. fowler/Alamy, p.158 Crown Copyright/Health & Safety Laboratory/Science Photo Library, p.160t H. Brauer/Shutterstock, p.160b vario images GmbH & Co.KG/Alamy, p.162 Martyn F. Chillmaid/Science Photo Library, p.164 Sander van Sinttruye/Shutterstock, p.165 GustoImages/Science Photo Library, p.166t Chris Price/iStockphoto, p.166b Danny E Hooks/Shutterstock, p.167 sciencephotos/Alamy, p.168t Bart Coenders/iStockphoto, p.168b Bart Coenders/iStockphoto, p.169 Steve Allen/Science Photo Library, p.176t Scott Rothstein/Shutterstock, p.176c Piotr Zajc/Shutterstock, p.176b Krivosheev Vitaly/Shutterstock, p.177t David Asch/Shutterstock, p.177c kilukilu/Shutterstock, p.177b Germanskydiver/Shutterstock, p.178 Philippe Plailly/Science Photo Library, p.180 ilFede/Shutterstock, p.182 Petr Mašek/Shutterstock, p.183 Chris Pearsall/Alamy, p.184 Tommounsey/iStockphoto, p.186 Andy Geldman/iStockphoto, p.188t Richard Watson/iStockphoto, p.188b Andrei Nekrassov/Shutterstock, p.190t Vladimir Vydrin/iStockphoto, p.190b brinkstock/iStockphoto, p.192t thaikrit/Shutterstock, p.192l Art Directors & TRIP/Alamy, p.192r sciencephotos/Alamy, p.194 sixninepixels/Shutterstock, p.195 blackwaterimages/iStockphoto, p.197l ssuaphotos/Shutterstock, p.197r Scott Andrews/NASA, p.198 Loren Winters, Visuals Unlimited/Science Photo Library, p.200 Edward Shaw/iStockphoto, p.201 narvikk/iStockphoto, p.202 Vuk Vukmirovic/Shutterstock, p.204 Giordano Aita/Shutterstock, p.206t NASA/Science Photo Library, p.206c Luc Viatour/Wikimedia Commons, p.206br Harrison Schmitt, Ron Evans (of the Apollo 17 crew)/Wikimedia Commons, p.206bl Martyn F. Chillmaid/Science Photo Library, p.208l Vince Clements/Shutterstock, p.208r Jiri Hera/Shutterstock, p.208b adziohiciek/Shutterstock, p.216t Rena Schild/Shutterstock, p.216c MrJafari/Shutterstock, p.216b polat/Shutterstock, p.217t Cheryl Casey/Shutterstock, p.217c Peeratam/Shutterstock, p.217b Lasse Kristensen/Shutterstock, p.218t Carla Thomas/NASA, p.218b Sergio Schnitzler/Shutterstock, p.220 Johnny Greig UK/Alamy, p.222t Thomas Eckstadt/iStockphoto, p.222b Caro/Alamy, p.223 Дмитрий Верещагин/iStockphoto, p.224t jaileybug/Alamy, p.224b Yuri Arcurs/Shutterstock, p.225 akva/Shutterstock, p.226t Four Oaks/Shutterstock, p.226b Andrey Pavlov/Shutterstock, p.228 Rechitan Sorin/Shutterstock, p.230t Dainis Derics/Shutterstock, p.230b Graham J. Hills/Science Photo Library, p.231 Kletr/Shutterstock, p.232t C. Powell, P. Fowler & D. Perkins/Science Photo Library, p.232s isobel flynn/Alamy, p.233 GoodMood Photo/Shutterstock, p.234 Traroth/Wikimedia Commons, p.236 Melvin A. Miller/US National Archives and Records Administration/Science Photo Library, p.237 Philippe Psaila/Science Photo Library, p.238 Adchariyaphoto/Shutterstock, p.239 Mikkel Juul Jensen/Science Photo Library, p.240t ribeiroantonio/Shutterstock, p.240b Crown Copyright/Health Protection Agency and British Geological Survey, p.241 Health Protection Agency/Science Photo Library, p.242t Cordelia Molloy/Science Photo Library, p.242b Health Protection Agency/Science Photo Library, p.244t ppl/Shutterstock, p.244u GustoImages/Science Photo Library, p.244l fusebulb/Shutterstock, p.244b Philippe Plailly/Science Photo Library, p.245l Oguz Aral/Shutterstock, p.245r Mark Kostich/iStockphoto, p.245b Simon Fraser/Royal Victoria Infirmary, Newcastle-Upon-Tyne/Science Photo Library, p.248t James King-Holmes/Science Photo Library, p.246b Stephen Gray/Shutterstock, p.248t Martin Bond/Science Photo Library, p.248c Ria Novosti/Science Photo Library, p.248b Andrew Lambert Photography/Science Photo Library, p.249 US Department of Energy/Science Photo Library, p.250t michaeljung/Shutterstock, p.250bl mambo/Alamy, p.250br mambo/Alamy, p.254bl zhu difeng/Shutterstock, p.254c George Dolgikh/Shutterstock, p.254br Rechitan Sorin/Shutterstock, p.255 David W Hughes/Shutterstock, p.256l Huguette Roe/Shutterstock, p.256r Tilmann von Au/iStockphoto, p.258-259 Tischenko Irina/Shutterstock, p.258 Kletr/Shutterstock, p.260-261 Diego Cervo/Shutterstock, p.262-263 Dmitry Naumov/Shutterstock, p.274 Martyn F. Chillmaid/Science Photo Library.